Quantum Theory of Many-Particle Systems

Frontiers in Physics

A Lecture Note and Reprint Series

DAVID PINES, *Editor*

N. Bloembergen **NUCLEAR MAGNETIC RELAXATION:** *A Reprint Volume*

Geoffrey F. Chew **S-MATRIX THEORY OF STRONG INTERACTIONS:** *A Lecture Note and Reprint Volume*

R. P. Feynman **QUANTUM ELECTRODYNAMICS:** *A Lecture Note and Reprint Volume*

R. P. Feynman **THE THEORY OF FUNDAMENTAL PROCESSES:** *A Lecture Note Volume*

Hans Frauenfelder **THE MÖSSBAUER EFFECT:** *A Collection of Reprints with an Introduction*

David Pines **THE MANY-BODY PROBLEM:** *A Lecture Note and Reprint Volume*

L. Van Hove, N. M. Hugenholtz, and L. P. Howland **PROBLEMS IN THE QUANTUM THEORY OF MANY-PARTICLE SYSTEMS**

Problems in Quantum Theory of Many-Particle Systems

A Lecture Note and Reprint Volume

L. VAN HOVE
Professor of Theoretical Physics, The University, Utrecht

N. M. HUGENHOLTZ
Professor of Physics, The University, Groningen

L. P. HOWLAND
Department of Physics, Dartmouth College

W. A. BENJAMIN, INC.
New York 1961

PROBLEMS IN THE QUANTUM THEORY
OF MANY-PARTICLE SYSTEMS
A Lecture Note and Reprint Volume

Library of Congress Catalog Card Number: 61-18183
Manufactured in the United States of America

W. A. Benjamin, Inc.
2465 Broadway, New York 25, New York

EDITOR'S FOREWORD

The problem of communicating in a coherent fashion the recent developments in the most exciting and active fields of physics seems particularly pressing today. The enormous growth in the number of physicists has tended to make the familiar channels of communication considerably less effective. It has become increasingly difficult for experts in a given field to keep up with the current literature; the novice can only be confused. What is needed is both a consistent account of a field and the presentation of a definite "point of view" concerning it. Formal monographs cannot meet such a need in a rapidly developing field, and, perhaps more important, the review article seems to have fallen into disfavor. Indeed, it would seem that the people most actively engaged in developing a given field are the people least likely to write at length about it.

"Frontiers in Physics" has been conceived in an effort to improve the situation in several ways. First, to take advantage of the fact that the leading physicists today frequently give a series of lectures, a graduate seminar, or a graduate course in their special fields of interest. Such lectures serve to summarize the present status of a rapidly developing field and may well constitute the only coherent account available at the time. Often, notes on lectures exist (prepared by the lecturer himself, by graduate students, or by postdoctoral fellows) and have been distributed in mimeographed form on a limited basis. One of the principal purposes of the "Frontiers in Physics" series is to make such notes available to a wider audience of physicists.

It should be emphasized that lecture notes are necessarily rough and informal, both in style and content, and those in the series will prove no exception. This is as it should be. The point of the series is to offer new, rapid, more informal, and, it is hoped, more effective ways for physicists to teach one another. The point is lost if only elegant notes qualify.

A second way to improve communication in very active fields of physics is by the publication of collections of reprints of recent articles. Such collections are themselves useful to people working in the field. The value of the reprints would, however, seem much enhanced if the collection would be accompanied by an introduction of moderate length, which would serve to tie the collection together and, necessarily, constitute a brief survey of the present status of the field. Again, it is appropriate that such an introduction be informal, in keeping with the active character of the field.

A third possibility for the series might be called an informal monograph, to connote the fact that it represents an intermediate step between lecture notes and formal monographs. It would offer the author an opportunity to present his views of a field that has developed to the point at which a summation might prove extraordinarily fruitful, but for which a formal monograph might not be feasible or desirable.

Fourth, there are the contemporary classics—papers or lectures which constitute a particularly valuable approach to the teaching and learning of physics today. Here one thinks of fields that lie at the heart of much of present-day research, but whose essentials are by now well understood, such as quantum electrodynamics or magnetic resonance. In such fields some of the best pedagogical material is not readily available, either because it consists of papers long out of print or lectures that have never been published.

"Frontiers in Physics" is designed to be flexible in editorial format. Authors are encouraged to use as many of the foregoing approaches as seem desirable for the project at hand. The publishing format for the series is in keeping with its intentions. Photo-offset printing is used throughout, and the books are paperbound, in order to speed publication and reduce costs. It is hoped that the books will thereby be within the financial reach of graduate students in this country and abroad.

Finally, because the series represents something of an experiment on the part of the editor and the publisher, suggestions from interested readers as to format, contributors, and contributions will be most welcome.

DAVID PINES

Urbana, Illinois
August 1961

PREFACE

In June,1958, at the invitation of Professor J. C. Slater, I gave at the Massachusetts Institute of Technology a series of ten lectures entitled "Interactions of Elastic Waves in Solids." The aim was to present the application to a concrete physical problem of rather general techniques developed by N. M. Hugenholtz and me for the study of interaction effects in quantum systems of many particles. The first part of the present book contains an expanded version of these lectures, prepared by L. P. Howland and originally circulated as a Technical Report of the Solid State and Molecular Theory Group of M.I.T. A number of original papers by G. Placzek, N. M. Hugenholtz, and me, dealing with problems or methods discussed in the lectures, are represented in the second part.

By presenting first a detailed discussion of a special and rather simple physical system, an anharmonic crystal lattice at the absolute zero of temperature, and then a number of articles of greater generality, we hope to give the reader a convenient and self-contained introduction to one of the methods that has been developed and used in recent years for the study of interactions in quantum systems containing a large number of particles. In the study of anharmonic crystals we have considered among other things the effect of the interaction between elastic waves on slow neutron scattering by the crystal. It is for this reason that a few somewhat older papers on slow neutron scattering have been included.

On behalf of L. P. Howland and myself I gladly express our gratitude to Professor J. C. Slater for his stimulating interest in the lecture series and in the preparation of the lecture notes.

Authors and publishers are indebted to the Solid State and Molecular Theory Group of M.I.T., and to the editors of the *Physical Review* and *Physica*, for permission to republish the material contained in this book.

L. VAN HOVE

Geneva, Switzerland
August 1961

CONTENTS

ACKNOWLEDGMENTS

The publisher wishes to acknowledge the assistance of the following persons and organizations in the preparation of this volume:

The Massachusetts Institute of Technology, Department of Physics, especially Professor John C. Slater, for permission to reproduce Dr. Van Hove's lecture notes.

The Physica Foundation, for permission to reprint five articles from Physica.

The American Institute of Physics, for permission to reprint three articles from the Physical Review.

Quantum Theory of Many-Particle Systems

TABLE OF CONTENTS

INTERACTIONS OF ELASTIC WAVES IN SOLIDS

INTERACTIONS OF ELASTIC WAVES IN SOLIDS

1. INTRODUCTION

In this report it is intended to discuss several problems in solid-state physics by means of a new perturbation method for many-particle, quantum-mechanical systems. The particular problems to be discussed concern effects of the interactions of elastic waves in ideal single crystals, especially non-conducting crystals. Some of these problems have been treated earlier by other methods, but they still serve well as illustrative applications of the new method.

The solid-state problems to be discussed have much in common with other many-particle problems. Examples of these are the Fermi gas with interactions (Brueckner and Levinson, 1955; Bethe, 1956; Goldstone, 1957) and the Bose gas with interactions (Bogolyubov, 1947; Huang and Yang, 1957; Brueckner and Sawada, 1957). The perturbation method presented here was actually developed in a treatment of the Fermi gas (Hugenholtz, 1957 a,b), but it is applicable to all of the problems mentioned above. Furthermore, the method is closely related to methods used in field theory, and, in fact, it was largely inspired by those methods (Van Hove, 1955 b and 1956; Frazer and Van Hove, 1958).

There are many types of waves in addition to elastic waves which are familiar in solid-state physics. Among these are the Bloch-type wave functions for electrons, the spin waves of magnetic materials at low temperatures, and the waves of x-rays and neutrons which are used to study solids in scattering experiments. In each of these examples the wave is a useful concept because it is relatively independent and long-lived in the total system. When the system is described in terms of such waves, there only remains the problem of treating small interactions between the waves to obtain a complete description of the system. When the interactions are not small, of course, the concept of the wave is not so useful. Even when the wave description is quite good, however, some of the most important properties of the system derive from the small interactions which remain. This is the case for all transport properties, for example, and the new method actually originated as a new approach to the related irreversible statistics (Van Hove, 1955 a and 1957).

In an ideal non-conducting crystal the vibrational problem is generally treated in the following way. The crystal is assumed to have a total potential energy which is only a function of nuclear positions (the electrons are assumed to follow the nuclei), and this energy is written as a series in powers of the displacements of nuclei from their equilibrium positions. The potential energy is therefore given by a constant plus quadratic and higher-order terms in the nuclear displacements. If only the quadratic, or harmonic, terms are significant, the crystal vibration problem can be completely solved in terms of independent elastic waves, each wave being characterized by a wave vector $\vec{q}$, a polarization vector $\vec{e}$, and a frequency ω. In a quantum-mechanical description of the vibrations, the energy of each elastic wave is quantized, and there is said to be one phonon present for each quantum of energy, $\hbar\omega$.

The higher-order or anharmonic terms in the expanded potential energy give rise to interactions between the elastic waves or phonons of the harmonic approximation. Except near the melting point of the solid, these interaction terms turn out to be small enough that the elastic waves or phonons still provide a good basis for treating the vibrational problem. Once the harmonic problem is solved, then, there remains the problem of calculating the effects of small phonon-phonon interactions. The calculation of such effects when the crystal is at equilibrium or in its ground state is the main problem which is treated in the present report.

In an ideal conducting crystal the vibrational problem is complicated by the presence of conduction electrons, which are not constrained to follow the vibrations of the nuclei (or the ionic cores). If the nuclei were fixed rigidly in their equilibrium positions, these conduction electrons could be described by Bloch-type one-electron wave functions, each of these functions being characterized by a wave vector, an energy, and a spin quantum number. If the nuclei make displacements from their equilibrium positions, however, as they do in an actual vibrating crystal, the crystal symmetry is no longer that appropriate to Bloch electrons, and, furthermore, the electrons cannot be assumed to follow the nuclei, as they do in a non-conducting crystal. In the usual treatment of this problem, the conduction electrons are described in terms of the Bloch functions of the non-vibrating crystal, and they are then allowed to interact with the lattice vibrations or phonons. When a conducting crystal is thus described in terms of phonons and Bloch electrons, there remains the problem of calculating the effects of three different types of interaction: phonon-phonon, phonon-electron, and electron-electron.

The interactions described above for non-conductors and conductors are responsible for important physical effects. The phonon-phonon interaction gives rise to heat conduction, and it also leads to the effect of thermal expansion. The phonon-electron interaction also gives rise to heat conduction, and it is responsible for electrical resistance and superconductivity. The electron-electron interaction gives rise to plasma oscillations. There are other effects, of course, but those given should be sufficient to illustrate the point.

Theoretical treatments of these and other interaction effects are generally quite difficult, and the best treatments of some are still far from satisfactory. Since the interactions of interest are small and non-singular, some form of perturbation theory is the natural basis for any treatment. Standard perturbation theory is generally inadequate for a large system, however, because some high-order terms may be quite large, even though the interaction forces are small.

There are also other difficulties which arise in treating many-particle systems by perturbation methods, and some of these can be related to certain physical characteristics of the interaction effects. In the first place, many of the interaction effects are at least partly dissipative in character. This is not surprising, of course, since a solid could not come to thermal equilibrium without such effects. Thermal conductivity is one dissipative effect, and electrical conductivity is another.

For a dissipative effect which is somewhat simpler theoretically, consider the decay of an extra phonon in a non-conducting solid. Such a phonon might have been excited by neutron bombardment, for example. In any case, the phonon decays with a finite lifetime into two or more phonons, and the secondary phonons and all the later products also decay. The original system containing the single extra phonon thus decays irreversibly into a system in which the energy of the original extra phonon is distributed among all the vibrational degrees of freedom of the system and thermal equilibrium is restored. Such effects are involved in many physical processes of interest, and one of the difficulties in many-particle perturbation theory is to account for them in a natural and practical way.

In the second place, some of the effects depend upon interaction-produced energy shifts and involve the physical characteristics of such shifts. The particular characteristic which is of interest here is the volume dependence of an energy shift, as will be seen below. Thermal expansion is an energy-shift effect, since it occurs because of an interaction-produced shift in the free energy of a crystal. The equilibrium value of the lattice constant at O°K also involves an energy-shift effect, since it depends upon an interaction-produced shift in the zero-point energy of a crystal. In both of these examples the energy shift is an extensive (bulk) quantity, and it should be proportional to the volume of the crystal.

For a different energy-shift effect, consider again the extra phonon in a non-conducting solid. The energy of this phonon (the energy required to excite it) is not exactly equal to $\hbar\omega$, as predicted by harmoinc theory, but it is shifted from this value by the anharmonic forces. This energy shift is an intensive (local) quantity, and it should be independent of the volume of the crystal.

One of the difficulties in many-particle perturbation theory is to obtain expressions for energy-shift effects which exhibit the expected volume-dependence in a simple way. For many of these effects a straightforward calculation leads to an expression in which intensive and extensive effects are intermixed, even though the effect itself is expected to be purely extensive or intensive.

Finally, many interaction effects involve both dissipative processes and energy shifts, and these mixed effects exhibit further difficulties. The extra phonon in a non-conducting solid again provides a good example. The lifetime of this phonon is a dissipative effect, but it is influenced by the energy-shift effect, since energy conservation is involved in each decay. The mixing of the effects is really more complete than this, however. In view of the finite lifetime of the phonon, its energy cannot be perfectly well defined. The phonon therefore has an energy spectrum, and the spectrum must have a width corresponding to an imaginary part of the phonon frequency and depending on the decay probability of the phonon. The spectrum may also have a peak position which depends upon the decay probability. If the mixing in such mixed effects is quantitatively important, intuitive perturbation treatments become impossible and a completely systematic perturbation method is required.

In this report a general many-particle perturbation method which handles the difficulties mentioned above is presented. The presentation is accomplished in the course of a discussion of a relatively simple system consisting of interacting phonons in a non-conducting crystal. The problems for this system which are discussed are the ground-state energy and wave function at O°K, the cross-section for neutron scattering at O°K, the free energy at an arbitrary temperature, and, very briefly, the cross-section for neutron scattering at an arbitrary temperature. In view of the purpose of this report the results presented are not in general those in which an experimentalist would be interested. Important factors such as the presence of impurities are neglected, mainly low-temperature properties are discussed, and many other simplifications are made. Results of interest to experimentalists can be obtained by the new perturbation method, but they will not be presented here. No quantitative calculations have as yet been made for any of the problems considered in this report, but the theory has reached a point where such calculations are feasible and desirable.

2. INTERACTING PHONONS IN AN IDEAL NON-CONDUCTING CRYSTAL: HAMILTONIAN

The vibrations of the nuclei in a crystal are described here in terms of the displacements of the nuclei from rigid-lattice equilibrium positions, which are defined below in terms of the Born-Oppenheimer approximation. The crystal is assumed to be perfect, having no impurities, vacancies, interstitials, grain boundaries, dislocations, or disorder.

If the nuclei are all fixed in their rigid-lattice equilibrium positions, the resulting crystal can be considered as constructed from a large number of identical (except near the surface) cells packed together with no space left over. A cell of this sort containing the least number of nuclei is called a unit cell of the crystal. The shape of the unit cell for a particular crystal is not uniquely defined, but in the following discussion it is assumed that some choice has been made.

In the particular unit cell which contains the origin of coordinates the different nuclei will be designated by indices n running from 1 to n_o. The rigid-lattice equilibrium positions of all the nuclei in the crystal then will be designated by vectors $\vec{R}_{sn}$ which are given by

$$\vec{R}_{sn} = \vec{s} + \vec{R}_{on}. \qquad (2\text{-}1)$$

Here $\vec{R}_{on}$ is the position of nucleus n in the unit cell on the origin, $\vec{s}$ is a crystal translation vector (a vector from the origin to the equivalent point in another unit cell in the crystal), and the arrow over a letter which designates a vector is omitted when the letter appears as a subscript (as with $\vec{s}$ in $\vec{R}_{sn}$). Each of the translation vectors $\vec{s}$ can be written as an integral linear combination of three primitive translation vectors, $\vec{a}_1$, $\vec{a}_2$, and $\vec{a}_3$ as follows:

$$\vec{s} = s_1\vec{a}_1 + s_2\vec{a}_2 + s_3\vec{a}_3. \qquad (2\text{-}2)$$

Here s_1, s_2, and s_3 are positive or negative integers or zero.

Finally, the actual positions of all the nuclei in the crystal will be designated by vectors $\vec{r}_{sn}$, each equal to the corresponding equilibrium vector $\vec{R}_{sn}$ plus a displacement vector $\vec{u}_{sn}$. A position vector $\vec{r}_{sn}$ is therefore given by the following equation:

$$\vec{r}_{sn} = \vec{R}_{sn} + \vec{u}_{sn}. \qquad (2\text{-}3)$$

For an ideal, non-conducting crystal the Born-Oppenheimer or adiabatic approximation offers a good starting point for a quantum-mechanical treatment. In this approximation a ground-state electronic wave function for the crystal is calculated from a Hamiltonian which neglects the nuclear kinetic energy and thus assumes a rigid lattice. The electronic wave function and the total crystal energy obtained from this Hamiltonian only depend upon the nuclear coordinates as parameters. The total wave function for the crystal is then written as the product of a nuclear wave function and this rigid-lattice electronic wave function, the nuclear coordinates appearing in both. To a good approximation, the nuclear wave function can be determined from a Hamiltonian consisting of just the kinetic energies of all the nuclei and a potential energy which is the rigid-lattice energy determined in the original electronic calculation. In the Born-Oppenheimer approximation, therefore, the electrons are taken to follow the nuclear motions without excitations and without inertia, on the assumption that any electronic excitation would require an appreciable energy transfer.

In the standard treatment of the nuclear part of the problem, the potential energy in the nuclear Hamiltonian described above is expanded in powers of the displacements of the nuclei from their equilibrium rigid-lattice positions. The resulting Hamiltonian can then be written in the following form:

$$H = H^{(2)} + V, \tag{2-4}$$

where $H^{(2)}$ includes all the terms through second order in products of the displacements and V includes all the terms of higher order. The energies $H^{(2)}$ and V will be called the harmonic and anharmonic energies respectively.

The harmonic energy $H^{(2)}$ in Eq. (2-4) is given by the following equation:

$$H^{(2)} = \varepsilon_o + \frac{1}{2}\Sigma_{sn} m_n |\dot{\vec{u}}_{sn}|^2 + V^{(2)}, \tag{2-5}$$

where

$$V^{(2)} = \Sigma_{s,s'}\Sigma_{n,n'}\Sigma_{\alpha,\alpha'} C^{(2)}_{s-s',nn'\alpha\alpha'} u_{sn\alpha} u_{s'n'\alpha'}. \tag{2-6}$$

In these equations ε_o is the equilibrium rigid-lattice energy of the crystal, m_n is the mass of a nucleus of type n, $\vec{u}_{sn}$ is a nuclear displacement as defined in Eq. (2-3), the dot over $\vec{u}_{sn}$ designates a time derivative, and $u_{sn\alpha}$ is the α'th rectangular component of the vector $\vec{u}_{sn}$. For a proper Hamiltonian, of course, the kinetic energy terms in Eq. (2-5) should be rewritten explicitly in terms of the conjugate momenta $\vec{p}_{sn}$, where each $\vec{p}_{sn}$ is equal to $m_n\dot{\vec{u}}_{sn}$.

The anharmonic energy V in Eq. (2-4) is given by the following equation:

$$V = \sum_{\nu=3}^{\infty} V^{(\nu)}, \tag{2-7}$$

where

$$V^{(\nu)} = \Sigma_{s_1,s_2,\ldots s_\nu}\Sigma_{n_1,n_2,\ldots n_\nu}\Sigma_{\alpha_1,\alpha_2,\ldots\alpha_\nu} C^{(\nu)}_{s_1n_1\alpha_1,s_2n_2\alpha_2,\ldots s_\nu n_\nu\alpha_\nu} \times u_{s_1n_1\alpha_1}u_{s_2n_2\alpha_2}\cdots u_{s_\nu n_\nu\alpha_\nu}. \tag{2-8}$$

2. INTERACTING PHONONS IN AN IDEAL NON-CONDUCTING CRYSTAL: HAMILTONIAN

Each of the coefficients $C^{(\nu)}\ldots$ (including ν equals 2) in the foregoing equations is proportional to a ν'th-order derivative of the rigid-lattice energy, evaluated for the equilibrium lattice. Each is essentially an atomic force constant, therefore.

The second-order coefficients $C^{(2)}_{\vec{s}-\vec{s}', nn'\alpha\alpha'}$ only depend on the cell positions $\vec{s}$ and $\vec{s}'$ through the separation vector $\vec{s}-\vec{s}'$. This is because of the equivalence of all the unit cells in the infinite crystal. In addition the second-order coefficients obey the following symmetry relations:

$$C^{(2)}_{s, nn'\alpha\alpha'} = C^{(2)}_{-s, n'n\alpha'\alpha}. \tag{2-9}$$

In general the expectation value of a ν'th-order potential energy term $V^{(\nu)}$ (including ν equals 2) is of the order of magnitude $\omega(u/a)^{\nu-2}$ per unit volume. Here ω is a characteristic nuclear vibration frequency, u is an average nuclear displacement for a given temperature, and a is the smallest equilibrium distance between two nuclei. At the melting point of the crystal u is smaller than a, but it is of the same order or magnitude. At temperatures which are low compared to the melting point, however, u is much smaller than a. Under these circumstances the expectation values of the terms $V^{(\nu)}$ decrease rapidly with increasing ν, and V itself can be considered as a small term in the Hamiltonian of Eq. (2-4). This fact provides the basis for the use of perturbation methods in treating the effects of anharmonic forces on crystal vibration phenomena.

3. THE CLASSICAL THEORY OF LATTICE VIBRATIONS

The classical theory of lattice vibrations is described here as a means of introducing concepts and notations which will be used throughout this report. The theory is the Born-von Kármán theory, and complete descriptions of it may be found in many books and articles (Liebfried, 1955; Born and Huang, 1954).

In the Born-von Kármán theory anharmonic forces are entirely neglected. The Hamiltonian for the system is therefore given by Eq. (2-4) with V set equal to zero, and it is just equal to $H^{(2)}$. The equilibrium lattice is defined somewhat differently in the classical problem than in the quantum-mechanical problem, but this does not affect the form of the Hamiltonian. The equations of motion for the nuclei are obtained from the Hamiltonian $H^{(2)}$ by use of Hamilton's equations, and they are given by:

$$m_n \ddot{u}_{sn\alpha} = -2\Sigma_{s'n'\alpha'} C^{(2)}_{s-s', nn'\alpha\alpha'} u_{s'n'\alpha'} . \qquad (3\text{-}1)$$

The mathematical treatment of the equations of motion is simplified by use of the periodic boundary conditions of Born and von Kármán. For this the crystal is taken to be a parallelopiped with its edges parallel to the principal translation vectors $\vec{a}_1$, $\vec{a}_2$, and $\vec{a}_3$ and with L unit cells along each direction. This crystal contains N_o unit cells, where N_o equals L^3, and it has a volume Ω, where Ω equals $N_o v_o$, v_o being the volume of a unit cell. The total number of cells, N_o, is taken to be very large. The crystal is then extended in all directions to infinity by translations $L\vec{s}$ of the original crystal, where $\vec{s}$ is any translation vector of the form shown in Eq. (2-2) The resulting infinite crystal is exactly periodic at every instant of time, and a nuclear displacement $\vec{u}_{s'n}$ is identical to another displacement $\vec{u}_{s''n}$ if the separation vector $\vec{s}''-\vec{s}'$ is equal to one of the translations $L\vec{s}$. The number of degrees of freedom of this infinite crystal is finite and equal to $3n_oN_o$.

Consider the following plane wave as a trial solution to the equations of motion (3-1):

$$\vec{u}_{sn} = a_q m_n^{-1/2} [\vec{e}_q^{(n)} \cos(\vec{s} \cdot \vec{q}) + \vec{f}_q^{(n)} \sin(\vec{s} \cdot \vec{q})] . \qquad (3\text{-}2)$$

Here $\vec{q}$ is the wave vector of the plane wave, a_q is a real amplitude coordinate, and $\vec{e}_q^{(n)}$ and $\vec{f}_q^{(n)}$ are real vector coefficients which determine the phase and polarization of the wave. If this vibrational wave is to satisfy the periodic boundary conditions, the dot product of $\vec{q}$ with any of the crystal translation vectors $L\vec{s}$ must be equal to an integral multiple of 2π. To explain the effect of this condition it is usual to introduce the reciprocal lattice.

The reciprocal lattice for a particular crystal is the infinite, periodic lattice which is defined by a particular set of primary translation vectors, $\vec{b}_1$, $\vec{b}_2$, and $\vec{b}_3$. These vectors are determined by the following set of equations:

$$\vec{a}_i \cdot \vec{b}_j = \delta_{ij}. \tag{3-3}$$

Here $\vec{a}_1$, $\vec{a}_2$, and $\vec{a}_3$ are the primary translation vectors of the real crystal, and δ_{ij} is a Kronecker delta. A translation vector of the reciprocal lattice then can be written in the following way:

$$\vec{\tau} = \tau_1\vec{b}_1 + \tau_2\vec{b}_2 + \tau_3\vec{b}_3. \tag{3-4}$$

Here τ_1, τ_2, and τ_3 are positive or negative integers or zero. The translation vector $\vec{\tau}$ has the important property that its dot product with any translation vector $\vec{s}$ of the real crystal is an integer, as is easily verified by examination of Eqs. (2-2), (3-3) and (3-4).

In terms of the above definitions the trial wave of Eq. (3-2) satisfies the periodic boundary conditions if and only if the wave vector $\vec{q}$ satisfies the following equation:

$$\vec{q} = 2\pi\,(\vec{\tau}/L), \tag{3-5}$$

where $\vec{\tau}$ is one of the translation vectors of the reciprocal lattice. The dot product of such a wave vector with a translation vector $L\vec{s}$ is clearly equal to an integral multiple of 2π, as required.

Not all of the wave vectors $\vec{q}$ satisfying Eq. (3-5) give different trial solutions when used in Eq. (3-2), however. In the first place, using $\vec{q}$ plus any of the vectors $2\pi\vec{\tau}$ for $\vec{q}$ in that equation gives essentially the same trial solution as using $\vec{q}$ itself. The coefficients $\vec{e}_q^{\,(n)}$ and $\vec{f}_q^{\,(n)}$ can therefore be taken to obey the following relation:

$$\vec{e}_{q+2\pi\tau}^{\,(n)} = \vec{e}_q^{\,(n)}, \quad \vec{f}_{q+2\pi\tau}^{\,(n)} = \vec{f}_q^{\,(n)}. \tag{3-6}$$

Furthermore, using $-\vec{q}$ for $\vec{q}$ in Eq. (3-2) gives essentially the same trial solution as using $\vec{q}$ itself. The coefficients $\vec{e}_q^{\,(n)}$ and $\vec{f}_q^{\,(n)}$ can therefore be taken to obey the following relations in addition to those in Eq. (3-6):

$$\vec{e}_{-q}^{\,(n)} = \vec{e}_q^{\,(n)}, \quad \vec{f}_{-q}^{\,(n)} = -\vec{f}_q^{\,(n)}. \tag{3-7}$$

On the basis of Eqs. (3-6) and (3-7) the coefficients $\vec{e}_q^{\,(n)}$ and $\vec{f}_q^{\,(n)}$ are periodic functions in $\vec{q}$-space, and they are symmetric and antisymmetric respectively on inversion of $\vec{q}$. They are only defined at the discrete values of $\vec{q}$ given in Eq. (3-5), but as N_o approaches infinity these values approach a continuum.

In view of the results above, all the different allowed trial solutions of the form of Eq. (3-2) can be obtained by considering only a finite set of wave vectors $\vec{q}$. The wave vectors in this set are conveniently defined (to within an inversion) by the following three conditions: first, each satisfies Eq. (3-5); second, each belongs to the central unit cell in $\vec{q}$-space (which is understood to be just the ordinary first Brillouin zone of the crystal); and, third, no one is the inverse of any other. These vectors will be described hereafter as those belonging to half the central unit cell in $\vec{q}$-space. The linear independence or orthogonality of two trial solutions with different wave vectors in this set can be established by use of the orthogonality relations for the functions $\sin \vec{s} \cdot \vec{q}$ and $\cos \vec{s} \cdot \vec{q}$.

In the discussion which follows there should really be special consideration of complications which arise for wave vectors which are zero or belong to the surface of a unit cell. This is omitted for the sake of brevity, but it should be remembered that these complications do exist.

When the trial solution of Eq. (3-2) is substituted into the equation of motion, Eq. (3-1), the following equation is obtained:

$$\ddot{a}_q m_n^{1/2}[e_{q\alpha}^{(n)}\cos(\vec{s} \cdot \vec{q}) + f_{q\alpha}^{(n)}\cos(\vec{s} \cdot \vec{q})]$$

$$= -2a_q \Sigma_{n'\alpha'}(m_n m_{n'})^{1/2}\Big\{[C_{qnn'\alpha\alpha'}^{(2)}\cos(\vec{s} \cdot \vec{q}) + S_{qnn'\alpha\alpha'}^{(2)}\sin(\vec{s} \cdot \vec{q})]\, e_{q\alpha'}^{(n')}$$

$$+ [C_{qnn'\alpha\alpha'}^{(2)}\sin(\vec{s} \cdot \vec{q}) - S_{qnn'\alpha\alpha'}^{(2)}\cos(\vec{s} \cdot \vec{q})]\, f_{q\alpha'}^{(n')}\Big\}, \tag{3-8}$$

where

$$C_{qnn'\alpha\alpha'} = (m_n m_{n'})^{-1/2}\Sigma_{sn} C_{snn'\alpha\alpha'}^{(2)}\cos(\vec{s} \cdot \vec{q}) \tag{3-9}$$

and

$$S_{qnn'\alpha\alpha'} = (m_n m_{n'})^{-1/2}\Sigma_{sn} C_{snn'\alpha\alpha'}^{(2)}\sin(\vec{s} \cdot \vec{q}). \tag{3-10}$$

Because of Eq. (2-9) the new quantities $C_{qnn'\alpha\alpha'}$ and $S_{qnn'\alpha\alpha'}$ obey the following useful symmetry relations:

$$C_{-q,\,nn'\alpha\alpha'} = C_{qnn'\alpha\alpha'},\quad S_{-q,\,nn'\alpha\alpha'} = -S_{qnn'\alpha\alpha'}. \tag{3-11}$$

It is now assumed that the quantity $\ddot{a}_q$ in Eq. (3-8) can be replaced by $-\omega_q^2 a_q$, where ω_q^2 is real and positive. Under this assumption a_q obeys the equation of motion of a linear harmonic oscillator of frequency ω_q. On the basis of this assumption and the orthogonality relations for $\sin \vec{s} \cdot \vec{q}$ and $\cos \vec{s} \cdot \vec{q}$, Eq. (3-8) can be transformed to the following pair of equations:

$$2\Sigma_{n'\alpha'}[C_{qnn'\alpha\alpha'}e_{q\alpha'}^{(n')} - S_{qnn'\alpha\alpha'}f_{q\alpha'}^{(n')}] = \omega_q^2 e_{q\alpha}^{(n)}$$

$$2\Sigma_{n'\alpha'}[S_{qnn'\alpha\alpha'}e_{q\alpha'}^{(n')} + C_{qnn'\alpha\alpha'}f_{q\alpha'}^{(n')}] = \omega_q^2 f_{q\alpha}^{(n)} \qquad (3\text{-}12)$$

These equations are actually quite practical, since there are only a few of them for each value of the wave vector $\vec{q}$ (as will be seen below), and since the summations in the associated equations (3-9) and (3-10) only involve a few terms and can be calculated for reasonable models of many crystals.

For a particular wave vector $\vec{q}$, Eqs. (3-12) define a standard eigenvalue problem. The associated secular equation is of order $6n_o$ in general, since α runs over the three rectangular components of a vector, n runs over the n_o nuclei in a single unit cell, and both $\vec{e}_q^{(n)}$ and $\vec{f}_q^{(n)}$ are to be determined. The number of eigenvalues of a secular equation is equal to the order of the equation. In the present case, then, there must be $6n_o$ eigenvalues ω_q^2. For each of these $6n_o$ eigenvalues there is an independent eigenvector $(\vec{e}_q^{(n)}, \vec{f}_q^{(n)})$, where the first vector in parentheses is the coefficient of cos $(\vec{s} \cdot \vec{q})$ and the second of sin $(\vec{s} \cdot \vec{q})$ in the trial solution of Eq. (3-2). For each eigenvector $(\vec{e}_q^{(n)}, \vec{f}_q^{(n)})$, however, there is a second, $(-\vec{f}_q^{(n)}, \vec{e}_q^{(n)})$, having the same wave vector, which is degenerate with the first. For a given wave vector $\vec{q}$, then, there are only $3n_o$ eigenvalues which can be different. These $3n_o$ eigenvalues will be written as ω_{qj}^2 with j running from 1 to $3n_o$. The two independent eigenvectors corresponding to an eigenvalue ω_{qj}^2 will then be written as $(\vec{e}_{qj}^{(n)}, \vec{f}_{qj}^{(n)})$ and $(-\vec{f}_{qj}^{(n)}, \vec{e}_{qj}^{(n)})$.

The following set of equations express the condition for the linear independence of different eigenvectors with the same wave vector, and they also express a convenient normalization for the eigenvectors:

$$\Sigma_n[\vec{e}_{qj}^{(n)} \cdot \vec{e}_{qj'}^{(n)} + \vec{f}_{qj}^{(n)} \cdot \vec{f}_{qj'}^{(n)}] = \delta_{jj'},$$

$$\Sigma_n[-\vec{e}_{qj}^{(n)} \cdot \vec{f}_{qj'}^{(n)} + \vec{f}_{qj}^{(n)} \cdot \vec{e}_{qj'}^{(n)}] = 0. \qquad (3\text{-}13)$$

Here j and j' can each have any one of $3n_o$ values. The orthogonality expressed by these equations can be proved directly from Eqs. (3-12).

The eigenvalues and eigenvectors discussed above comprise the solutions of Eqs. (3-12). If one of these solutions is substituted into Eq. (3-8), that equation reduces to the expected harmonic oscillator equation for the appropriate amplitude coordinate. This result justifies the assumption made in the derivation of Eqs. (3-12). Each solution describes what is called a normal mode of vibration for the crystal, and the associated amplitude coordinate is called the amplitude of the normal mode. There are found to be just $3n_oN_o$ independent normal modes, and this is just equal to the original number of degrees of freedom, as should be expected.

At this point it is useful to mention a few characteristics of the solutions discussed above. For a given wave vector $\vec{q}$, there are eigenvalues ω_{qj}^2 with j running from 1 through $3n_o$. If the order of the indices j is chosen to arrange the eigenvalues in order of increasing magnitude, the frequency ω_{qj} for a given j can be considered a continuous function of $\vec{q}$ (in the limit of infinite N_o). Since there are $3n_o$ values for j, there are $3n_o$ such frequency functions. Three of these functions are found to become proportional to the magnitude q as $\vec{q}$ approaches zero, and these frequencies correspond to acoustic vibrational modes of the crystal. The acoustic modes with $\vec{q}$ equal to zero represent pure translations of the crystal. The remaining $3(n_o-1)$ frequency functions approach non-zero values as $\vec{q}$ approaches zero, and these correspond to optical vibrational modes. The modes themselves (acoustic and optical) are both longitudinal and transverse, and there are two modes for each frequency.

The solutions discussed above are all obtained by considering only the wave vectors $\vec{q}$ in half of the central unit cell in $\vec{q}$-space. For later work, however, it is useful to consider other values of $\vec{q}$ as well. The solution for an arbitrary value of $\vec{q}$ can be obtained from the basic solutions by use of Eqs. (3-6) and (3-7). When these equations are used, the following relations are obtained:

$$\vec{e}_{q+2\pi\tau,\,j} = \vec{e}^{(n)}_{q,\,j}, \quad \vec{f}_{q+2\pi\tau,\,j} = \vec{f}^{(n)}_{qj}, \quad \omega^2_{q+2\pi\tau,\,j} = \omega^2_{qj}$$

$$\vec{e}^{(n)}_{-q,\,j} = \vec{e}^{(n)}_{qj}, \quad \vec{f}^{(n)}_{-qj} = -\vec{f}^{(n)}_{qj}, \quad \omega^2_{-qj} = \omega^2_{qj}. \tag{3-14}$$

These relations should be taken to mean that the wave vector associated with a particular normal mode or frequency is only defined modulo $2\pi\vec{\tau}$ and to within an inversion. The reason for this convention will become clear in later sections.

The instantaneous displacement of an individual nucleus in a crystal is equal to the sum of its instantaneous displacements in each of the normal modes of the crystal. This fact is expressed in the following equation:

$$\vec{u}_{sn} = (2N_o m_n)^{-1/2} \Sigma_q^{u.c.} \Sigma_j \Big\{ a_{qj}[\vec{e}^{(n)}_{qj} \cos(\vec{s}\cdot\vec{q}) + \vec{f}^{(n)}_{qj} \sin(\vec{s}\cdot\vec{q})]$$

$$+ a'_{qj}[-\vec{f}^{(n)}_{qj} \cos(\vec{s}\cdot\vec{q}) + \vec{e}^{(n)}_{qj} \sin(\vec{s}\cdot\vec{q})] \,. \tag{3-15}$$

Here the superscript u. c. on the summation sign indicates that the summation is to run over the entire central cell in $\vec{q}$-space, and the constant factor $(2N_o)^{-1/2}$, which does not appear in Eq. (3-2), has been introduced to simplify later expressions. The summation on $\vec{q}$ only needs to run over half a unit cell to include all the different normal modes, but it is formally convenient to extend it as shown. With this extension, each normal mode having a general wave vector appears twice.

If the extension of the summation in Eq. (3-15) is to make sense, the amplitude of a particular normal mode must be taken to be independent of how the wave vector of the mode is specified. On the basis of Eqs. (3-14) for the normal modes, then, the amplitudes can be taken to obey the following relations:

$$\alpha_{q+2\pi\tau,j} = \alpha_{qj}, \quad \alpha'_{q+2\pi\tau,j} = \alpha'_{qj}$$

$$\alpha_{-q,j} = \alpha_{qj}, \quad \alpha'_{-q,j} = -\alpha'_{qj} \tag{3-16}$$

These relations are obviously more general than is required for Eq. (3-15), but they will prove useful in later work.

Eq. (3-15) can be described as a transformation to normal coordinates for the vibrating crystal. The normal coordinates are the independent amplitudes of the normal mode vibrations. As shown by earlier results the number of degrees of freedom of the system is preserved by this transformation.

The harmonic Hamiltonian for a crystal can be obtained in terms of the normal coordinates by substituting the transformation of Eq. (3-15) into the energy expression of Eq. (2-5). The resulting Hamiltonian must correspond to an infinite energy, since Eq. (2-5) must be taken to give the energy of the infinite crystal with periodic boundary conditions. The energy per independent region of the infinite crystal is easily extracted, however, and this is given by the following equation:

$$H^{(2)} = \varepsilon_o + (1/4)\,\Sigma_q^{u.c.}\,\Sigma_{j=1}^{3n_o}\,[\dot{\alpha}_{qj}^2 + \dot{\alpha}'^2_{qj}) + \omega_{qj}^2(\alpha_{qj}^2 + \alpha'^2_{qj})]\,. \tag{3-17}$$

The symbols $H^{(2)}$ and ε_o used here are the same as those used in Eq. (2-5), but they are now to be interpreted as energies per independent region of the crystal, such a region containing N_o cells and having a volume $\mathbf{\Omega}$. The Hamiltonian $H^{(2)}$ with its new meaning still involves all of the degrees of freedom of the infinite crystal, and it is a perfectly good Hamiltonian on which to base either a classical or a quantum-mechanical description of the infinite crystal. In Eq. (3-17) for $H^{(2)}$ the contribution for each normal mode with a general wave vector appears twice because the summation on $\vec{q}$ again runs over an entire unit cell in $\vec{q}$-space.

Eq. (3-17) may be used to verify various properties of the transformation to normal coordinates. In the first place, the equations of motion for the normal coordinates are easily obtained from it by use of Hamilton's equations. The momenta which are conjugate to the coordinates α_{qj} and α'_{qj} are $\dot{\alpha}_{qj}$ and $\dot{\alpha}'_{qj}$ respectively. The equations of motion are therefore found to be

$$\ddot{a}_{qj} = -\omega_{qj}^2 a_{qj}, \quad \ddot{a}'_{qj} = -\omega_{qj}^2 a'_{qj}, \tag{3-18}$$

and these are the equations of motion of simple harmonic oscillators, as expected.

In the second place, the eigenvalues ω_{qj}^2 can be proved to be positive from the form of $H^{(2)}$ in Eq. (3-17), and they must be positive if Eqs. (3-18) are to lead to undamped harmonic oscillation. The eigenvalues are positive because the potential energy in $H^{(2)}$ must be positive for every set of values of the normal coordinates, this energy being the deviation of the potential energy of the crystal from its minimum in the limit of small nuclear displacements (when V is negligible).

Since the solutions of the equations of motion (3-18) are well known, the classical problem of lattice vibrations in the harmonic approximation is solved. Once the procedures outlined above have been carried out, it is only necessary to specify a set of initial conditions in order to know the nuclear displacements of a crystal at ever instant of time.

As a final note, it is useful to express the nuclear displacements of a crystal in terms of complex modes instead of the real modes of Eq. (3-15). This is done by rewriting the trigonometric functions in Eq. (3-15) in terms of exponentials, and the result is as follows:

$$\vec{u}_{sn} = (2N_o m_n)^{-1/2} \Sigma_q^{u.c.} \Sigma_{j=1}^{3n_o} (a_{qj} - ia'_{qj}) [\vec{e}_{qj}^{(n)} - if_{qj}^{(n)}) e^{i q \cdot s}] . \tag{3-19}$$

In this expansion each pair of indices $\vec{q}$ and j designates a distinct complex mode, and there are $3n_oN_o$ such modes, which is the same as the number of distinct real modes. The amplitude of a complex mode is itself complex, and it has no simple behavior under inversion of $\vec{q}$. Since both a_{qj} and a'_{qj} oscillate harmonically with the same frequency ω_{qj}, the complex amplitude $(a_{qj} - ia'_{qj})$ also oscillates harmonically with this frequency.

4. QUANTIZATION OF LATTICE VIBRATIONS; CREATION AND ANNIHILATION OPERATORS

The quantum theory of harmonic lattice vibrations is based on the harmonic Hamiltonian $H^{(2)}$ which is given in Eq. (3-17). It thus assumes that the secular equation arising from Eqs. (3-12) have been solved and that the normal modes and their frequencies are known. The harmonic Hamiltonian $H^{(2)}$ is then quantized in a fashion familiar from second quantization in field theory. This procedure is outlined below.

The momenta conjugate to the normal coordinates a_{qj} and a'_{qj} will be symbolized by p_{qj} and p'_{qj} respectively, as mentioned in Section 3. These momenta are given by the following equations:

$$p_{qj} = \dot{a}_{qj}, \; p'_{qj} = \dot{a}'_{qj}. \qquad (4\text{-}1)$$

In view of Eqs. (3-16), these momenta must have the following symmetry properties:

$$p_{q+2\pi\tau,\, j} = p_{qj}, \; p'_{q+2\pi\tau,\, j} = p'_{qj},$$

$$p_{-q,\, j} = p_{qj}, \; p'_{-q,\, j} = p'_{qj}. \qquad (4\text{-}2)$$

Quantization proceeds by treating the normal coordinates a_{qj} and a'_{qj} and their conjugate momenta p_{qj} and p'_{qj} as operators, although retaining in them the symmetry with respect to $\vec{q}$ of the classical quantities. As operators they are taken to obey the following set of commutation rules:

$$[p_{qj}, a_{q'j'}] = (\hbar/i)\delta_{jj'} \times \begin{cases} 1 \text{ if } \vec{q}' = \vec{q} + 2\pi\vec{\tau} \text{ or } \vec{q}' = -\vec{q}' = 2\pi\vec{\tau} \\ 0 \text{ otherwise} \end{cases}$$

$$[p'_{qj}, a'_{q'j'}] = (\hbar/i)\delta_{jj'} \times \begin{cases} 1 \text{ if } \vec{q}' = \vec{q} + 2\pi\vec{\tau} \neq -\vec{q} + 2\pi\vec{\tau}' \\ -1 \text{ if } \vec{q}' = -\vec{q} + 2\pi\vec{\tau} \neq +\vec{q} + 2\pi\vec{\tau}' \\ 0 \text{ otherwise} \end{cases}$$

$$\text{All other commutators} = 0. \qquad (4\text{-}3)$$

Here the symbol $[x, y]$ denotes the commutator of the operators x and y (which is just the operator xy-yx), $\hbar$ is $h/2\pi$, the reduced Planck's constant, $\vec{\tau}$ is any vector of the reciprocal lattice, and "all other commutators" means all those which can be obtained by choosing pairs from the normal coordinates and their conjugate momenta.

The commutation rules discussed above are somewhat different than those which are usual for coordinates and momenta because the indices $\vec{q}$ and j do not always designate distinct operators. They reduce to the ordinary rules if the wave vectors $\vec{q}$ and $\vec{q}'$ are restricted to half of the central unit cell in $\vec{q}$-space, however.

As in field theory it is convenient at this point to introduce a transformation from the operators defined above to creation and annihilation operators. This transformation is defined by the following equations:

$$a_{qj} = (1/2)(\omega_{qj}/\hbar)^{1/2}(a_{qj}-ia'_{qj}) + (1/2)i(\hbar\omega_{qj})^{-1/2}(p_{qj}-ip'_{qj}),$$

$$a^*_{qj} = (1/2)(\omega_{qj}/\hbar)^{1/2}(a_{qj}+ia'_{qj}) - (1/2)i(\hbar\omega_{qj})^{-1/2}(p_{qj}+ip'_{qj}). \qquad (4\text{-}4)$$

Here a^*_{qj} and a_{qj} are respectively creation and annihilation operators, and one is the Hermitian conjugate of the other.

On the basis of Eqs. (4-4) the coordinate and momentum operators can be written out in terms of the creation and annihilation operators as follows:

$$a_{qj} = \frac{1}{2}(\hbar/\omega_{qj})^{1/2}\,[(a^*_{qj}+a_{qj}) + (a^*_{-q,j}+a_{-q,j})]$$

$$p_{qj} = i\frac{1}{2}(\hbar\omega_{qj})^{1/2}\,[(a^*_{qj}-a_{qj}) + (a^*_{-q,j}-a_{-q,j})]$$

$$a'_{qj} = -i\frac{1}{2}(\hbar/\omega_{qj})^{1/2}\,[(a^*_{qj}-a_{qj}) - (a^*_{-q,j}-a_{-q,j})]$$

$$p_{qj} = \frac{1}{2}(\hbar\omega_{qj})^{1/2}\,[(a^*_{qj}+a_{qj}) - (a^*_{-q,j}+a_{-q,j})]\,. \qquad (4\text{-}5)$$

By the nature of their definitions a^*_{qj} and a_{qj} are both transformed into different operators by the inversion of $\vec{q}$. This fact is reflected in the appearance of these operators with both plus and minus $\vec{q}$ in Eqs. (4-5). In order to define all the distinct operators a^*_{qj} and a_{qj}, therefore, it is necessary to consider all the wave vectors in a whole unit cell in $\vec{q}$-space. In view of this there are $6n_oN_o$ distinct creation and annihilation operators just as there were $6n_oN_o$ distinct coordinate and momentum operators.

In view of Eqs. (3-16) and (4-2) the creation and annihilation operators are carried into themselves by lattice translations in $\vec{q}$- space. This is expressed by the following equations:

$$a_{q+2\pi\tau,\,j} = a_{qj}, \quad a^*_{q+2\pi\tau,\,j} = a_{qj}. \qquad (4\text{-}6)$$

Although the creation and annihilation operators do not have the simple properties under inversion which the coordinate and momentum operators have, they have the advantage of very simple and useful commutation rules. These rules are the following:

4. QUANTIZATION OF LATTICE VIBRATIONS: CREATION AND ANNIHILATION OPERATORS

$$[a_{qj}, a^*_{q'j'}] = \delta_{jj'}\Delta_{q-q'}$$

$$[a_{qj}, a_{q'j'}] = [a^*_{qj}, a^*_{q'j'}] = 0, \qquad (4\text{-}7)$$

where the wave vectors $\vec{q}$ and $\vec{q}'$ can be either general or special. The quantity Δ_q appearing here is defined by the following equation:

$$\Delta_q = \Sigma_\tau \delta_{q, 2\pi\tau}. \qquad (4\text{-}8)$$

It is therefore equal to one if $\vec{q}$ is equal to any vector $2\pi\vec{\tau}$ and zero otherwise.

If the harmonic Hamiltonian of Eq. (3-17) is written out in terms of creation and annihilation operators, on the basis of Eqs. (4-5), it is given by the following expression:

$$H^{(2)} = \varepsilon_o + \Sigma_q^{u.c.} \Sigma_{j=1}^{3n_o} \hbar\omega_{qj}(a^*_{qj}a_{qj} + \frac{1}{2}). \qquad (4\text{-}9)$$

In this form the Hamiltonian is a sum of $3n_oN_o$ terms, each of which is independent of the others.

The eigenfunctions and eigenvalues of the Hamiltonian given above can be constructed formally in a very simple way. Each eigenfunction can be generated (to within a normalizing constant) by the operation of some product of creation operators on the ground-state eigenfunction. The corresponding eigenvalue is then given by the following expression:

$$\varepsilon_o + \Sigma_q^{u.c.} \Sigma_{j=1}^{3n_o} \hbar\omega_{qj}(n_{qj} + \frac{1}{2}), \qquad (4\text{-}10)$$

where n_{qj} is the number of times (including zero) that the operator a^*_{qj} appears in the product which generates the eigenfunction. These facts are easily verified by operating on the proposed eigenfunctions with the Hamiltonian of Eq. (4-9) and by then using the commutation relations (4-7) and the fact that an annihilation operator operating on the ground state wave function gives zero.

Each eigenfunction generated by a product of creation operators is uniquely characterized by the set of $3n_oN_o$ numbers n_{qj} which tell the number of times the creation operator of each mode appears in the product. The order of the creation operators in a product is immaterial. The orthogonality of different eigenfunctions is easily proved by use of the commutation relations (4-7).

If Eq. (3-19) for the nuclear displacements is written out in terms of creation and annihilation operators on the basis of Eqs. (4-5), the result is as follows:

$$\vec{u}_{sn} = \Sigma_q^{u.c.} \Sigma_j (2m_nN_o\omega_{qj})^{-1/2}(a_{qj} + a^*_{-q,j})(\vec{e}^{(n)}_{qj} - i\vec{f}^{(n)}_{qj})e^{i\vec{q}\cdot\vec{s}} \qquad (4\text{-}11)$$

or

$$\vec{u}_{sn} = \Sigma_q^{u.c.} \Sigma_j (2m_n N_o \omega_{qj})^{-1/2} \Big\{ a_{qj}(\vec{e}_{qj}^{(n)} - i\vec{f}_{qj}^{(n)}) e^{i\vec{q}\cdot\vec{s}} + a^*_{-q,j}(\vec{e}_{qj}^{(n)} + i\vec{f}_{qj}^{(n)}) e^{-i\vec{q}\cdot\vec{s}} \Big\}. \qquad (4\text{-}12)$$

From either of these equations it can be shown that the expectation value of a nuclear displacement is zero for any eigenstate of $H^{(2)}$, as should be expected.

The time-dependence of the operator for a nuclear displacement can be obtained from that of the appropriate creation and annihilation operators. Since all of the matrix elements of an annihilation operator a_{qj} between the eigenfunctions defined above are independent of time, a_{qj} must obey the following equation

$$\dot{a}_{qj} = (i\hbar)^{-1} [a_{qj}, H^{(2)}], \qquad (4\text{-}13)$$

which is obtained from the Heisenberg equation of motion. On use of the Hamiltonian $H^{(2)}$ as given in Eq. (4-9) and the commutation rules, this becomes:

$$\dot{a}_{qj} = -i\omega_{qj} a_{qj}, \qquad (4\text{-}14)$$

which gives

$$a_{qj}(t) = a_{qj}(0) \exp(-i\omega_{qj} t). \qquad (4\text{-}15)$$

With this result the following expression is obtained from Eq. (4-12) for a nuclear displacement:

$$\vec{u}_{sn}(t) = \Sigma_q^{u.c.} \Sigma_j (2m_n N_o \omega_{qj})^{-1/2} \Big\{ a_{qj}(0)(\vec{e}_{qj}^{(n)} - i\vec{f}_{qj}^{(n)}) \exp[i(\vec{q}\cdot\vec{s} - \omega_{qj}t)] + a^*_{qj}(0)(\vec{e}_{qj}^{(n)} - i\vec{f}_{qj}^{(n)} \quad \exp[-i(\vec{q}\cdot\vec{s} - \omega_{qj}t)] \Big\}. \qquad (4\text{-}16)$$

The operator for a nuclear displacement is thus seen to be given by a linear combination of traveling waves with coefficients containing creation and annihilation operators. Each of these traveling waves is characterized by a single pair of indices $\vec{q}$ and j.

For convenience the quantum-mechanical vibrating crystal is generally described in terms of phonons. For each creation operator a^*_{qj} in the product which generates an eigenfunction of the vibrating crystal there is said to be a phonon $\vec{q}j$ in the crystal. For each phonon $\vec{q}j$ in a crystal, then, there is a contribution to the total energy of $\hbar\omega_{qj}$, according to Eq. (4-10). The phonon itself is therefore said to have an energy $\hbar\omega_{qj}$. A creation operator a^*_{qj} acting on any eigenfunction of the crystal produces another eigenfunction (to within a normalizing constant) with one more phonon $\vec{q}j$ than the original, and it is therefore said to create a phonon $\vec{q}j$. An annihilation operator a_{qj} acting on any eigenfunction can be shown to annihilate one phonon $\vec{q}j$ if there is such a phonon in the eigenfunction and to give zero if there is not. Because of the form of Eq. (4-16) each phonon is to be thought of as a traveling quantum of vibrational energy. The name "phonon" reflects the fact that sound waves in a crystal are just lattice vibrations of small $\vec{q}$, but the word is generally taken to apply to optical as well as acoustic vibrations.

5. FORMULATION OF THE PERTURBATION PROBLEM

In the preceding section the nuclear vibrations in a crystal were assumed to be determined entirely by the harmonic Hamiltonian $H^{(2)}$, and this led to a description of the vibrations in terms of independent phonons. The problem now is to determine the effects of the anharmonic energy V which appears with $H^{(2)}$ in the total Hamiltonian of Eq. (2-4). If V is sufficiently small, the concept of phonons is still meaningful, and V can just be regarded as causing interactions between the phonons. In this case the effects of V can be investigated by means of perturbation theory. In anticipation of such an investigation it is useful to study the complete Hamiltonian in some detail and to introduce an improved notation.

The Hamiltonian which is the basis of all of the work to follow is the quantum-mechanical form of the Hamiltonian H which is given by $H^{(2)} + V$. The harmonic part of this Hamiltonian, $H^{(2)}$, is given in a form suitable for present purposes in Eq. (4-9). The anharmonic part, V, can be obtained in a suitable form from Eqs. (2-7) and (2-8) by use of the transformation to creation and annihilation operators which is given in Eq. (4-5). The resulting anharmonic energy is infinite, since Eqs. (2-7) and (2-8) give the anharmonic energy of the infinite crystal with periodic boundary conditions, but the anharmonic energy per independent region, which is finite, is easily extracted from this. This anharmonic energy per independent region is given by the following equation:

$$V = \sum_{\nu=3}^{\infty} V^{(\nu)}, \tag{5-1}$$

where

$$V^{(\nu)} = (8\pi^3/N_o v_o)^{(\nu/2)-1} \Sigma^{u.c.}_{q_1, q_2, \ldots q_\nu} \Sigma_{j_1, j_2, \ldots j_\nu} B^{(\nu)}_{q_1 j_1, q_2 j_2, \ldots q_\nu j_\nu}$$

$$\times [a_{q_1 j_1} + a^*_{-q_1 j_1}][a_{q_2 j_2} + a^*_{-q_2 j_2}] \ldots [a_{q_\nu j_\nu} + a^*_{-q_\nu j_\nu}]$$

$$\times \Delta_{q_1 + q_2 + \ldots q_\nu}. \tag{5-2}$$

In the latter equation v_o is the volume of the unit cell of the crystal, and the factor $(8\pi^3/v_o)^{(\nu/2)-1}$ is introduced to simplify later expressions. The other quantities are discussed below.

The symbols V and $V^{(\nu)}$ used in Eqs. (5-1) and (5-2) are the same as were used in Eqs. (2-7) and (2-8), but they are now to be interpreted as energies per independent region of the infinite crystal. Since $H^{(2)}$ in Eq. (4-9) has a similar interpretation, the sum of the new $H^{(2)}$ and the new V gives a new total Hamiltonian H which also is an energy per independent region. Like $H^{(2)}$ this new total Hamiltonian H involves all the degrees of freedom of the infinite crystal, and it is perfectly adequate as the basis for a quantum-mechanical description of this crystal.

The quantity $\Delta_{q_1+q_2+\ldots q_\nu}$ which appears in Eq. (5-2) is equal to one or zero depending on whether the total wave vector $(\vec{q}_1+\vec{q}_2+\ldots\vec{q}_\nu)$ is or is not equal to one of the translation vectors of q-space, $2\pi\vec{\tau}$. It occurs in Eq. (5-2) as a result of the following equality:

$$(1/N_o)\,\Sigma_s\, e^{i\vec{q}\cdot\vec{s}} = \Delta_q; \tag{5-3}$$

and it leads to important consequences, which will be discussed later.

The quantity $B^{(\nu)}_{q_1j_1,q_2j_2,\ldots q_\nu j_\nu}$ appearing in Eq. (5-2) is essentially the Fourier transform of the appropriate coefficient $C^{(\nu)}_{s_1n_1\alpha_1,s_2n_2\alpha_2\ldots s_\nu n_\nu\alpha_\nu}$ in Eq. (2-8), but in view of the scope of the present report it need not be written out explicitly here. Several properties of this quantity should be mentioned, however. Most importantly, $B^{(\nu)}_{\ldots}$ turns out to be a finite quantity which is independent of the size of the crystal (as long as the crystal is reasonably large). It does contain a factor $[\omega_{q_1j_1}\omega_{q_2j_2}\ldots\omega_{q_\nu j_\nu}]^{-1/2}$ which can become infinite if one of the frequencies corresponds to an acoustical mode with a wave vector of zero (or $2\pi\vec{\tau}$), but the infinities arising from this factor are not important. In the few cases in which these infinities are not eliminated by weighting factors multiplying the coefficients $B^{(\nu)}_{\ldots}$, they are excluded explicitly on the ground that an acoustical mode with a wave vector zero (or $2\pi\vec{\tau}$) is just a pure translation of the crystal as a whole. Other properties of $B^{(\nu)}_{\ldots}$ are that it is unchanged by permutations of its index pairs $\vec{q}j$, and that it is changed into its complex conjugate by an inversion of all its wave vectors.

The effect of the perturbing term $V^{(\nu)}$ acting on an eigenstate of the harmonic Hamiltonian $H^{(2)}$ is easy to describe in the phonon representation. If the operators in square brackets in Eq. (5-2) for $V^{(\nu)}$ are multiplied together, $V^{(\nu)}$ is given by a linear combination of ν'th-order products of creation and annihilation operators. One such product operating on a phonon state gives either another phonon state (to within a normalizing constant) or zero. Because of the factor $\Delta_{q_1+q_2+\ldots q_\nu}$ multiplying each of these products of operators, however, the only new phonon states which can be generated are those having the same total wave vector, module $2\pi\vec{\tau}$, as the initial phonon state.

As an illustration, consider the following typical contribution to the third-order perturbing term $V^{(3)}$:

$$(8\pi^3/N_o v_o)^{1/2} B^{(3)}_{q_1j_1q_2j_2q_3j_3}\, a_{q_1j_1}\, a_{q_2j_2}\, a^*_{-q_3j_3}\, \Delta_{q_1+q_2+q_3}.$$

Let us apply this on a phonon state containing phonons $\vec{q}_1 j_1$ and $\vec{q}_2 j_2$ among others. Then $a^*_{-q_3 j_3}$ creates a phonon $-\vec{q}_3 j_3$, $a_{q_2 j_2}$ annihilates a phonon $\vec{q}_2 j_2$ and $a_{q_1 j_1}$ annihilates a phonon $\vec{q}_1 j_1$. The total wave vector of the final state equals that of the initial state plus a vector $-\vec{q}_1 - \vec{q}_2 - \vec{q}_3$, and this vector must be zero or $2\pi\tau$ if the final state is not to be multiplied by a factor of zero.

In view of the remarks above, the effect of the total perturbing term $V^{(\nu)}$ on a phonon state is to induce transitions to other states having the same total wave vector, modulo $2\pi\vec{\tau}$, as the initial state. The selection rule on these transitions resembles a momentum conservation except for the qualification "modulo $2\pi\tau$" ($\hbar$ times a wave vector $\vec{q}$ has the dimensions of momentum). The total wave-vector for a particular phonon state cannot correspond to an actual momentum of the crystal, however, because the only modes of vibration which correspond to non-vanishing values of the total crystal momentum are the acoustical modes with wave vectors which are zero, and these are excluded from the total wave vector. The total wave-vector is therefore only associated with the propagation of internal energy through the crystal. In scattering problems this wave vector multiplied by $\hbar$ does enter into conservation equations with real momenta, however, and this will be shown later. In view of these facts, the wave vector times $\hbar$ is called a pseudo-momentum. The selection rule on the transitions induced by $V^{(\nu)}$ can therefore be called a conservation of pseudo-momentum, modulo $2\pi\vec{\tau}$.

In the limit of very large N_o (the number of cells in an independent region of the crystal with periodic boundary conditions) the density of wave vectors $\vec{q}$ satisfying Eq. (3-5) becomes very large. In this limit it is necessary to replace all sums over wave vectors, such as appear in Eqs. (4-9) and (5-2), by integrations. Before going on to actual perturbation calculations, it is desirable to introduce a notation which is suited to this limit.

The new notation is based on the following definitions:

$$(8\pi^3/\Omega)\, \Sigma_q^{u.c.}(\ldots) = \textstyle\int_q(\ldots), \tag{5-4}$$

$$(\Omega/8\pi^3)\Delta_q = \Delta(\vec{q}), \tag{5-5}$$

and

$$(\Omega/8\pi^3)^{1/2} a_{qj} \equiv A_{qj}. \tag{5-6}$$

Here Ω is the volume of an independent region of the crystal and is equal to $N_o v_o$. In the first of these equations, (5-4), the summation of a quantity over all wave vectors in a unit cell in q-space multiplied by the volume of q-space per wave vector is given a special name, $\int_q(\ldots)$, because this combination becomes the integral $\int d\vec{q}\,(\ldots)$ in the limit of large N_o. Integration over just one unit cell in $\vec{q}$-space is to be understood in this notation. In Eq. (5-5) the quantity $\Delta(\vec{q})$ is defined from Δ_q in such a way that it has the following property:

5. FORMULATION OF THE PERTURBATION PROBLEM

$$\int_q \Delta(\vec{q}) = 1 . \tag{5-7}$$

With this property, $\Delta(\vec{q})$ can be treated as a Dirac delta-function in the limit of large N_o, and it can then be replaced as follows:

$$\Delta(\vec{q}) = \Sigma_\tau \delta(\vec{q} + 2\pi\vec{\tau}).$$

Finally, in Eq. (5- 6), the operator A_{qj} is defined from the operator a_{qj} in such a way that the following useful commutation rules are obtained:

$$[A_{qj}, A^*_{q'j'}] = \delta_{jj'}\Delta(\vec{q}-\vec{q}'),$$

$$[A_{qj}, A_{q'j'}] = [A^*_{qj}, A^*_{q',j'}] = 0. \tag{5-8}$$

With these new notations the transition to the limit of large N_o is usually quite easy.

On the basis of the new notations the Hamiltonian H (which now corresponds to the total energy per independent region of the infinite crystal) can be written out as follows:

$$H = \varepsilon_o + \varepsilon_{zp} + H_o + V \tag{5-9}$$

where the individual terms are given by the following equations:

$$\varepsilon_{zp} = (\Omega/8\pi^3)\Sigma_j \int_q (1/2)\hbar\omega_{qj} \tag{5-10}$$

$$H_o = \Sigma_j \int_q \hbar\omega_{qj} A^*_{qj} A_{qj} \tag{5-11}$$

$$V = \Sigma^{\infty}_{\nu=3} V^{(\nu)} \tag{5-12}$$

$$V^{(\nu)} = \Sigma_{j_1, j_2 \ldots j_\nu} \int_{q_1, q_2 \ldots q_\nu} B^{(\nu)}_{q_1 j_1, q_2 j_2, \ldots q_\nu j_\nu} \times [A_{q_1} + A^*_{-q_1 j_1}][A_{q_2 j_2} + A^*_{-q_2 j_2}] \ldots [A_{q_\nu j_\nu} + A^*_{-q_\nu j_\nu}] \times \Delta(\vec{q}_1 + \vec{q}_2 \ldots + \vec{q}_\nu). \tag{5-13}$$

These equations are based on Eqs. (4-9), (5-1) and (5-2), but the harmonic Hamiltonian $H^{(2)}$ in Eq. (4-9) has been divided into the following three parts; ε_o, which is the equilibrium rigid-lattice energy, ε_{zp}, which is the zero-point energy (the vibrational energy of the crystal in its ground state in the harmonic approximation), and H_o, which is the phonon energy and contains all of the dependence of $H^{(2)}$ on creation and annihilation operators. In the present notation, the zero-point energy has a form which directly shows its expected proportionality to Ω, the volume of the independent region of the crystal.

The new operators A^*_{qj} and A_{qj} are creation and annihilation operators in the same sense as the original operators a^*_{qj} and a_{qj} are. For this reason the earlier discussion of the quantum mechanical crystal in terms of creation and annihilation operators is just as valid if the new notation is employed rather than the old one.

The ground-state wave function for the harmonic Hamiltonian $H^{(2)}$ will be designated hereafter by the symbol $|0>$, and it will be called the vacuum state, since it involves no phonons. This vacuum state is assumed to be normalized such that

$$<0|0> = 1, \tag{5-14}$$

where $<0|0>$ is a diagonal matrix element of the identity operator.

The excited states of the harmonic Hamiltonian will be designated by symbols such as $|\vec{q}j, \vec{q}'j', \vec{q}''j'', \ldots >$, which is supposed to represent the state in which phonons $\vec{q}j, \vec{q}'j', \vec{q}''j'', \ldots$ are excited. The normalizing constants for these excited states will be fixed by the following definition:

$$|qj, q'j', q''j'', \ldots > = A^*_{qj} A^*_{q'j'} A^*_{q''j''} \cdots |0>. \tag{5-15}$$

From this definition and the commutation rules of Eq. (5-8), the following sample normalization integrals for excited states are easily obtained:

$$<qj|q'j'> = \delta_{jj'} \Delta(\vec{q}-\vec{q}') \tag{5-16}$$

$$<qj\, q'j'|q''j'', q'''j'''> = \delta_{jj''}\delta_{j'j'''} \Delta(\vec{q}-\vec{q}'')\Delta(\vec{q}'-\vec{q}''')$$
$$+ \delta_{jj'''}\delta_{j'j''} \Delta(\vec{q}-\vec{q}''')\Delta(\vec{q}'-\vec{q}''). \tag{5-17}$$

The normalizations are quite convenient in the limit of large Ω. The existence of the two terms on the right in Eq. (5-17) is a reflection of the fact that phonons obey Bose statistics.

The effect of an annihilation operator A_{qj} acting on a phonon state like that given in Eq. (5-15) is to annihilate a phonon $\vec{q}j$ if one is present and to give zero otherwise. This statement is expressed in the following equation:

$$A_{qj}|\alpha> = n_{qj}\Delta(0)|\beta>, \tag{5-18}$$

where state $|\alpha>$ contains n_{qj} phonons $\vec{q}j$, and where the state $|\beta>$ differs from $|\alpha>$ only in that it has one less phonon $\vec{q}j$. This result is easily proved by use of Eq. (5-15) and the commutation relations (5-8). From Eq. (5-5), $\Delta(0)$ is equal to $\Omega/8\pi^3$, which is the density of wave-vectors in $\vec{q}$-space, and therefore the constant $n_{qj}\,\Delta(0)$ in Eq.(5-18) above can be interpreted as a density of phonons in $\vec{q}$-space, n'_{qj}.

5. FORMULATION OF THE PERTURBATION PROBLEM

As can be shown by operating on both sides of Eq. (5-18) with A^*_{qj}, a phonon state is an eigenstate of the operator $A^*_{qj}A_{qj}$. The eigenvalue is just the phonon density n'_{qj} or $n_{qj}\Delta(0)$ for that state. Since the operator H_o in Eq. (5-11) is just a sum of operators $A^*_{qj}A_{qj}$, then, a phonon state is also an eigenfunction of H_o (it was constructed for this, of course). The effect of H_o acting on a phonon state $|\alpha>$ is expressed in the following equation:

$$H_o|\alpha> = \left\{ \Sigma_{qj}\hbar\omega_{qj}n_{qj} \right\}|\alpha> = \left\{ \int_q \Sigma_j \hbar\omega_{qj}n'_{qj} \right\}|\alpha>. \qquad (5\text{-}19)$$

The eigenvalue of H_o given here is consistent with the corresponding eigenvalue given in Eq. (4-10).

6. ELEMENTS OF THE PERTURBATION FORMALISM

The remainder of this report is devoted to formal calculations of effects of the anharmonic perturbation V in the Hamiltonian of Eq. (5-9). The perturbation theory by which these effects are calculated is based on the use of the following operator,

$$R_z = 1/(H_o + V - z). \tag{6-1}$$

which can also be written as

$$R_z = 1/(H - \varepsilon_o - \varepsilon_{zp} - z). \tag{6-2}$$

In both of these equations the term on the right is meant to represent the inverse of the operator which is written as a denominator; z is a complex variable with the units of energy, and the other quantities are defined in Eqs. (5-9) through (5-13). The operator R_z will be called the resolvent operator, or simply the resolvent, a name established for it in mathematics some time ago. In the coordinate representation this operator reduces to the Green function for Schrödinger's equation.

The effects of the anharmonic perturbation V which are of interest are calculated in terms of matrix elements of the resolvent and related operators between eigenstates of the harmonic Hamiltonian (phonon states). For the determination of these matrix elements the resolvent is expanded in powers of the operator V, and it is this expansion which makes the method a perturbation method.

The expansion of the resolvent in powers of V is obtained from the following equation:

$$R_z(H_o + V - z) = 1, \tag{6-3}$$

which is equivalent to the definition of R_z in Eq. (6-1). By manipulation this becomes

$$R_z = (1/H_o - z) - R_z V(1/H_o - z). \tag{6-4}$$

If R_z on the right side of this equation is replaced by use of the whole equation, if R_z on the right side of the resulting expression is also replaced by use of Eq. (6-4), and if the iteration is repeated ad infinitum, the following expansion of R_z in powers of the operator V is obtained:

$$R_z = (1/H_o - z) - (1/H_o - z)V_z(1/H_o - z) \tag{6-5}$$

where V_z is defined by

$$V_z = V - V(1/H_o - z)V + V(1/H_o - z)V(1/H_o - z)V \ldots . \tag{6-6}$$

6. ELEMENTS OF THE PERTURBATION FORMALISM

Since the operator H_o is diagonal with respect to phonon states and since z is merely a number, the operator $1/H_o - z$ is diagonal with respect to phonon states. On the basis of Eq. (5-19), the operation of $1/H_o - z$ on a phonon state $|a>$ gives the following result:

$$(1/H_o - z)|a> = (1/\Sigma_{qj}\omega_{qj}n_{qj} - z)|a>. \qquad (6\text{-}7)$$

In this equation and in all further work it is assumed that, in the units being used, the reduced Planck's constant $\hbar$ is equal to one.

Consider the matrix element of the second-order operator $V(1/H_o - z)V$ in Eq. (6-6) between the two one-phonon states $<q'j'|$ and $|qj>$. Since the phonon states form a complete set, the following equation is true:

$$V|qj> = \Sigma_a |a><a|V|\vec{q}j> \qquad (6\text{-}8)$$

The complete matrix element can therefore be written as follows:

$$<\vec{q}'j'|V(1/H_o - z)V|\vec{q}j> = \Sigma_a <\vec{q}'j'|V|a>(1/E_a - z)<a|V|\vec{q}j>, \qquad (6\text{-}9)$$

where $1/E_a - z$ is an abbreviation for the eigenvalue in Eq. (6-7). This result is quite similar to expressions which occur in ordinary second-order perturbation theory. It exhibits the familiar energy denominator (though with a complex energy parameter) and the product of two elements of V in the numerator. The resolvent formalism to be used here is closely related to the formalism of ordinary perturbation theory, but it has a much more condensed mathematical structure than the latter. Because of this condensed structure it is well suited to handle the complications which arise in the treatment of a many-particle system.

The remainder of the present section is devoted to sample calculations of matrix elements of terms in the expanded resolvent. Only in later sections is it shown how these elements arise in actual problems. In later sections also it is shown how the matrix elements of other operators can be calculated by methods analagous to those used for the resolvent.

Since the operator $1/H_o - z$ is diagonal, the problem of finding matrix elements of R_z reduces directly to the problem of finding matrix elements of the operator V_z, as can be seen by Eq. (6-5). When each operator V in Eq. (6-6) for V_z is expanded in terms of the operators $V^{(\nu)}$, V_z is seen to be made up of a sum of products of the following general form:

$$\pm V^{(\nu)}(1/H_o - z)V^{(\nu')}(1/H_o - z)V^{(\nu'')}\ldots(1/H_o - z)V^{(\mu)}. \qquad (6\text{-}10)$$

Products such as this with any number of $V^{(\nu)}$'s can occur. A matrix element of V_z

can then be calculated approximately by calculating enough of the largest of the matrix elements of these products, at least if the infinite series involved is reasonably convergent.

Matrix elements of a few products of the form of Eq. (6-10) are calculated below to illustrate the general method. This general method is based upon analysis of the matrix element in terms of Goldstone diagrams (Goldstone, 1957), which are closely related to the Feynman diagrams of field theory (Feynman, 1949). Diagram analysis not only simplifies the calculation of the matrix elements; it also helps point the way out of some of the characteristic difficulties of many-particle perturbation theory.

Example 1: Calculate the matrix element $< 0 | V^{(3)}(1/H_0 - z)V^{(3)} | 0 >$. The operator involved in this element comes from the second-order term in the expression for V_z, Eq. (6-6). The effects of an operator like $V^{(3)}$ acting on a phonon state have already been discussed, and these effects will now be used. The defining equation for $V^{(3)}$ is taken to be Eq. (5-13) with the products of creation and annihilation operators multiplied out.

One class of contributions to the desired matrix element can be said to occur when a term in the first $V^{(3)}$ (on the right in the complete operator) generates a 3-phonon state and a term in the second $V^{(3)}$ (on the left) annihilates these three phonons. This class of contributions is represented by the diagram in Fig. 6-1. The diagram is to be read from right to left as the sequence of states and operations just described, starting with the state $|0>$ and ending with the state $< 0|$. At any particular "time" in this sequence the existing state is specified by the number and names of the lines in the diagram, each line representing a phonon. Each vertex in the diagram represents the operation of a term in some $V^{(\nu)}$ on the state to the right of the vertex. The total number of lines entering a vertex is equal to the order ν of the $V^{(\nu)}$ which that vertex represents, and a vertex of ν lines is said to describe a ν'th-order process.

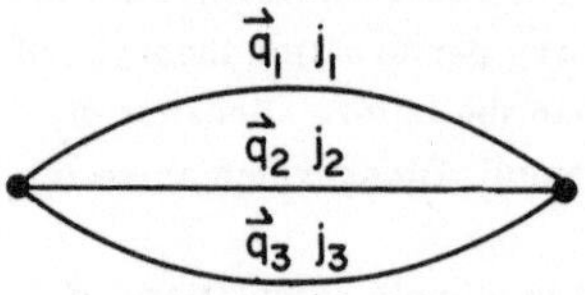

Fig. 6-1
First diagram for Example 1

The total contribution to the desired matrix element from all of the processes characterized by the diagram of Fig. 6-1 is given by the following expression:

$$(3!)\Sigma\,(j_1, j_2, j_3)\int(\vec{q}_1, \vec{q}_2, \vec{q}_3)|B^{(3)}_{1,2,3}|^2\Delta\,(\vec{q}_1+\vec{q}_2+\vec{q}_3)^2(1/\omega_1+\omega_2+\omega_3-z). \qquad (6\text{-}11)$$

In this expression the indices of summation are indicated in parentheses after the summation signs, and each subscript i on $B^{(3)}$ or one of the ω's stands for the pair of indices $\vec{q}_i j_i$.

The result in Eq. (6-11) above is obtained by using Eq. (5-13) and Eq. (6-7) in conjunction with the diagram of Fig. 6-1, as is now described. The three intermediate-state phonons $\vec{q}_1 j_1$, $\vec{q}_2 j_2$, and $\vec{q}_3 j_3$ are generated from the vacuum by a term in the first $V^{(3)}$ which contains the product of creation operators $A_1^* A_2^* A_3^*$ (where each subscript i again stands for $\vec{q}_i j_i$). Since a summation over all phonon indices $\vec{q}_1 j_1$, $\vec{q}_2 j_2$, and $\vec{q}_3 j_3$ is to be performed below, terms in $V^{(3)}$ containing the operators A_1^*, A_2^*, and A_3^* in a different order should not be considered separately. When operating on the vacuum state $|0>$, this term containing the product $A_1^* A_2^* A_3^*$ yields the following result:

$$B^{(3)}_{-1,\,-2,\,-3}\Delta(-\vec{q}_1-\vec{q}_2-\vec{q}_3)|\vec{q}_1 j_1, \vec{q}_2 j_2, \vec{q}_3 j_3> , \tag{6-12}$$

where each subscript -i on $B^{(3)}$ stands for $-\vec{q}_i j_i$. The operation of $(1/H_0 - z)$ on this then introduces an additional factor of $(1/\omega_1+\omega_2+\omega_3-z)$.

The three intermediate-state phonons in expression (6-12) above are annihilated by a term in the second $V^{(3)}$ which contains the product of annihilation operators $A_1 A_2 A_3$ or one of its 3! permutations. Any one of these 3! terms operating on the intermediate state $|\vec{q}_1 j_1, \vec{q}_2 j_2, \vec{q}_3 j_3>$ gives the following result:

$$\Delta(0)^3 B^{(3)}_{1,\,2,\,3}\Delta(\vec{q}_1+\vec{q}_2+\vec{q}_3)|0> , \tag{6-13}$$

where it is assumed for simplicity that the three intermediate phonons are all different. This result is obtained by use of Eqs. (5-13) and (5-18).

The final result in Eq. (6-11) is obtained by combining the result above, closing the matrix element with the vacuum state $<0|$, and introducing the summations from the equation for $V^{(3)}$. The normality integral $<0|0>$ which appears in this process is just one. The summation from the first $V^{(3)}$ gives the summation over intermediate phonons in Eq. (6-11), and the summation from the second $V^{(3)}$ gives a combinatorial factor of 3!, the number of terms in $V^{(3)}$ which can annihilate the three intermediate-state phonons, and a factor $\Delta(0)^{-3}$, from the three essentially unused summations $\int_q$. In introducing these summations the special cases in which two or three phonons are the same can be included without special consideration. This procedure leads to a correct result in this simple example, as can be readily verified by explicit consideration of the special cases. The procedure is also valid in the general case, however, and this will be illustrated shortly. In the present example it should be noted that the factors $\Delta(0)$ cancel one another exactly.

The quantity $\Delta(\vec{q}_1+\vec{q}_2+\vec{q}_3)^2$ which appears in Eq. (6-11) does not make much sense as it stands. It can be replaced by $\Delta(0)\Delta(\vec{q}_1+\vec{q}_2+\vec{q}_3)$, however, as can be proved by squaring both sides of the equality (5-3) from which it arises. With this substitution, the total contribution to the matrix element $< 0|V^{(3)}(1/H_o-z)V^{(3)}|0 >$ from all of the processes characterized by the diagram of Fig. 6-1 is given by

$$(3!)(\Omega/8\pi^3)\,\Sigma(j_1, j_2, j_3)\int(\vec{q}_1, \vec{q}_2, \vec{q}_3)\,|B^{(3)}_{1,2,3}|^2\Delta(\vec{q}_1+\vec{q}_2+\vec{q}_3)(1/\omega_1+\omega_2+\omega_3-z). \qquad (6\text{-}14)$$

One important result which has been achieved in Eq. (6-14) is that the dependence of the contribution on the size of the crystal (or, more properly, on the size of an independent region of the infinite crystal with periodic boundary conditions) is exhibited explicitly. Except for the simple factor of Ω , expression (6-14) is essentially independent of the size of the crystal in the limit of a large crystal. The resulting proportionality to Ω for the complete expression is consistent with the fact that this expression with z set equal to zero occurs as a term in the ground state energy of the crystal, which is an extensive quantity.

There is only one other class of contributions to the matrix element of this example, and this class is represented by the diagram in Fig. 6-2. In this diagram the loop at each vertex describes what will be called an instantaneous phonon, a phonon which is created and annihilated at the same vertex. An instantaneous phonon belongs to the vertex alone and not to a state preceding or following the vertex. The first instantaneous phonon in the diagram of Fig. 6-2 arises from the presence of a product $A_1A_1^*$ in a term in the first $V^{(3)}$. The same term must contain another operator, A_2^*, as a factor, however, and A_2^* can be the first, second, or third operator in the term. The first vertex therefore represents any one of three terms in the first $V^{(3)}$. Similar considerations apply to the second vertex.

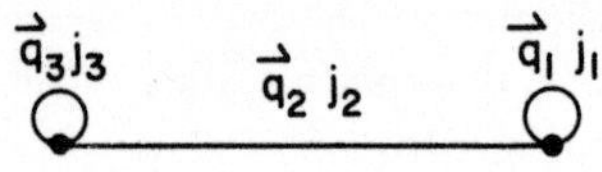

Fig. 6-2
Second diagram for Example 1

The total contribution to the desired matrix element from all of the processes characterized by the diagram in Fig. 6-2 is given by the following expression:

$$9(\Omega/8\pi^3)\Sigma(j_1, j_2, j_3)\int(\vec{q}_1, \vec{q}_2, \vec{q}_3)\, B^{(3)}_{1,-1,2}B^{(3)}_{3,-3,2}(1/\omega_2-z)\,\Delta(\vec{q}_2). \qquad (6\text{-}15)$$

This result is obtained by much the same procedure as is described above for the first contribution. Again a factor $\Delta(0)^3$ arising from three annihilations is canceled by a factor $\Delta(0)^3$ arising from three essentially unused summations $\int_q$. Again also a square of a delta function is replaced by $\Delta(0)$ times the delta function, giving proportionality to Ω. The combinatorial factor of nine in Eq. (6-15) is made up of a factor of three for the three terms in the first $V^{(3)}$ and another factor of three for the three terms in the second $V^{(3)}$.

According to the selection rule in expression (6-15), the intermediate phonon $\vec{q}_2j_2$ must have a wave vector of zero or $2\pi\vec{\tau}$. The only intermediate phonons of interest are the optical phonons, therefore, because acoustical phonons with wave vectors of zero only describe pure translations of the crystal.

Example 2: Calculate the matrix element $< \vec{q}j\,|V^{(3)}(1/H_0-z)V^{(3)}\,|\vec{q}'j'>$. This is an element between one-phonon states of the same operator which appeared in Example 1. One class of contributions to this element is represented by the diagram in Fig. 6-3. According to this diagram a term in the first $V^{(3)}$ annihilates the initial-

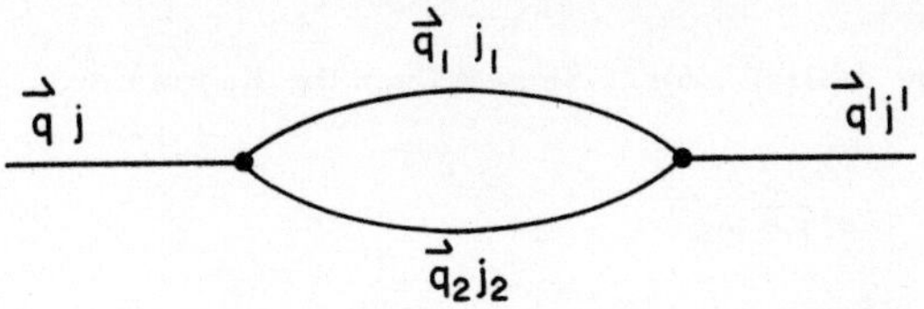

Fig. 6-3 First diagram for Example 2

state phonon and creates two intermediate-state phonons. A term in the second $V^{(3)}$ then annihilates the intermediate-state phonons and creates the final state phonon.

The total contribution to the desired element from the diagram in Fig. 6-3 is given by the following expression:

$$18\,\Delta(\vec{q}-\vec{q}')\Sigma(j_1,j_2)\int(\vec{q}_1,\vec{q}_2)B^{(3)}_{-qj,\,1,\,2}B^{(3)}_{q'j',\,-1,\,-2}(1/\omega_1+\omega_2-z)\,\Delta(\vec{q}'-\vec{q}_1-\vec{q}_2). \quad (6\text{-}16)$$

The first part of the calculation of this result can be carried out like the calculations in the first example. Then, after the last operation in the diagram, there remains a normalization integral $< \vec{q}j\,|\,\vec{q}j >$. This integral is equal to $\Delta(0)$ from Eq. (5-16), and it is canceled exactly by a factor $\Delta(0)^3$ from the three annihilations and a factor $\Delta(0)^{-4}$ from the four essentially unused sums $\int_q$. In order to obtain the result in Eq. (6-13) it is also necessary to use the following identity:

$$\Delta(\vec{q}_1+\vec{q}_2-\vec{q})\Delta(\vec{q}'-\vec{q}_1-\vec{q}_2) = \Delta(\vec{q}-\vec{q}')\Delta(\vec{q}'-\vec{q}_1-\vec{q}_1).$$

Because of the factor $\Delta(\vec{q}-\vec{q}')$ which this identity introduces, the initial and final wave vectors $\vec{q}$ and $\vec{q}'$ must be equal modulo $2\pi\vec{\tau}$ if the total contribution to the matrix element is to be non-zero. Except for this factor, the total contribution is independent of Ω in the limit of large Ω.

A second class of contributions to the desired matrix element is represented by the diagram in Fig. 6-4. This diagram is said to be disconnected, since it con-

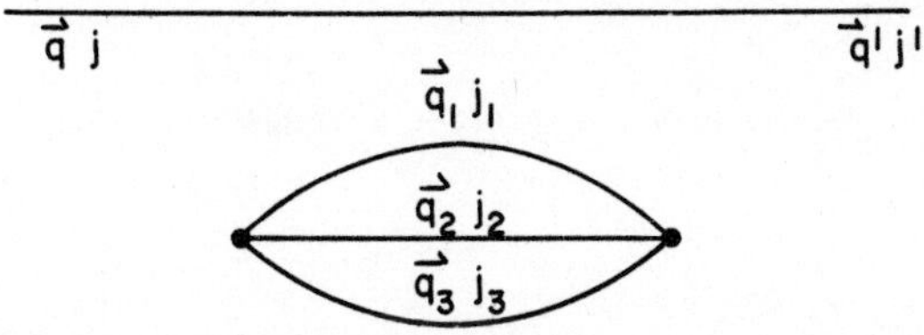

Fig. 6-4 Second diagram for Example 2

tains components which are not connected to one another by any phonon lines. One of the components in the diagram looks just like the diagram in Fig. 6-1, and the other is a simple line with no vertices. Disconnected diagrams such as this cause much of the difficulty in the perturbation theory of many-particle systems, as will become apparent later.

The total contribution to the desired matrix element from the diagram in Fig. 6-4 is given by:

$$\left\{\Delta(\vec{q}-\vec{q}')\delta_{jj'}\right\}$$

$$\times\left\{6(\Omega/8\pi^3)\Sigma(j_1,j_2,j_3)\int(\vec{q}_1,\vec{q}_2,\vec{q}_3)\left|B^{(3)}_{1,2,3}\right|^2\Delta(\vec{q}_1+\vec{q}_2+\vec{q}_3)(1/\omega_{q'j'}+\omega_1+\omega_2+\omega_3-z)\right\}. \tag{6-17}$$

This result is easily calculated by the methods already described. It is seen to be the product of two factors, one which is the same as if the simple line were alone in the diagram, and another which is almost the same as if the second component were alone in the diagram, as it is in Fig. 6-1. Only the energy denominator reflects the co-existence of the two components. It should be noted that the contribution (6-17) contains the same factor $\Delta(\vec{q}-\vec{q}')$ as the contribution (6-16), and that it is otherwise independent of Ω in the limit of large Ω.

There are other diagrams which give contributions to the matrix element of this example, but for the sake of brevity they are not considered here. Instead some matrix elements of first-order operators are considered. The diagrams for the latter elements can have only one vertex each, while the diagrams considered above have two vertices each.

Example 3: Calculate the matrix element $<\vec{q}j\,|V^{(3)}|\,0>$. The only diagram is that shown in Fig. 6-5, and the corresponding contribution to the matrix element is

$$3\,\Delta(\vec{q})\,\Sigma(j_1)\int(\vec{q}_1)B^{(3)}_{-qj,1,-1}. \tag{6-18}$$

Because of the selection rule on $\vec{q}$, the only final states of interest are those in which the single phonon is an optical phonon.

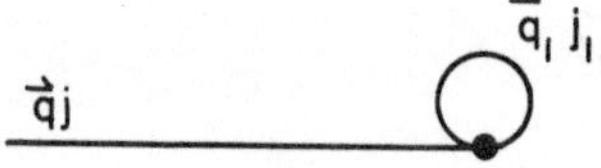

Fig. 6-5 Diagram for Example 3

Example 4: Calculate the matrix element $<\vec{q}j, \vec{q}'j', \vec{q}''j''|\,V^{(3)}|\,0>$. The only diagram is that shown in Fig. 6-6, and the corresponding contribution to the matrix element is

$$6\Delta\,(\vec{q}+\vec{q}'+\vec{q}'')B^{(3)}_{-qj,\,-q'j',\,-q''j''}. \tag{6-19}$$

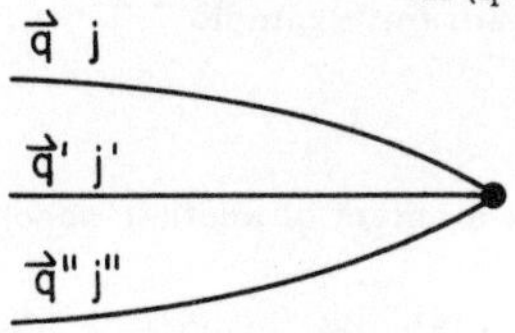

Fig. 6-6
Diagram for Example 4

To obtain this result the normalization integral for the state $|\vec{q}j, \vec{q}'j', \vec{q}''j''>$ is required, but this is just $\Delta(0)^3$, as found by an extension of the procedures which lead to Eq. (5-17). This factor $\Delta(0)^3$ is canceled by a factor $\Delta(0)^{-3}$, which arises from the three essentially unused sums $\int_q$.

Example 5: Calculate the matrix element $<\vec{q}'j'|\,V^{(4)}\vec{q}j>$. The only diagram is that shown in Fig. 6-7, and the corresponding contribution to the matrix element is

$$12\,\Delta(\vec{q}-\vec{q}')\,\Sigma(j_1)\int(\vec{q}_1)B^{(4)}_{qj,\,-q'j',\,1,\,-1}. \tag{6-20}$$

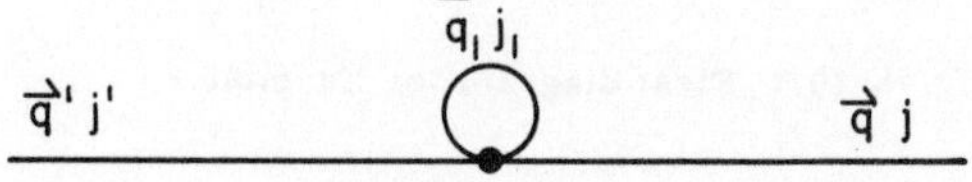

Fig. 6-7 Diagram for Example 5

Example 6: Calculate the matrix element $<\vec{q}j, \vec{q}'j'|\,V^{(4)}|\,0>$. The only diagram is that shown in Fig. 6-8, and the corresponding contribution to the matrix element is

$$12\Delta(\vec{q}+\vec{q}')\Sigma(j_1)\int(q_1)B^{(4)}_{-qj,\,-q'j,\,1,\,-1}. \tag{6-21}$$

To obtain this result the normalization integral of the state $|\vec{q}j, \vec{q}'j'>$ is required, but this is just $\Delta(0)^2$ by Eq. (5-17).

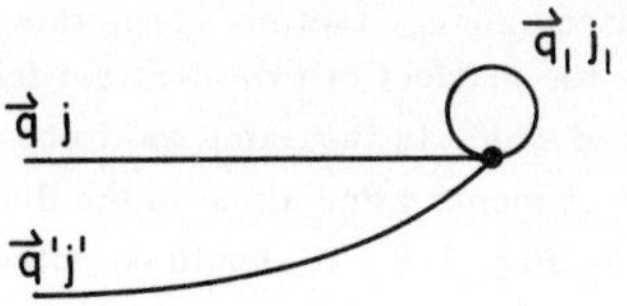

Fig. 6-8 Diagram for Example 6

Example 7: Calculate the matrix element $<0|\,V^{(4)}|\,0>$. The only diagram is that shown in Fig. 6-9. The diagram represents two instantaneous phonons belonging to the same vertex. The corresponding contribution to the matrix element is

$$3(\Omega/8\pi^3)\Sigma(j_1, j_2)\int(\vec{q}_1, \vec{q}_2)B^{(4)}_{1,-1,2,-2}. \tag{6-22}$$

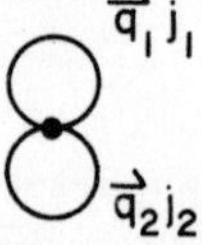

Fig. 6-9 Diagram for Example 7

The final example, which is given below, is the matrix element of another second-order operator.

Example 8: Calculate the matrix element $< 0 | V^{(4)}(1/H_0 - z)V^{(4)} | 0 >$. One diagram for this element is shown in Fig. 6-10, and the contribution corresponding to this diagram is

$$4!(\Omega/8\pi^3)\Sigma(j_1, j_2, j_3, j_4)\int(\vec{q}_1, \vec{q}_2, \vec{q}_3, \vec{q}_4)|B^{(4)}_{1,2,3,4}|^2(1/\omega_1+\omega_2+\omega_3+\omega_4-z)\ \Delta(\vec{q}_1+\vec{q}_2+\vec{q}_3+\vec{q}_4) \tag{6-23}$$

This contribution is proportional to Ω.

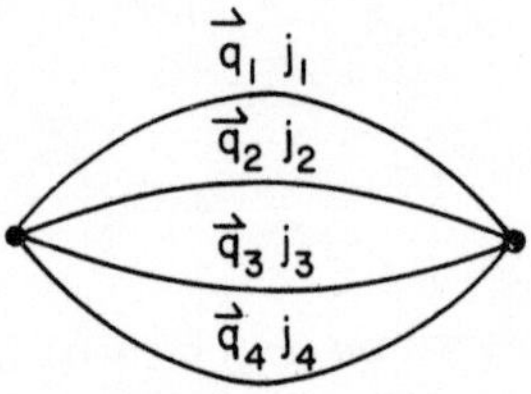

Fig. 6-10 First diagram for Example 8

Another diagram for this element is shown in Fig. 6-11. This is a disconnected diagram in which each of the two components is identical to the diagram of Fig. 6-9. The two components do not coexist, however. The contribution to the matrix element corresponding to this diagram is

$$(-1/z)[(3\Omega/8\pi^3)\Sigma(j_1, j_2)\int(\vec{q}_1, \vec{q}_2)B^{(4)}_{1,-1,2,-2}]^2 \tag{6-24}$$

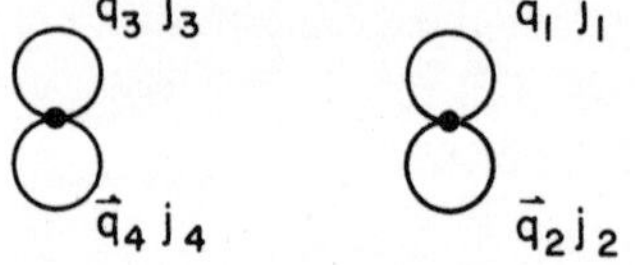

Fig. 6-11
Second diagram for Example 8

Except for the energy factor, $-1/z$, this is seen to be the product of two identical factors, each of which is the same as if one of the two components were alone in the diagram, as in Fig. 6-9. It should be noted that the total contribution is proportional to Ω^2, even though the contribution (6-23) is proportional to Ω.

There is a third diagram for the matrix element of this example, but it need not be considered here, as it does not involve anything new.

6. ELEMENTS OF THE PERTURBATION FORMALISM

At this point it is useful to summarize the procedure for calculating matrix elements which is illustrated in the foregoing examples. First, it should be noted that because of the way in which the matrix elements will be used there should never be any explicit identities among the initial- and final-state phonons in a particular matrix element. The procedure for calculating a matrix element is then the following: first, construct all possible diagrams for the element; and second, calculate the total contribution from each diagram, performing the summations over intermediate-state phonons without introducing any correction factors for the special cases of identical phonons. The justification of this treatment of the special cases will be discussed shortly. The calculation of the contribution from a particular diagram is simplified by the use of certain rules, which will now be stated. These rules are suggested by the results in the examples which have been presented, and they are born out by further analysis.

In the first place, each component in a given diagram contributes an almost separate factor to the corresponding contribution, and only the energy denominators prevent these factors from being entirely separate. Except for the energy denominators, which are easily incorporated, the factor for a particular component is the same as if that component were alone in the diagram. The energy denominators depend on complete states, and they therefore link all components which coexist when an operation $(1/H_0-z)$ is performed. Two Goldstone diagrams which differ in the relative locations of their components are therefore not equivalent, and in this property the Goldstone diagrams differ from Feynman diagrams.

In the second place, the almost-separate factor which is contributed by each component of a given diagram always can be written to contain a factor $\Delta(\vec{q})$, where $\vec{q}$ here is the total wave vector of the final state in the component minus the total wave vector of the initial state. For a vacuum component (a component with no initial or final-state phonons), the factor $\Delta(\vec{q})$ just mentioned becomes $\Delta(0)$ or $(\Omega/8\pi^3)$.

The delta factors $\Delta(\vec{q})$ described above are the only factors in the contribution to a matrix element which can depend on the size of the crystal, in the limit of a large crystal. The other factors $\Delta(0)$ which arise because of annihilations, unused sums, and normalization integrals can always be shown to cancel one another exactly, and they can therefore be ignored entirely.

The application of the rules given above will be illustrated briefly by consideration of the diagram in Fig. (6-12). This diagram belongs to the matrix element

$$< \vec{q}'j', \vec{q}''j'', \vec{q}'''j''', \vec{q}^{iv}j^{iv} | V^{(3)}(1/H_0-z)V^{(4)}(1/H_0-z)V^{(3)}(1/H_0-z)$$
$$\times V^{(4)}(1/H_0-z)V^{(3)} | \vec{q}j >.$$

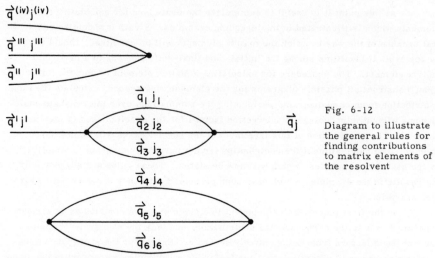

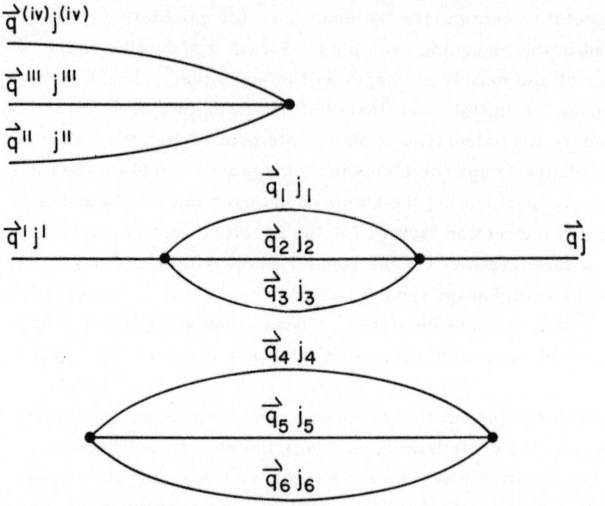

Fig. 6-12
Diagram to illustrate the general rules for finding contributions to matrix elements of the resolvent

Since the diagram has three components, the corresponding total contribution to the matrix element is made up of three almost separate factors, one for each component. The energy denominators which link these components are easily determined. As for the size-dependence of the total contribution, the uppermost component in the diagram yields a factor $\Delta(\vec{q}''+\vec{q}'''+\vec{q}^{iv})$, the middle component yields a factor $\Delta(\vec{q}'-\vec{q})$, and the lowest component, which is a vacuum component, yields a factor $\Delta(0)$, or $\Omega/8\pi^3$. The total contribution from the diagram is therefore given by the factor

$$\Delta(\vec{q}''+\vec{q}'''+\vec{q}^{iv})\,\Delta(\vec{q}'-\vec{q})(\Omega/8\pi^3)$$

times a quantity which is easy to write out and which is essentially independent of the size of the crystal.

In view of the general rules given above, the contribution to a matrix element from a particular diagram contains an explicit factor Ω for each vacuum component in the diagram. It is therefore clear that the matrix element of an operator which contains many $V^{(\nu)}$'s can have contributions proportional to high powers of Ω. Such matrix elements appear in the high-order terms of standard perturbation theory, and, because of these high powers of Ω, the terms in question are important even when the phonon interaction is small. As stated in Sec. 1, the importance of such high-order terms is one of the principal difficulties in the perturbation theory of many-particle systems. The observation that the high powers of Ω result from disconnected diagrams helps point the way out of this difficulty, however, as will be seen later.

6. ELEMENTS OF THE PERTURBATION FORMALISM

One feature of the calculation of matrix elements still remains to be discussed, and that concerns the special cases of two or more identical phonons. According to the procedure which is described above, the summation over intermediate phonons for a particular diagram is to be performed without including correction factors for identities of the phonons. This leads to a rigorously correct expression for the matrix element when the contributions from all the diagrams are added together, and the proof of this was given by Wick (1955). The result is due to a compensation of errors, and it is illustrated by examples below.

Consider the diagram of Fig. 6-1 and the resulting contribution in Eq. (6-14). The sum which makes up this contribution includes some terms in which two of the three intermediate-state phonons are identical and others in which all three are identical. From Eq. (6-14) the sum of all those terms in which just two phonons are identical is given by the following expression:

$$18(\Omega/8\pi^3)\Sigma(j_1, j_2)\int{}'(\vec{q}_1, \vec{q}_2)|B^{(3)}_{1,2,2}|^2\Delta(\vec{q}_1+2\vec{q}_2)(1/\omega_1+2\omega_2-z) \qquad (6\text{-}25)$$

where the prime on the summation sign means that if j_1 equals j_2, $\vec{q}_1$ should not equal $\vec{q}_2$. It turns out that this expression is the same as is obtained by explicit consideration of the special case, and that it is therefore correct as it stands. The numerical coefficient in the expression is only correct due to a compensation of errors, however. To verify this statement, consider the diagram of Fig. 6-1 when it is modified to make phonons 2 and 3 identical. The numerical coefficient in the corresponding contribution is a product of a combinatorial factor of 3 from the first vertex, another combinatorial factor of 3 from the second vertex, and a factor of 2 from the annihilation of the first of the two identical phonons at the second vertex. The complete coefficient is 18, therefore, in agreement with Eq. (6-25). The annihilation factor of 2 here is a new feature, and it appears because of the factor n_{qj} in Eq. (5-18). The errors which compensate to give the correct coefficient in Eq. (6-25) are the use of the wrong combinatorial coefficient at the second vertex and the omission of the annihilation factor at the second vertex.

The other special case in the diagram of Fig. 6-1 is that of three identical phonons. The sum of all the terms in Eq. (6-14) in which the three phonons are identical is given by the following expression:

$$6(\Omega/8\pi^3)\Sigma(j_1)\int(\vec{q}_1)|B^{(3)}_{1,1,1}|^2\Delta(3\vec{q}_1)(1/3\omega_1-z). \qquad (6\text{-}26)$$

This expression is also the same as is obtained by explicit consideration of the special case, and the correctness of the numerical coefficient again results from a compensation of errors. The errors which compensate here are the use of the wrong combinatorial coefficients at both vertices and the omission of the annihilation factors at the second vertex (3 for the first annihilation and 2 for the second).

For an example in which contributions must be added before a special case is correctly included, consider the diagram in Fig. 6-13. One special case arising from this diagram is that in which phonons 5 and 7 are identical. In this case the diagram in question is identical to another diagram for the same matrix element. That other diagram is shown in Fig. 6-14. The contributions from these two diagrams will not be written out, but when all the terms in which phonons 5 and 7 are identical are added together from both general contributions, the resulting expression contains a numerical factor of 4×3^5 which is the sum of a factor 2×3^5 for each diagram. The factor for each diagram is the product of combinatorial factors for each vertex, and these factors are given below the vertices in the figures. The total contribution for the special case which is obtained in this way by the general procedure is exactly the same as the contribution which is obtained by explicit consideration of the special case. In the explicit consideration the numerical coefficient of 4×3^5 is obtained as the product of the same combinatorial factors which occur for either of the general diagrams (the two diagrams being identical in the special case) and a factor of 2 from the annihilation at the fourth vertex. The errors which compensate to give the correct result in the general procedure are the treatment of two diagrams separately when only one process is involved and the omission of annihilation factors.

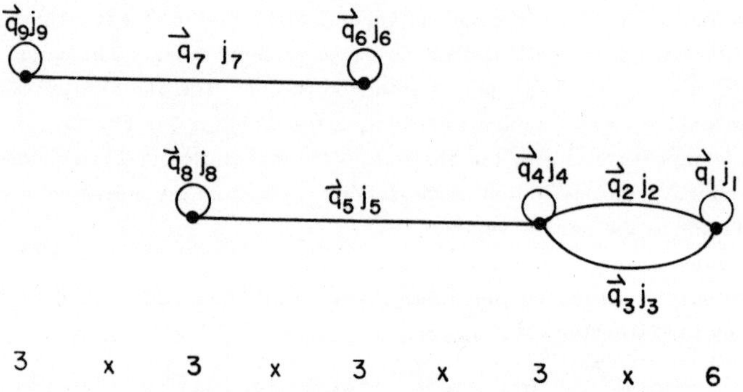

Fig. 6-13

Diagram illustrating a special case of identical phonons

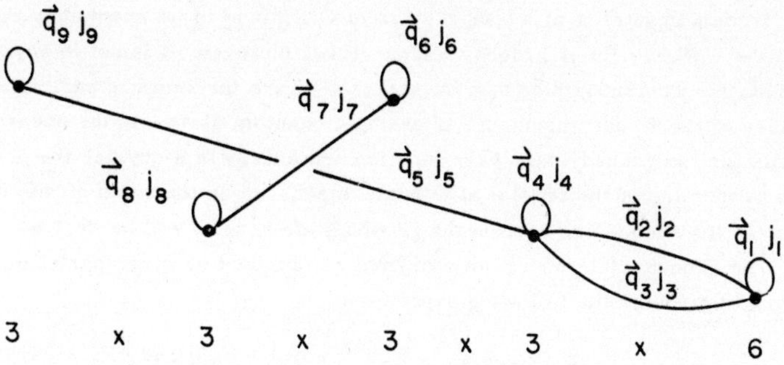

Fig. 6-14
Second diagram illustrating a special case of identical phonons

For an example with still another feature, consider the diagram in Fig. 6-13 again, and consider the special case in which phonons 5 and 8 are identical. Again the general procedure yields the correct result for the special case. In the general procedure the numerical coefficient is obtained as a product of the combinatorial factors shown in Fig. 6-13. In the explicit calculation, each vertex yields the same factor as in the general procedure, but the factor from the fourth vertex is made up in a very different way. In the special case the operator for this fourth vertex is a product of two creation operators and an annihilation operator, all with the same phonon indices. If the annihilation comes last, it yields an annihilation factor of 2, but if it comes second, it yields an annihilation factor of one. Since each of these possibilities can occur in only one way, the numerical factor for the fourth vertex is 3, just as in the general procedure. The coefficient obtained by the general procedure is again correct, therefore.

The examples given above show how the general procedure for calculating matrix elements does give correct results even though the special cases of identical phonons are not considered explicitly. Other examples lead to the same result. The fact that the general procedure does give the correct result is fortunate, of course, since much of the utility of diagram analysis depends upon this.

7. RESULTS FOR THE PERTURBED GROUND STATE

When a crystal is at a temperature of O°K, it is in its quantum-mechanical ground state. When it is at a higher temperature, however, it is not in any single quantum state. The properties of a crystal at O°K are therefore of particular interest because of the direct importance of a single quantum state. In the present section the results for the ground-state wave function and energy of a crystal are presented, andsome properties of the crystal at O°K are discussed on the basis of this wave function. In the succeeding section the ground state results will be derived.

The ground-state energy of a crystal as obtained by many-particle perturbation theory is given by the following expression:

$$E_o = \varepsilon_o + \varepsilon_{zp} + \Sigma_\delta^{conn} < 0 | \left\{ V_o \right\}_\delta | 0 >. \qquad (7-1)$$

This expression was first derived by Goldstone (Goldstone, 1957). In the present case it represents the expectation value of the Hamiltonian of Eq. (5-9) with respect to the perturbed ground-state wave function of the crystal. In the expression δ designates a diagram for the matrix element $< 0 | V_o | 0 >$, and the symbol $< 0 | \left\{ V_o \right\}_\delta | 0 >$ refers to the contribution to the matrix element which is represented by the diagram δ. The operator V_o is simply Vz with z set equal to zero. The superscript on the summation sign in Eq. (7-1) means that the summation over diagrams δ is to be restricted to connected diagrams (diagrams with only one component each). The last term in Eq. (7-1) is therefore the sum of all the contributions to the matrix element $< 0 | V_o | 0 >$ which come from connected diagrams. This term by itself is the expectation value of the anharmonic energy of the crystal at O°K.

Since the anharmonic energy in Eq. (7-1) is given by a sum of contributions from only connected vacuum-to-vacuum diagrams, it is proportional to the volume Ω in the limit of a large crystal. This follows from the discussion of diagrams and their contributions to a matrix element in the preceding section. The anharmonic energy therefore has the proper dependence on crystal volume (as do ε_o and ε_{zp}), and it does not exhibit any of the spurious dependence on high powers of the volume which is characteristic of the terms obtained in standard perturbation theory. The spurious dependence on Ω is absent because the troublesome contributions from disconnected diagrams do not enter the final expression for the energy. The reasons for this will become apparent later.

Eq. (7-1) gives the exact ground-state energy of a crystal. For practical purposes, however, it is useful to classify contributions to the anharmonic energy in this equation in rough orders of magnitude and only retain the largest of these. Consider the diagram in Fig. 7-1. This is a diagram which enters the calculation of the

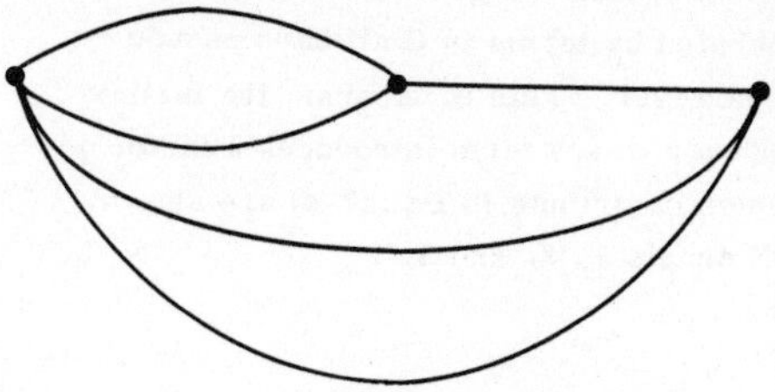

anharmonic energy. The order of magnitude of the contribution from this diagram is determined in the figure on the assumption that an energy $V^{(\nu)}$ is of the order of magnitude of $\omega(u/a)^{\nu-2}$ per unit cell (the notation is explained Sec. 2) and that an eigenvalue of $1/H_o$ is of the order of magnitude of $1/\omega$. Since the first vertex in the diagram of Fig. 7-1 represents a term in $V^{(3)}$, it yields a factor proportional to something like $\omega(u/a)$; the succeeding operation of $1/H_o$ then yields a factor of $1/\omega$; etc. In this way

$$\omega\left(\frac{u}{a}\right)^2 \times \frac{1}{\omega} \times \omega\left(\frac{u}{a}\right) \times \frac{1}{\omega} \times \omega\left(\frac{u}{a}\right) = \omega\left(\frac{u}{a}\right)^4$$

Fig. 7-1 Diagram for illustration of an order-of-magnitude calculation

the complete contribution from the diagram is about equal to $N_o\omega(u/a)^4$, in which the known size-dependence is included. The contribution is therefore of fourth order in (u/a). For comparison, the zero-point energy in Eq. (7-1) is about equal to $N_o\omega$, and this is of zeroth order in (u/a). The order of magnitude of any contribution to the anharmonic energy in Eq. (7-1) can be determined by this method.

The ground-state wave function of a crystal as obtained by many-particle perturbation theory is given by the following equation:

$$|\psi_o\rangle = e^{n/2}[1+O+(1/2!)O^2+(1/2!)O^3+\ldots(1/m!)O^m+\ldots]\,|0\rangle, \qquad (7\text{-}2)$$

where n is the following constant:

$$n = \left[\frac{d}{dz}\,\Sigma^{conn}_{\delta} < 0|\left\{V_z\right\}_{\delta}|0>\right]_{z=0}, \qquad (7\text{-}3)$$

and where O is the following operator:

$$O = -\sum_{N=1}^{\infty}\ \Sigma(j_1, j_2 \ldots j_N)\int(\vec{q}_1, \vec{q}_2, \ldots \vec{q}_N)\left[\Sigma^{conn}_{\delta} < \vec{q}_1 j_1, \vec{q}_2 j_2, \ldots \vec{q}_N j_N|\left\{V_o\right\}_{\delta}|0>\right]$$

$$\times\ (1/\omega_1+\omega_2+\ldots\omega_N)A^*_1A^*_2\ldots A^*_N. \qquad (7\text{-}4)$$

The wave function in Eq. (7-2) is normalized such that

$$<\psi_o|\psi_o> = 1, \qquad (7\text{-}5)$$

as can be proved by methods which will be described later.

The operator O defined in Eq. (7-4) is a linear combination of products of creation operators. The products for which N equals one generate one-phonon states from the vacuum state, the products for which N equals two generate two-phonon states, and so on. The states which are generated by terms in O all have pseudo-momenta of either zero or some vector $2\pi\vec{\tau}$, however. This is because the matrix element $< \vec{q}_1 j_1 \cdots \vec{q}_N j_N | \{V_o\}_\delta | 0 >$ which appears in any term introduces a factor $\Delta(\vec{q}_1 + \vec{q}_2 + \cdots \vec{q}_N)$. A few of the diagrams δ which contribute in Eq. (7-4) are shown in Fig. (7-2). The diagrams shown are for N equals 1, 2, and 3.

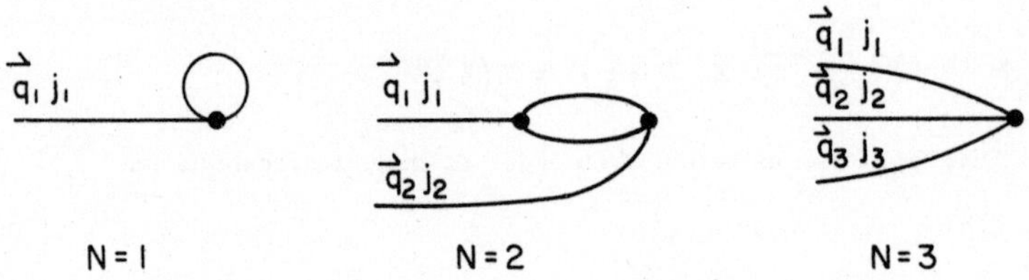

Fig. 7-2

Sample diagrams contributing to O in Eq. (7-4)

In view of the nature of O as described above, the ground-state wave function in Eq. (7-2) is a linear combination of unperturbed states containing all numbers of phonons, each unperturbed state having a pseudo-momentum of zero or some vector $2\pi\vec{\tau}$. The first term in the square brackets in Eq. (7-2) generates the vacuum state, the second generates unperturbed states with one or more phonons, the third generates unperturbed states with two or more phonons, and so on. This series of terms extends to infinity, and the resulting wave function is only intended to apply in the limit of infinite volume.

The constant n as defined in Eq. (7-3) is obtained from only matrix-element contributions which have connected vacuum-to-vacuum diagrams and which are therefore proportional to Ω. Because of this, n itself is proportional to Ω. In fact it can be shown that n is given by $-\Omega c$, where c is a finite, positive constant. The factor $e^{n/2}$ which appears as a normalizing constant in Eq. (7-2) is therefore equal to $e^{-\Omega c/2}$. This exponential dependence of the normalizing constant on Ω is reasonable in view of the fact that wave functions are essentially multiplicative as large sections of a crystal are put together.

The constant n discussed above has a further meaning which is related to the probability of finding the perturbed crystal in the unperturbed ground state. This probability is given by $|<0|\psi_o>|^2$. Upon examination of Eq. (7-2), this quantity is seen to reduce to just e^n or $e^{-c\Omega}$. In the limit of infinite Ω, then, the probability of finding the crystal in its unperturbed ground state is infinitessimally small. This is reasonable, of course, since the density of unperturbed states available for mixing becomes infinite in this limit.

Because of the anharmonic forces in a crystal, the equilibrium positions of the nuclei are not equal to those predicted by rigid-lattice theory or by harmonic-vibration theory. This effect occurs even at O°K, as a result of the zero-point vibrations. Part of this effect can be calculated by simply evaluating the expectation value of the nuclear displacements with respect to the perturbed ground-state wave function $|\psi_o>$. As will be seen below, however, the expectation value of a displacement $\vec{u}_{sn}$ is necessarily the same as that of any other displacement $\vec{u}_{s'n}$ with the same n. These expectation values therefore can only describe shifts of the equilibrium positions within a unit cell. The remainder of the effect is the change of the unit cell itself, and this must be calculated by minimizing the perturbed ground state energy E_o with respect to the primitive translation vectors. The first part of the effect, the change within a cell, is treated in detail below. This provides an example of the use of the perturbed ground-state wave function.

The expectation value of a displacement $\vec{u}_{sn}$ with respect to the wave function $|\psi_o>$ is $<\psi_o|\vec{u}_{sn}|\psi_o>$. The operator for the displacement $\vec{u}_{sn}$ can be obtained from Eq. (4-12) by introducing the notation of Sec. 5. This leads to the following equation:

$$\vec{u}_{sn} = (v_o/16\pi^3 m_n)^{1/2}\Sigma_j \int_q (\omega_{qj})^{-1/2}[A_{qj}+A^*_{-q,j}] \times [\vec{e}^{(n)}_{qj} - i\vec{f}^{(n)}_{qj}] \exp(i\vec{q}\cdot\vec{s}). \quad (7\text{-}6)$$

If the expectation value of A_{qj} with respect to $|\psi_o>$ can be determined, the expectation value of this operator $\vec{u}_{sn}$ can be evaluated easily. The expectation value of A^*_{-qj} is just the complex conjugate of that of A_{-qj}, and it does not require special treatment.

As a first step in the evaluation of $<\psi_o|A_{qj}|\psi_o>$, consider the function $A_{qj}|\psi_o>$. When use is made of the definition of $|\psi_o>$, this function can be written out as follows:

$$A_{qj}|\psi_o> = e^{n/2}A_{qj}[1+O+(1/2!)O^2+\ldots]|0>. \quad (7\text{-}7)$$

A term $A_{qj}|O^{m+1}|0>$ which occurs in this equation will now be rewritten as follows:

$$A_{qj}O^{m+1}|0> = (m+1)O^{m}(A_{qj}O)|0> \tag{7-8}$$

Eq. (7-8) can be proved by use of the following equation, which in turn can be proved by using Eq. (7-4) for O:

$$[A_{qj}, O]\, O = O[A_{qj}, O] + O^2 A_{qj}. \tag{7-9}$$

When use is made of Eq. (7-8), Eq. (7-7) can be rewritten in the following way:

$$A_{qj}|\psi_o> = e^{n/2}[1+O+(1/2!)O^2+\ldots](A_{qj}O)|0>. \tag{7-10}$$

In the equation above the operator $(A_{qj}O)$ on the right can be treated as a single operator acting on the vacuum. This is desirable because $(A_{qj}O)$ can be written as a linear combination of just creation operators, as in the following equation:

$$A_{qj}O|0> = -\sum_{\nu=1}^{\infty} \nu\Sigma(j_2, j_3, \ldots j_\nu)\int(\vec{q}_2, \vec{q}_3, \ldots \vec{q}_\nu)(1/\omega_1+\omega_2+\ldots\omega_\nu)$$
$$\times\ \Sigma_\delta^{conn} < \vec{q}j, \vec{q}_2 j_2, \ldots \vec{q}_\nu j_\nu | \{V_o\}_\delta |0> A_2^* A_3^* \ldots A_\nu^* |0>. \tag{7-11}$$

The annihilation operator A_{qj} has been absorbed by what will be called contraction with a creation operator in O. The advantage of having $(A_{qj}O)$ in a form which contains no annihilation operators will become clear shortly.

In view of the results above, the desired expectation value of A_{qj} can be written out in either of the following ways:

$$<\psi_o|A_{qj}|\psi_o> = e^n <0|\left\{1+O^* + (1/2!)O^{*2}+\ldots\right\}\left\{[1+O+(1/2!)O^2+\ldots]\, A_{qj}O\right\}|0> \tag{7-12}$$

or

$$<\psi_o|A_{qj}|\psi_o> = \sum_{m=0}^{\infty}\ \sum_{p=0}^{\infty} e^n(1/m!)(1/p!)<0|\left\{O^{*m}\right\}\left\{O^p(A_{qj}O)\right\}|0>. \tag{7-13}$$

From the second way it is apparent that $<\psi_o|A_{qj}|\psi_o>$ can be calculated from auxiliary matrix elements of the following form:

$$e^n(1/m!)(1/p!)<0|\left\{O^{*m}\right\}\left\{O^p(A_{qj}O)\right\}|0>. \tag{7-14}$$

These auxiliary elements in turn can be calculated readily by means of a pictorial analysis which is quite similar to the diagram analysis already described. An example of this is presented below.

The picture in Fig. 7-3 is supposed to represent a contribution to the auxiliary matrix element of Eq. (7-14) when m and p are equal to 3 and 4 respectively. It is called a picture rather than a diagram because it does not involve vertices. The set of circles on the right in the picture represents one term in the product operator $\left\{ O^4(A_{qj}O) \right\}$, where $(A_{qj}O)$ is the operator given in Eq. (7-11), and the set of circles on the left represents one term in the product operator O^{*3}. By one term is meant one product of creation operators with their coefficient. Each term of this sort is a product of terms from each of the individual operators $(A_{qj}O)$ and O on the right and O^* on the left. These terms from the individual operators are represented by the individual circles in the picture, and the right-to-left order of the terms is represented by the top-to-bottom order of the circles. The cross-hatched circle represents a term in the operator $(A_{qj}O)$, and each shaded circle represents a term in an operator O if it is on the right and O^* if it is on the left.

For each phonon created by a term in the product operator $\left\{ O^4(A_{qj}O) \right\}$ a line emanates from the appropriate circle on the right in the picture, and for each phonon annihilated by a term in the product operator O^{*3} a line enters the appropriate circle on the left. The emanating and entering lines are numbered in the picture, and each number i is meant to designate a set of phonon indices $\vec{q}_i j_i$. For a non-zero contribution to the desired matrix element, the number of phonons annihilated on the left must be equal to the number created on the right, and each phonon which is created must be annihilated.

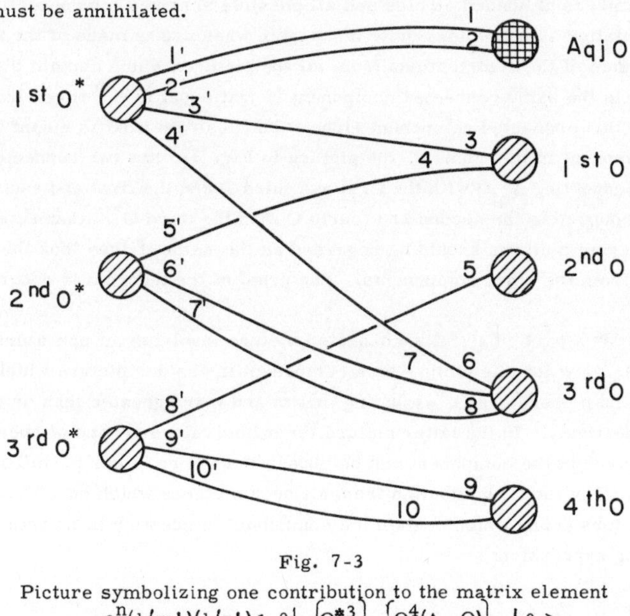

Fig. 7-3

Picture symbolizing one contribution to the matrix element

$$e^n(1/m!)(1/p!)\langle 0| \left\{O^{*3}\right\} \left\{O^4(A_{qj}O)\right\} |0\rangle$$

The total contribution to the desired matrix element from the picture in Fig. 7-3 contains a factor $\Delta(\vec{q}-\vec{q}')\delta_{jj'}$ for each phonon line, and it involves summations over all the initial and final phonon indices $\vec{q}j$ and $\vec{q}'j'$. Because of the presence of the delta factors, however, half of the summations can be performed immediately. As in the case of diagrams, the summations here are supposed to be performed without introducing correction factors for the special cases in which phonons are identical. The justification for this procedure is the same as for diagrams.

By convention one picture is changed into a new picture if the roles of the successive operators O or O^* are interchanged. For example, the picture in Fig. 7-3 is changed into a new picture if the three phonons 6, 7, and 8 are said to be created by a term in the first O instead of the third and the phonons 3 and 4 are said to be created by a term in the third O instead of the first. All pictures differing only by interchanges of the roles of the operators O or O^* yield the same total contribution to the desired matrix element, however. If there are m operators O^* and p operators O, there are m! p! such pictures.

According to Eq. (7-13) the desired expectation value $<\psi_o|A_{qj}|\psi_o>$ is given by the sum of all matrix elements having the form (7-4). In view of this it is also given by the sum of the contributions to such matrix elements from all pictures with all possible numbers of shaded circles and all possible schemes for connecting the circles. This latter sum becomes quite managable when use is made of the following theorem: the sum of the contributions from all the pictures which contain the cross-hatched circle in the same connected component is just equal to e^{-n} times the contribution from that connected component alone. To illustrate what is meant by connected component in this context, the picture in Fig. 7-3 has two connected components, one connecting $A_{qj}O$ with the first and third O and the first and second O^*, and the other connecting the second and fourth O with the third O^*. Connected components in different pictures should be regarded as the same if they look the same when isolated from the other components. The proof of the theorem is outlined below.

Consider a particular fully-connected picture involving m' operators O^* and p' operators O. Now let this picture be a component in another picture which involves m operators O^* and p operators O, assuming that m and p are greater than or equal to m' and p' respectively. In the latter picture the m' operators O^* and p' operators O which are involved in the component can be chosen in any one of $[m!\,p!/m'!\,p'!\,(m-m')!\,(p-p')!]$ ways. The total contribution from all such pictures which have m operators O^* and p operators O and which contain the component in question is therefore given by the following expression:

$$(1/m!)(1/p!)[m!/m'!(m-m')!][p!/p'!(p-p')!]$$
$$\times (m'!p'!)\{\text{contribution from the connected picture involving } A_{qj}O\}$$
$$\times (m-m')!(p-p')!\{\text{contribution from all pictures containing } (n-n')O\text{'s and } (m-m')O^*\text{'s}\}. \quad (7\text{-}15)$$

The factor in the second line of this expression is equal to

$$<0|\{O^{*m'}O^{p'}(A_{qj}O)\}_\delta|0>,$$

where δ designates the particular component,and the factor in the third line is equal to

$$<0|\{O^{*m-m'}\}\{O^{p-p'}\}|0>.$$

On the basis of the results above, the sum of the contributions from all the pictures which contain the connected component δ is given by the following expression:

$$e^n(1/m'!)(1/n'!)<0|\{O^{*m'}O^{p'}(A_{qj}O)\}_\delta|0>$$
$$\times <0|\{1+O^*+(1/2!)O^{*2}+\ldots\}\{1+O+(1/2!)O^2+\ldots\}|0>. \quad (7\text{-}16)$$

On examination of Eq. (7-2) for $|\psi_o>$ however, the last matrix element in the expression above is seen to be just the normalization integral $<\psi_o|\psi_o>$ times a factor e^{-n}. Since $<\psi_o|\psi_o>$ is equal to one, the theorem is proved.

It should be noted that the proof given above is the result of a rigorous formal treatment of an infinite number of pictures. In a certain sense this treatment corresponds to carrying out standard perturbation theory to infinite order. The elimination of all but connected pictures which is achieved by such a treatment is a characteristic result in many-particle perturbation theory.

On the basis of the theorem given above, the expectation value $<\psi_o|A_{qj}|\psi_o>$ is given by the sum of expression (7-16) over all connected pictures which involve p' operators O and m' operators O^* and over all non-negative integers m' and p'. The expectation value can therefore be written in the following way:

$$<\psi_o|A_{qj}|\psi_o> = \Sigma_{mp}\Sigma_\delta^{conn}(1/m!)(1/n!)<0|\{O^{*m}O^p(A_{qj}O)\}_\delta|0> \quad (7\text{-}17)$$

or

$$<\psi_o|A_{qj}|\psi_o> = \Sigma_\delta^{conn}<0|\{[1+O^*+(1/2!)O^{*2}+\ldots][1+O+(1/2!)O^2+\ldots](A_{qj}O)\}_\delta|0> \quad (7\text{-}18)$$

The latter equation is seen to be identical to Eq. (7-12) except for the restriction to connected pictures and the absence of the factor e^n. The present equation is much more practical than the earlier one, however. The pictures involved in the present equation give contributions which are easily classified as to order of magnitude in powers of u/a, and for any particular order there are only a finite number of pictures. The pictures involved in the earlier equation also give contributions which can be classified as to order of magnitude, but for a particular order there is an infinity of pictures.

As shown by examination of Eq. (7-18), the desired expectation value $<\psi_o|A_{qj}|\psi_o>$ involves no contribution which is independent of u/a. This is to be expected, of course, since the expectation value of a nuclear displacement with respect to the unperturbed ground state is zero. The desired expectation value does contain one contribution which is of first order in u/a, however. This contribution comes from a picture which is a single cross-hatched circle with no phonons at all, and it is given by the following expression:

$$(1/\omega_{qj})\, \Sigma_{\delta'}^{conn} < \vec{q}j | \left\{ V_o \right\}_{\delta'} | 0 >.$$

The first-order part of this contribution is obtained when V_o is replaced by just $V^{(3)}$. The matrix element $< \vec{q}j | V^{(3)} | 0 >$ which then appears is given by Eq. (6-18). To first order in u/a, then, the expectation value $<\psi_o|A_{qj}|\psi_o>$ is given by the following equation:

$$<\psi_o|A_{qj}|\psi_o> \cong -3\Delta(\vec{q})(1/\omega_{0j})\, \Sigma\, (j_1) f(\vec{q}_1) B^{(3)}_{0j,\,1,\,-1}. \qquad (7\text{-}19)$$

Once this expectation value of A_{qj} is known, it is a simple matter to find the expectation value of a nuclear displacement $\vec{u}_{sn}$, at least formally. On the basis of Eqs. (7-6) and (7-19), the first-order approximation to this expectation value of $\vec{u}_{sn}$ is given by the following equation:

$$<\psi_o|\vec{u}_{sn}|\psi_o> \cong -3/2\; \Sigma_j (v_o/m_n \pi^3 \omega_{0j}^3)^{1/2} \vec{e}^{(n)}_{0j}$$
$$\times \left\{ \Sigma\, (j_1) f(\vec{q}_1) B^{(3)}_{0j,\,1,\,-1} + c.\,c. \right\}, \qquad (7\text{-}20)$$

where c. c. stands for the complex conjugate of the preceding term. As shown by this equation, $<\psi_o|A_{qj}|\psi_o>$ is determined completely by the normal modes for which $\vec{q}$ is zero (modulo $2\pi\tau$), and this result occurs in all orders. The index j which appears in Eq. (7-20) and the corresponding index which appears in higher order equations should therefore be restricted to the optical modes, since acoustical modes with q equal to zero only lead to pure translations.

Since only optical modes with q equal to zero contribute to the expectation value of $\vec{u}_{sn}$, the expectation values of two displacements $\vec{u}_{sn}$ and $\vec{u}_{s'n}$ must be identical. This is the justification for the statement made earlier that the expectation values $<\psi_o|A_{qj}|\psi_o>$ cannot describe an alteration of the unit cell but can only that diagram to $R_z|0>$ can be written as a product of two factors, one factor for the part of the diagram to the left of the last intermediate vacuum state (not the final state) and one factor for the part of the diagram to the right of this state. Because of the structure of Eqs. (6-5) and (6-6) for the resolvent, the first of these factors is a contribution to the function $(1/H_o-z)V_z|0>$, and the second is a contribution to the matrix element $<0|R_z|0>$, which is $D_z(0)$. When all of the contributions to $R_z|0>$ which involve intermediate vacuum states are treated in this way, the sum of these contributions can be rewritten to give Eq. (8-2).

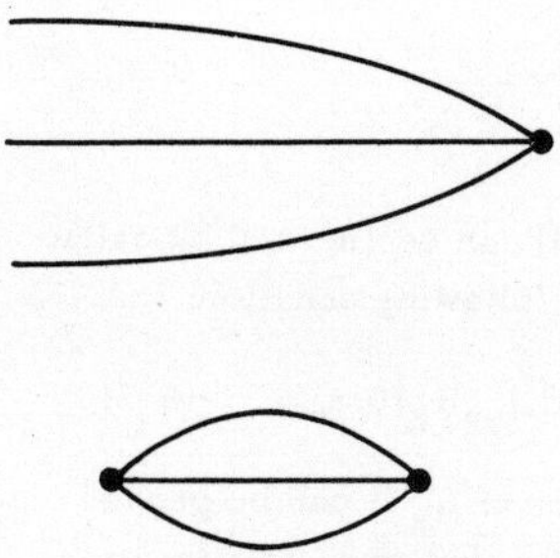

Fig. 8-1
Sample diagram contributing to $R_z|0>$ in Eq. (8-2)

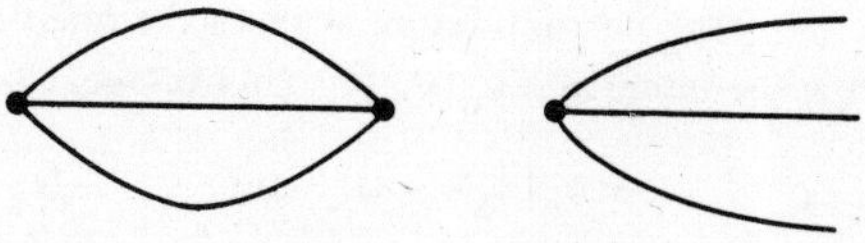

Fig. 8-2
Sample diagram which is excluded from Eq. (8-2)

On the basis of Eq. (8-2) the pole at z equals x_o in $D_z(0)$ gives rise to a pole at the same location in $R_z|0>$. The first factor in Eq. (8-2) can be shown to be finite and well-behaved at x_o. The pole in $R_z|0>$ is therefore simple, as is the pole in $D_z(0)$.

Now consider the following function:

$$|\psi_o> = Q_o^{-1/2} \lim_{z\to x_o \pm i0} (x_o-z)R_z|0>. \qquad (8\text{-}3)$$

The limit on z here means that the imaginary part of z approaches zero from either above or below the real axis, and the factor $Q_o^{-1/2}$ is included for normalization. The function defined in Eq. (8-3) turns out to be an eigenfunction of the Hamiltonian H of Eq. (5-9), and its eigenvalue is given by

$$E_o = \varepsilon_o + \varepsilon_{zp} + x_o. \qquad (8\text{-}4)$$

In this equation x_o is found to approach zero as the perturbation V approaches zero. It is therefore natural to assume that for small perturbations Eqs. (8-3) and (8-4) represent the wave function and energy of the ground state of the perturbed crystal.

To see that $|\psi_o>$ in Eq. (8-3) is an eigenfunction of H, consider the operation of H on $|\psi_o>$. This can be written out as follows:

$$H|\psi_o> = (\varepsilon_o+\varepsilon_{zp})|\psi_o> + Q_o^{-1/2} \lim_{z \to x_o \pm i0} (x_o-z)(H_o+V)R_z|0>, \qquad (8\text{-}5)$$

Because of the definition of R_z, however, the product $(H_o+V)R_z$ is just equal to $1+zR_z$. When this relation is used in Eq. (8-5) and the limit is taken, the following equation is obtained:

$$H|\psi_o> = (\varepsilon_o + \varepsilon_{zp} + x_o)|\psi_o>. \qquad (8\text{-}6)$$

This verifies the results which are claimed above.

The normalization of the wave function in Eq. (8-3) can be checked by calculating the integral $<\psi_o|\psi_o>$. This integral is given by the following equation:

$$<\psi_o|\psi_o> = Q_o^{-1} \lim_{z \to x_o \pm i0} (x_o-z)(x_o-z^*) <0|R_{z*}R_z|0>, \qquad (8\text{-}7)$$

where z* is the complex conjugate of z. From the definition of R_z it can be proved that $R_{z*}R_z$ equals $(R_{z*}-R_z)/(z^*-x)$, however. Eq. (8-7) can therefore be rewritten in the following way:

$$<\psi_o|\psi_o> = Q_o^{-1} \lim_{z \to x_o \pm i0} (x_o-z)(x_o-z^*)[D_{z*}(0)-D_z(0)]/z^*-z. \qquad (8\text{-}8)$$

When the limit on z is taken in this equation $D_z(0)$ and $D_{z*}(0)$ can be replaced by (Q_o/x_o-z) and (Q_o/x_o-z^*)(Q_o is real), and the right side of the equation becomes just one. The wave function $|\psi_o>$ defined by Eq. (8-3) is therefore normalized to one.

The wave function $|\psi_o>$ can be obtained in somewhat different form by use of Eq. (8-2) for $R_z|0>$. Since $D_z(0)$ in that equation is given by (Q_o/x_o-z) near z equals x_o, $|\psi_o>$ can be written out as follows:

$$|\psi_o> = Q_o^{1/2} \lim_{z \to x_o \pm i0} [1+\Sigma_\delta^{\text{no states } |0>}(1/H_o-z)\{V_z\}_\delta]\,|0>. \qquad (8\text{-}9)$$

The wave function $|\psi_o>$ can therefore be determined entirely from diagrams which have no intermediate vacuum states.

All of the results above depend upon assumed properties of $D_z(0)$, and the existence of these properties must now be verified.

The quantity $D_z(0)$ which is to be investigated can be written out in the following way:

describe changes within the cell.

The problem of nuclear shifts which is discussed above illustrates one effect of the anharmonic forces for a crystal in its ground state. Other effects which can be calculated by similar techniques are the correlations of the displacements of pairs of nuclei and the distribution of phonons. The first of these effects is given by the expectation value of a product $\vec{u}_{sn}\vec{u}_{s'n'}$, and it requires the calculation of the quantities $< \psi_o | A_{qj} A_{q'j'} | \psi_o >$ and $< \psi_o | A_{qj} A^*_{q'j'} | \psi_o >$. The second effect is given by the expectation value of the operator for phonon density, $A^*_{qj} A_{qj}$.

8. DERIVATION OF RESULTS FOR THE GROUND STATE

In the following discussion a derivation of the expressions for the perturbed ground-state energy and wave function is outlined. For a more detailed presentation of some parts of this derivation, the reader is referred to the literature of Van Hove and Hugenholtz which is listed in the bibliography. In some respects the derivation outlined below is simpler than the original, however.

The derivation is based on a property of the vacuum-to-vacuum matrix element of the resolvent. This element will now be symbolized by $D_z(0)$, so that

$$D_z(0) = \langle 0|R_z|0\rangle. \tag{8-1}$$

The property of interest is that in the limit of an infinite crystal $D_z(0)$ has a simple pole on the positive, real z axis, z being a complex number. Near this pole, then, $D_z(0)$ can be approximated by the expression $(Q_o/x_o - z)$, where x_o is the location of the pole and $-Q_o$ is the residue. It also turns out that $D_z(0)$ has a cut along the positive, real z axis from x_o (which is positive) to plus infinity. The discontinuity across this cut approaches zero as the real part of z approaches x_o from the positive side, however, and the simple pole at x_o remains well-defined. The proof of these properties of $D_z(0)$ will be discussed later in the present section.

As a result of the simple pole in $D_z(0)$, the function $R_z|0\rangle$ also has a simple pole at z equals x_o in the limit of an infinite crystal. The proof of this is based on the diagram analysis by which $R_z|0\rangle$ is to be evaluated. For this the resolvent R_z is first expanded in powers of V according to Eqs. (6-5) and (6-6), and each V is then replaced by the $V^{(\nu)}$'s. With these expansions the resolvent is given by a linear combination of product operators of the form shown in Eq. (6-10). Each of these product operators generates a linear combination of phonon states when it acts on the vacuum state, and the coefficients of the phonon states are easily determined by using the diagram techniques described in Sec. 6.

As shown by this diagram analysis, which is outlined below, the function $R_z|0\rangle$ can be written in the following form:

$$R_z|0\rangle = [\,1+\Sigma_\delta^{\text{no states }|0\rangle} (1/H_o - z)\left\{V_z\right\}_\delta]\,|0\rangle\, D_z(0). \tag{8-2}$$

The notation in the superscript of the summation sign here is meant to restrict the summation to those diagrams δ which do not have $|0\rangle$ as an intermediate or final state. To illustrate this restriction, the diagram in Fig. 8-1 is included in the summation, while the diagram in Fig. 8-2 is excluded.

Eq. (8-2) is based on the following analysis. If a particular diagram contains the vacuum as an intermediate state one or more times, the contribution from

$$D_z(0) = \langle 0|R_z|0\rangle = (-1/z)-(-1/z)^2\Sigma_\delta \langle 0|\left\{V_z\right\}_\delta|0\rangle. \qquad (8\text{-}10)$$

Here $(-1/z)$ appears as the eigenvalue of $(1/H_0-z)$ operating on the vacuum state, and the summation is over all diagrams.

For reasons which will become clear later it is convenient to consider the contribution to Eq. (8-10) which comes from just one-component diagrams. This contribution can be written out as follows:

$$B_z = -(1/z)^2\Sigma_\delta^{conn} \langle 0|\left\{V_z\right\}_\delta|0\rangle. \qquad (8\text{-}11)$$

Each diagram in this expression gives a contribution to B_z which is proportional to Ω (in the limit of an infinite crystal), and B_z itself can therefore be written in the form

$$B_z = -\Omega(1/z)^2F_z. \qquad (8\text{-}12)$$

According to the discussion of Sec. 6, the factor F_z introduced here is made up of a linear combination of terms, each of which contains a product of energy denominators of the form

$$(1/\omega_1+\omega_2+\ldots-z)(1/\omega_1'+\omega_2'+\ldots-z)\ldots\ .$$

Because of these energy denominators F_z has a dense set of poles all along the positive, real z axis when the crystal in question is large and finite. If the quantity F_z is only calculated to some finite order in powers of V, these poles occur out to some finite value X, and as the order to which F_z is calculated is made arbitrarily large, the value X also becomes arbitrarily large. There is no pole in F_z at z equals zero, however.

As the crystal volume Ω increases the poles in F_z shift around in a complicated way and the number of poles increases. Except for these effects, however, F_z is essentially independent of Ω. In the limit of an infinite crystal the poles in F_z merge, and F_z acquires a z-dependence which is somewhat like that of the integral $\int_0^X f(x)(1/x-z)dx$ in the vicinity of the real z axis. In this limit, the line of poles between zero and X becomes a cut across which the function F_z has a finite discontinuity.

According to a theorem which was established by Hugenholtz, (Hugenholtz, 1957 a, b), the quantity $D_z(0)$ can be completely expressed in terms of just the function B_z defined in Eq. (8-11). The equation which Hugenholtz derives for $D_z(0)$ is the following:

$$D_z(0) = -(1/z) + B_z + (1/2!)(B_z)*(B_z) + (1/3!)(B_z)*(B_z)*(B_z)+\ldots\ . \qquad (8\text{-}13)$$

Here the quantity $(B_z)*(B_z)$ is a convolution product of the two B_z's. A general convolution product of this type is defined by the following equation:

$$(f_z)*(g_z) = (i/2\pi) \oint f_{z'} g_{z-z'} dz', \tag{8-14}$$

and for present purposes the contour of integration is taken to be that shown in Fig. 8-3. The functions $f_{z'}$ and $g_{z-z'}$ appearing in the definition (8-14) are assumed to have poles or cuts only along the real z' axis, and the contour of integration is supposed to include enough of the real axis to encircle all of these. Furthermore, the contour of integration in the z' plane is not to contain the point z. For the proof of Eq. (8-13) the reader is referred to the original paper by Hugenholtz.

Eq. (8-12) is somewhat complicated as it stands, but a fairly simple equation can be obtained from it by taking the Fourier transform of both sides. The Fourier transform of a function such as f_z is defined here by the following equation:

$$\tilde{f}_t = (i/2\pi) \oint e^{-itz'} f_{z'} dz', \tag{8-15}$$

where the contour of integration is again taken to be that shown in Fig. 8-3 (except that no second variable z is involved here). The function $f_{z'}$ may again have poles or cuts only on the real z' axis, and the contour in Fig. 8-3 is supposed to enclose all of these.

On the basis of Eq. (8-13), the Fourier transform of $D_z(0)$ is found to be given by the following equation:

$$\tilde{D}_t(0) = 1 + \tilde{B}_t + (1/2!)\tilde{B}_t^2 + (1/3!)\tilde{B}_t^3 + \ldots, \tag{8-16}$$

where $\tilde{B}_t$ is the Fourier transform of B_z. The power series above is always convergent, and it gives the following result for $\tilde{D}_t(0)$:

$$\tilde{D}_t(0) = \exp \tilde{B}_t. \tag{8-17}$$

Because of the large factor Ω in both B_z and $\tilde{B}_t$, many terms are required for the convergence of the series in Eqs. (8-13) and (8-16). For all practical purposes, then, each series must be treated in its entirety, as has been done above. The simple result in Eq. (8-17) (or its transform) is then obtained, and it is this result which takes care of the troublesome powers of Ω which occur in the ordinary perturbation treatment of the ground-state wave function and energy.

The only features of $D_z(0)$ which are presently of interest are its singularities. When the crystal is finite, singularities in the form of poles are expected because of the nature of B_z in Eq. (8-12) for $D_z(0)$. In the limit of an infinite crystal, however, most of these poles should merge to give a cut. If any pole remains in this limit, the Fourier transform $\tilde{D}_t(0)$ should be a periodic function of t at large t. The existence of such a pole can therefore be checked by studying the assymptotic behavior of $\tilde{D}_t(0)$.

8. DERIVATION OF RESULTS FOR THE GROUND STATE

The assymptotic behavior of $\tilde{D}_t(0)$ is related to that of $\tilde{B}_t$ through Eq. (8-17), and the latter behavior is easily determined from the known properties of B_z. In the limit of large t, $\tilde{B}_t$ is found to be given by the following equation:

$$\tilde{B}_t \stackrel{\sim}{=} -it\Omega F_o + \Omega(dF_z/dz)_{z=0}. \quad (8\text{-}18)$$

The derivation of this result makes use of Cauchy's residue theorem. When this result is substituted into Eq. (8-16), $\tilde{D}_t(0)$ is indeed seen to be a periodic function of t at large t, thus indicating that there is a pole in $D_z(0)$. This pole can be shown to be of first order by studying the Fourier transform of $(z-x_o)D_z(0)$, where x_o is the location of the pole. The quantity $D_z(0)$ can therefore be written as Q_o/x_o-z when z is near x_o, as was assumed at the beginning of this section, and the values of Q_o and x_o determined by the analysis outlined above turn out to be the following:

$$x_o = \Omega F_o = \Sigma_\delta^{conn} < 0|\left\{V_z\right\}_\delta|0>, \quad (8\text{-}19)$$

$$Q_o = -\exp[\Omega(dF_z/dz)_{z=0}] = e^{-n}, \quad (8\text{-}20)$$

where n is the same quantity that is defined in Eq. (7-3).

With these results, Eq. (8-4) for the ground-state energy of the crystal is seen to agree with the result which was claimed in Sec. 7, and Eq. (8-9) for the ground-state wave function is seen to reduce to the following equation:

$$|\psi_o> = e^{n/2}\lim_{z\to x_o\pm i0} [1+\Sigma_\delta^{no\ states\ |0>}(1/H_o-z)\left\{V_z\right\}_\delta]\,|0>. \quad (8\text{-}21)$$

With some algebra this equation for $|\psi_o>$ can also be shown to give the result which was claimed in Sec. 7.

Although this essentially completes the outline of the derivation, several comments remain to be made. As presented above, the derivation appears to be quite straightforward, but in actuality it is complicated mathematically by the interplay of the different limiting processes. These limiting processes are the approach of Ω to infinity, the approach of z to a pole or cut, and the approach of t to infinity.

When the volume Ω is large but finite, as it is for a real crystal, the dense sets of poles in F_z and $D_z(0)$ do not actually form continuous cuts as they would for an infinite crystal. In the case of finite Ω, then, the limit as z approaches $x \pm i0$ must be taken with care. The dense set of poles can only be treated as a cut if the length of i0 remains large compared to the very small spacing between the poles, and this restriction must be incorporated into the limits which have been used in the foregoing derivation.

Furthermore, when the volume Ω is large but finite, t cannot actually be allowed to approach infinity. If t is so large that e^{itx} varies significantly from one of the closely-spaced poles in F_z or $D_z(0)$ to the next, then these poles will give additional contributions to $\tilde{B}_t$ and $\tilde{D}_t(0)$. Specifically, the results for $\tilde{B}_t$ and $\tilde{D}_t(0)$ which have been used in the derivation are only valid when t is in the range

$$\omega^{-1} << t << N_o^{1/3} \omega^{-1}, \qquad (8\text{-}22)$$

where ω is a characteristic frequency of vibration. This limitation naturally affects the physical interpretation of the wave function $|\psi_o>$ and the energy E_o which have been derived, and this is discussed below.

The quantity $\tilde{D}_t(0)$ which is involved here is the Fourier transform of the vacuum-to-vacuum matrix element of the resolvent. The Fourier transform of the resolvent itself is the operator $e^{-it(H_o+V)}$, however, and $\tilde{D}_t(0)$ can therefore be written in the following way:

$$\tilde{D}_t(0) = < 0 | e^{-it(H_o+V)} | 0 >. \qquad (8\text{-}23)$$

To within a constant factor, the operator $e^{-it(H_o+V)}$ which appears here is just the operator e^{-itH} which generates a time-dependent wave function from a time-independent solution of Schrödinger's equation. The parameter t in $\tilde{D}_t(0)$ can therefore be interpreted as time.

From the fact that $|\psi_o>$ in Eq. (8-21) is obtained from an approximation to $\tilde{D}_t(0)$, then, it follows that $|\psi_o>$ might very well behave as a stationary state of H only for times t in the range (8-21). Since the upper limit of this range is extremely large for a crystal of normal size, however, the wave function $|\psi_o>$ in Eq. (8-21) provides an approximation to a stationary state of H which is satisfactory for all practical purposes. A simple formula for the wave function $|\psi_o>$ has thus been obtained by abandoning the demand for an exact stationary state and accepting a practical substitute.

It has been claimed by some investigators that the final results for the ground-state wave function $|\psi_o>$ and the energy E_o are better than their derivation would indicate. It is claimed that these results satisfy Schrödinger's equation exactly no matter what the size of the system, rather than just in the limit of an infinite system. Formally this seems to be true, but there are problems of convergence which are difficult to investigate. The only assumption of convergence which is really needed for applying the wave function and energy derived here is that the series in powers of V for E_o/Ω and for the operator O converge in the limit of infinite Ω. If this assumption is satisfied, the derivation is valid, and the wave function $|\psi_o>$ behaves as a stationary state with an energy of E_o for reasonably long times.

If the expressions for E_o/Ω and $|\psi_o>$ are written out for a system in which

Ω does not approach infinity, however, the series involved are likely to be quite different from their assymptotic limits as Ω becomes infinite. The differences occur in the high-order terms. The conditions under which these series for finite Ω will converge to give rigorous stationary states and energies are not known, and there do not seem to be any suitable examples for which the convergence of these series can be fairly tested. A suitable example would have to be simple enough to be carried out and yet hard enough to involve all the important features which are to be tested. In view of the situation as it stands, then, it seems best to take a conservative viewpoint at this stage and to regard the derived formulae for E_0 and $|\psi_0>$ as just good approximations to the energy and wave function of a very large system.

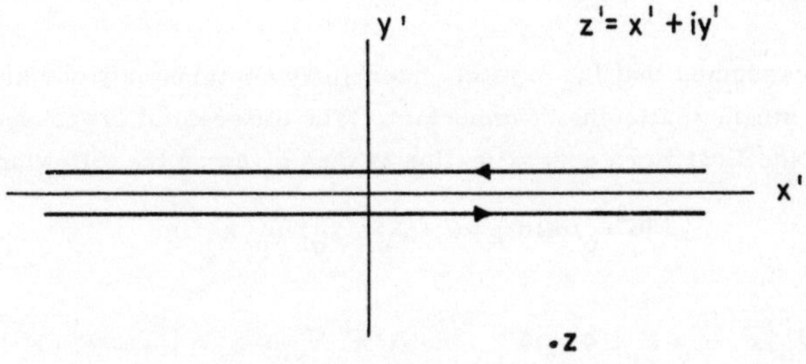

Fig. 8-3

Contour of integration for the convolution product of Eq. (8-14)

9. SCATTERING OF NEUTRONS BY A CRYSTAL IN ITS GROUND STATE: GENERAL DISCUSSION

As a second example of the application of many-particle perturbation theory, the scattering of neutrons by a crystal in its ground state will be considered. Since the crystal is in its ground state, the scattering is that which would occur at O°K. Anharmonic forces provide only a small correction to this scattering, but they give rise to effects which are expected to be measurable. They give rise to additional effects in scattering at non-zero temperatures, but this subject will be postponed to a later section. The present treatment for O°K provides a useful preliminary to the more general treatment, and it is theoretically interesting on its own merits for the same reason that the calculation of the ground-state energy and wave function were of interest.

It is assumed that the crystal under study contains only one kind of nucleus and that only single scattering is important. The differential cross-section for scattering in the first Born approximation is then given by the following equation:

$$(d^2\sigma_0/d\Omega\, d\varepsilon) = a\ (|\vec{k}|/|\vec{k}_0|)S_0(\vec{\kappa}, \omega), \tag{9-1}$$

where

$$S_0(\vec{\kappa}, \omega) = \Sigma_\nu | < \psi_\nu|\Sigma_{sn} \exp(i\ \vec{\kappa}\cdot \vec{r}_{sn})|\psi_0 > |^2 \delta(\omega + E_0 - E_\nu). \tag{9-2}$$

In these equations σ_0 is the scattering cross-section, $d\Omega$ is the element of solid angle into which the neutron is scattered, $d\varepsilon$ is the range of energy of the scattered neutron, a is the scattering length of the atomic nucleus, $\vec{k}$ is the wave vector or momentum of the scattered neutron ($\hbar$ is again set equal to one), $\vec{k}_0$ is the wave vector or momentum of the incident neutron, $\vec{\kappa}$ is the momentum transfered from the neutron to the crystal, ω is the energy transfered from the neutron to the crystal, $|\psi_\nu>$ is an excited eigenstate of the crystal, $|\psi_0>$ is the ground state of the crystal, E_ν is the energy of the eigenstate $|\psi_\nu>$, and E_0 is the ground-state energy. Some of these quantities are related to one another, and these relations are shown in the following equations:

$$\vec{\kappa} = \vec{k}_0 - \vec{k}$$

$$\omega = |\vec{k}_0|^2/2m - |\vec{k}|^2/2m = E_\nu - E. \tag{9-3}$$

where m is the mass of the neutron.

Eqs. (9-1) and (9-2) above can be derived from the following pseudo-potential for the scattering of a neutron by an atomic nucleus:

9. SCATTERING OF NEUTRONS BY A CRYSTAL IN ITS GROUND STATE: GENERAL DISCUSSION

$$V(r) = (2\pi a/m)\delta(\vec{r}). \tag{9-4}$$

The justification for the use of this potential is complicated and will not be discussed here. In writing the potential in Eq. (9-4) it has been assumed that the scattering length a is independent of the relative orientation of the spins of the neutron and nucleus if the nuclear spin is non-zero. This assumption is not necessary, but it is convenient here. It has also been assumed that a is independent of the energy of the incident neutron. This assumption is well justified for the low neutron energies which are used in scattering from solids. The derivation of Eq. (9-1) from the pseudo-potential V(r) requires the additional assumption that the range of V(r) is small compared to the smallest distance between nuclei, and this assumption is well justified.

As shown by the form of $S_0(\vec{\kappa}, \omega)$ in Eq. (9-2) the overall differential cross-section is the sum of the cross-sections for scattering processes in which the crystal is left in various excited states $|\psi_\nu\rangle$. Because of the delta function, however, only those states $|\psi_\nu\rangle$ whose energies differ from the ground state energy by ω give any contribution.

The problem is now to calculate the scattering function $S_0(\vec{\kappa}, \omega)$, taking into account the existence of anharmonic forces. Since the neutron does not manifest itself explicitly in Eq. (9-2), which defines the scattering function, the calculation is essentially a solid-state problem.

The scattering function as given in Eq. (9-2) appears to depend upon the exact excited states of the crystal. It can actually be evaluated without knowing these excited states, however, as will be shown below. It is quite fortunate that exact expressions for excited states are not required, because it does not seem possible to derive such expressions that are reasonably simple when anharmonic forces are included. The theoretical difficulty of finding formulae for exact excited states of many-particle systems seems to have an experimental analogue in the difficulty of finding information about single excited states. Since experimental results always seem to involve sums over excited states, however, simple theoretical expressions for individual excited states do not seem to be needed. The present calculation only provides a case in point.

In view of the factors just mentioned it is convenient to rewrite the scattering function in a form which does not explicitly involve the individual excited states $|\psi_\nu\rangle$. Such a form is shown in the following equation:

$$S_0(\vec{\kappa}, \omega) = \langle \psi_0 | T_{-\kappa}\, \delta(\omega + E_0 - H) T_\kappa | \psi_0 \rangle, \tag{9-5}$$

in which T_κ is the operator for the neutron interaction and is given by

$$T_{\kappa} = \Sigma_{sn} \exp(i\vec{\kappa} \cdot \vec{r}_{sn}). \tag{9-6}$$

Eq. (9-5) reduces to the original form in Eq. (9-2) when use is made of the expansion

$$T_{\kappa} |\psi_o> = \Sigma_{\nu} |\psi_{\nu}> <\psi_{\nu}| T_{\kappa} |\psi_o>, \tag{9-7}$$

which is valid because of the completeness of the set of functions $|\psi_{\nu}>$. The operator $\delta(\omega+E_o-H)$ acting on a function $|\psi_{\nu}>$ has an eigenvalue $\delta(\omega+E_o-E_{\nu})$, since $|\psi_{\nu}>$ is an eigenfunction of H.

Eq. (9-5) for the scattering function can be further rewritten to involve the resolvent operator instead of the operator $\delta(\omega+E_o-H)$. For this, use is made of relation

$$2\pi i\delta(x) = (1/x-i0) - (1/x+i0), \tag{9-8}$$

in which x is real. This relation is meant to be applied in the integrand of an integral over x. It is obtained from the relation

$$(1/x\pm i0) = (1/x)_{\text{principal part}} \pm i\pi\delta(x),$$

which is used in distribution theory. On the basis of Eq. (9-8), the scattering function can be rewritten as follows:

$$S_o(\vec{\kappa}, \omega) = (1/2\pi i) \lim_{z \to x_o+\omega+i0} [S_z(\vec{\kappa}) - S_z^*(\vec{\kappa})], \tag{9-9}$$

where

$$S_z(\vec{\kappa}) = <\psi_o| T_{-\kappa} R_z T_{\kappa} |\psi_o>, \tag{9-10}$$

and where x_o is related to E_o by Eq. (8-4).

The auxiliary function $S_z(\vec{\kappa})$ can be calculated by diagram analysis in much the same way as the matrix elements discussed in Sec. 6. For this the eigenfunction $|\psi_o>$ in Eq. (9-10) should be replaced by use of Eqs. (7-2) and (7-4), and the resolvent R_z should be replaced by its expansion in products of the operators $V^{(\nu)}$ and the operator $(1/H_o-z)$. The neutron operator T_{κ} should then be expanded in powers of the nuclear displacements, as the anharmonic energy V was expanded, and this is done in the following equation:

$$\begin{aligned} T_{\kappa} &= \Sigma_{sn} \exp[i\vec{\kappa} \cdot (\vec{s} + \vec{R}_{on} + \vec{u}_{sn})] \\ &= \Sigma_{sn} \exp[i\vec{\kappa} \cdot (\vec{s} + \vec{R}_{on})] \\ &\times [1 + i(\vec{\kappa} \cdot \vec{u}_{sn}) - (1/2!)(\vec{\kappa} \cdot \vec{u}_{sn})^2 - i(1/3!)(\vec{\kappa} \cdot \vec{u}_{sn})^3 + \ldots]. \end{aligned} \tag{9-11}$$

9. SCATTERING OF NEUTR ONS BY A CRYSTAL IN ITS GROUND STATE: GFNERAL DISCUSSION

The dot product $\vec{\kappa} \cdot \vec{u}_{sn}$ appearing in this equation is given in terms of creation and annihilation operators as follows:

$$\vec{\kappa} \cdot \vec{u}_{sn} = (v_o/16\pi^3 m_n)^{1/2} \Sigma_j \int_q (\omega_{qj})^{-1/2} [A_{qj} + A^*_{-qj}] \times \vec{\kappa} \cdot [\vec{e}^{(n)}_{qj} - i\vec{f}^{(n)}_{qj}] \exp(i\vec{q} \cdot \vec{s}). \tag{9-12}$$

This is derived from Eq. (7-6) for $\vec{u}_{sn}$. When the neutron operator T_κ is expanded as above it is given by a linear combination of products of creation and annihilation operators. In this form it can be treated by diagram analysis in much the same way as the resolvent operator was treated in earlier sections.

When the expansions described above are made, the function $S_z(\vec{\kappa})$ in Eq. (9-10) can be calculated by a form of diagram analysis. In addition to vertices arising from terms in the resolvent, however, each diagram has two vertices arising from the two neutron operators. The coefficient of a particular product of creation and annihilation operators for one of these neutron vertices is different than for one of the resolvent vertices, and different symbols must be used for the two types of vertices. A neutron vertex will therefore be designated by a dot with a small circle around it. Each neutron vertex should bear an index n, corresponding to the n which appears in Eq. (9-11), and an index $\vec{\kappa}$, but these will generally be omitted for convenience.

A few sample neutron vertices are illustrated in Fig. 9-1. The first of these (on the left) describes a first-order process in which one phonon is annihilated; the second describes a second-order process in which two phonons are created; and the third describes a second-order process in which one phonon is created and instantaneously annihilated. A somewhat more complicated neutron vertex is illustrated in Fig. 9-2. This describes a process of order eleven, involving two incoming phonons, three instantaneous phonons, and three outgoing phonons. The effect of any of these vertices in a diagram is easy to calculate when reference is made to Eqs. (9-11) and (9-12). The techniques involved are the same as those described in Sec. 6.

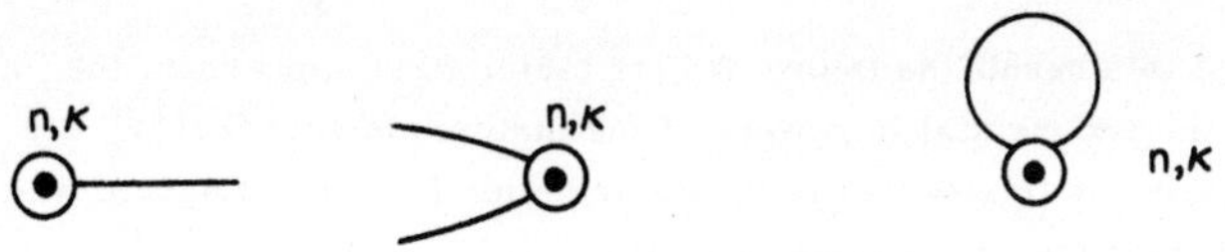

Fig. 9-1 Sample neutron vertices

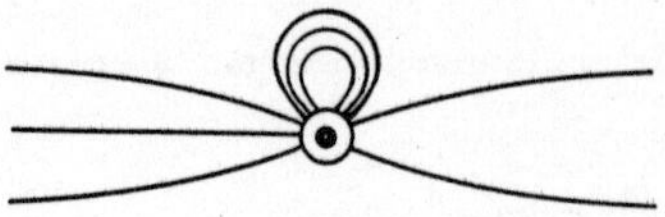

Fig. 9-2 Sample neutron vertex

One part of the effect of a neutron vertex in a diagram must be described in detail for future use, however. Consider a particular ν'th-order product of creation and annihilation operators which occurs in the expansion of T_κ in Eq. (9-11). Due to the summation over $\vec{s}$, the coefficient of this product contains a factor $\Delta(\vec{\kappa} + \vec{q})$, where $\vec{q}$ is the sum of the wave vectors of the phonons created minus the sum of the wave vectors of the phonons annihilated. Because of this factor the total pseudo-momentum of the state following a neutron vertex $(n, \vec{\kappa})$ is equal to $\vec{\kappa}$ plus the total pseudo-momentum of the state preceding the vertex. Since the neutron vertex represents an event in which a neutron is scattered from the crystal, the scattering event is seen to involve a form of momentum conservation. This conservation, which involves the real momentum of the neutron, provides the justification for calling the wave vector of a phonon a pseudo-momentum.

One simplification in the calculation of $S_z(\vec{\kappa})$ can now be described. Consider a diagram containing a neutron vertex which has no instantaneous phonons connected with it. Such a vertex is shown at the left in Fig. 9-3. Also consider all the other diagrams which differ from the original only in that one or more instantaneous phonons are connected with the particular neutron vertex which has been singled out. If the original diagram contains the neutron vertex which is at the left in Fig. 9-3, for example, consider all the other diagrams in which the original vertex is replaced by the other neutron vertices in Fig. 9-3 and its extension. The sum of the contributions from all of these diagrams is just equal to a constant times the contribution from the first diagram. The constant in this result turns out to be the well-known Debye-Waller factor for a crystal at O°K: it is given by the following expression:

$$\exp\left\{-(1/2) < 0 \,|\, (\vec{\kappa} \cdot \vec{u}_{on})^2 \,|\, 0 > \right\}. \tag{9-13}$$

In the proof of this result the Debye-Waller factor first appears as the infinite series exapnsion of the exponential in powers of the matrix element $< 0 \,|\, (\vec{\kappa} \cdot \vec{u}_{on})^2 \,|\, 0 >$, and the m'th term in this series is the contribution from the diagram which has m instantaneous phonons on the neutron vertex.

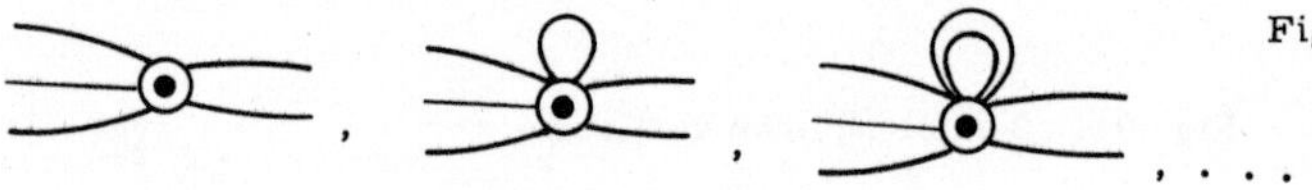

Fig. 9-3 Neutron vertices

9. SCATTERING OF NEUTRONS BY A CRYSTAL IN ITS GROUND STATE: GENERAL DISCUSSION

In view of the result above it is only necessary to consider explicitly those diagrams in which there are no instantaneous phonons on the neutron vertices. A factor like that in Eq. (9-13) must then be included for each neutron vertex to account for the diagrams which are omitted.

According to another theorem, it is really only necessary to consider two types of diagrams among those remaining; one type consists of just two connected components, each of which contains one of the neutron vertices, and the other type consists of just one component, which contains both neutron vertices. Again new factors must be introduced to account for the diagrams which are omitted, of course. The proof of this theorem is similar to the proof of Eq. (7-18). It will not be presented here, however, since the theorem is not needed in the discussion which follows. Only certain features of $S_z(\vec{\kappa})$ will be investigated here and for these there are specialized approaches which are fairly easy and which do not require the use of the theorem.

At this point it is useful to consider the nature of neutron-scattering results which are obtained in the harmonic approximation. This problem has been discussed extensively in the literature. Two of the papers are particularly appropriate to the present discussion, however, and these are the paper by Placzek and Van Hove (1954), and the paper by Sjölander (1954). In each of these papers a realistic phonon spectrum is used throughout the derivation.

As usual the neutron scattering can be considered as made up of elastic and inelastic scattering. Elastic scattering is characterized by the identity of the initial and final states of the crystal and hence by the absence of energy transfer between the neutron and the crystal. According to the harmonic theory, elastic scattering is only possible if the initial and final neutron momenta satisfy the following requirements:

$$\vec{\kappa} = \vec{k}_0 - \vec{k} = 2\pi\vec{\tau}, \quad \omega = (|\vec{k}_0|^2 - |\vec{k}|^2)/2m = 0, \tag{9-14}$$

in which $\vec{\tau}$ is any vector of the reciprocal lattice. These are the well-known Bragg conditions, and they turn out to apply whether or not anharmonic forces are neglected.

Inelastic scattering is characterized by the transfer of energy between the neutron and the crystal. For a particular momentum transfer $\vec{\kappa}$ (and therefore a particular angle of scattering) the inelastic spectrum predicted by harmonic theory has the general form indicated in Fig. 9-4. This figure is not meant to be quantitative. As suggested in the figure, the predicted spectrum is characterized by a set of delta-function peaks over a continuous background.

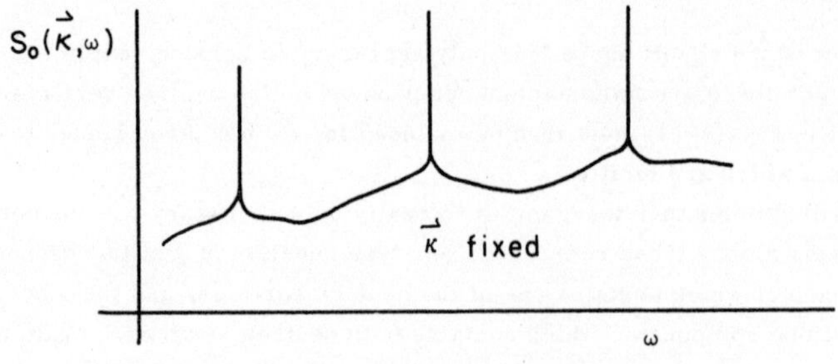

Fig. 9-4 Spectrum of scattered neutrons in the harmonic approximation

The delta-function peaks in the inelastic spectrum correspond to scattering in which each neutron excites a single phonon. For a given momentum transfer $\vec{\kappa}$ this process can only occur for certain values of the energy transfer ω. This follows from the conservation rules for energy and momentum, which take the following form when a phonon $\vec{q}j$ is excited:

$$\vec{\kappa} = k_o - \vec{k} = 2\pi\vec{\tau} + \vec{q}, \quad \omega = (|\vec{k}_o|^2 - |\vec{k}|^2)/2m = \omega_{qj}. \qquad (9\text{-}15)$$

For a given $\vec{\kappa}$ the peaks in the predicted inelastic spectrum occur at the values of ω for which these conditions are satisfied.

The background in the inelastic spectrum predicted by the harmonic theory corresponds to scattering in which each neutron excites more than one phonon in a single scattering event. The slight wings on the delta-function peaks in Fig. 9-4 belong to the background in the sense that they also are due to multiple excitations. In particular, they are due to two-phonon excitations in which one phonon has a very small pseudo-momentum. These wings are actually logarithmic infinities centered on the delta-function peaks.

The delta-function peaks in the spectrum described above are particularly interesting because they involve single phonons and because their locations can be investigated experimentally. The background does not exhibit features which are of such direct interest from the point of view of crystal dynamics.

The results of the harmonic theory have been presented above as a preliminary to considering the effects of anharmonic forces on neutron scattering. Since the anharmonic forces of a crystal are small compared to the harmonic forces, they only cause slight modifications of the results predicted by harmonic theory. The most significant of these modifications are the displacement and the broadening of the peaks in the inelastic spectrum. Since these peaks have no width (except for the

9. SCATTERING OF NEUTR ONS BY A CRYSTAL IN ITS GROUND STATE: GENERAL DISCUSSION

slight wings) according to the harmonic theory, their actual structure is an effect which is due solely to anharmonic forces. Such effects are obviously desirable as means of checking the predictions of many-particle perturbation theory.

10. PEAKS IN THE ENERGY SPECTRUM OF NEUTRONS SCATTERED AT O°K

The problem to be considered now is that of calculating the peaks in the energy spectrum of neutrons scattered from a crystal at O°K. Anharmonic forces are to be included in the calculation. Much information about the peaks can be obtained without a calculation of the complete spectrum, and the techniques required for this are fairly easy.

With the approximations introduced in the preceding section the important features of the desired spectrum are determined by the scattering function $S_o(\vec{\kappa}, \omega)$ which is defined in Eq. (9-2). If information is to be obtained about just the peaks in the spectrum, a formula for $S_o(\vec{\kappa}, \omega)$ must be found that separates the contributions of the peaks from that of the background. The procedure for doing this in general will be introduced here by first discussing the case of elastic scattering.

The straightforward method of obtaining the elastic scattering spectrum is to omit all terms but the ν-equals-zero term in Eq. (9-2) for the scattering function $S_o(\vec{\kappa}, \omega)$. This is equivalent to specifying that after the scattering event the crystal is again in its ground state $|\psi_o>$. The scattering function for elastic scattering which is obtained by this procedure is given by the following equation:

$$S_o^{(0)}(\vec{\kappa}, \omega) = | <\psi_o|T_\kappa|\psi_o> |^2 \delta(\omega). \qquad (10\text{-}1)$$

From this result the energy spectrum for elastic scattering at a given angle is seen to be a delta function centered at ω equals zero, as expected. Further consequences of this result will be considered after presentation of an alternative derivation.

The alternative derivation is quite artificial in view of the simple derivation above, but it is presented because of its connection to the more complicated problem of inelastic scattering. The starting point of the alternative derivation is Eq. (9-9) giving $S_o(\vec{\kappa}, \omega)$ in terms of the auxiliary function $S_z(\vec{\kappa})$, which is defined in Eq. (9-10). Since the elastic spectrum is a delta function centered on ω equals zero, it is necessary to investigate the function $S_z(\vec{\kappa})$ in the vicinity of z equals x_o. If $S_z(\vec{\kappa})$ can be shown to have a simple pole at x_o, for instance, the scattering function will have been proved to be a delta function at ω equals zero, as desired.

The auxiliary function $S_z(\vec{\kappa})$ can be completely calculated by diagram analysis using the techniques which were described in Sec. 9. Only the elastic spectrum is sought at present, however, and it is therefore desirable to isolate those contributions to $S_z(\vec{\kappa})$ which alone give rise to the elastic spectrum. For this purpose Eq. (9-9) for $S_z(\vec{\kappa})$ is rewritten in the following way:

$$S_z(\vec{\kappa}) = \Sigma_\delta < \psi_o|T_{-\kappa} \left\{R_z\right\}_\delta T_\kappa |\psi_o>. \qquad (10\text{-}2)$$

In this equation δ designates the part of a complete diagram which comes between (but does not include) the two neutron vertices. Two complete diagrams containing different partial diagrams δ are illustrated in Figs. 10-1 and 10-2. There are many complete diagrams which contain a particular diagram δ, of course, and all of them must be considered in the evaluation of Eq. (10-2).

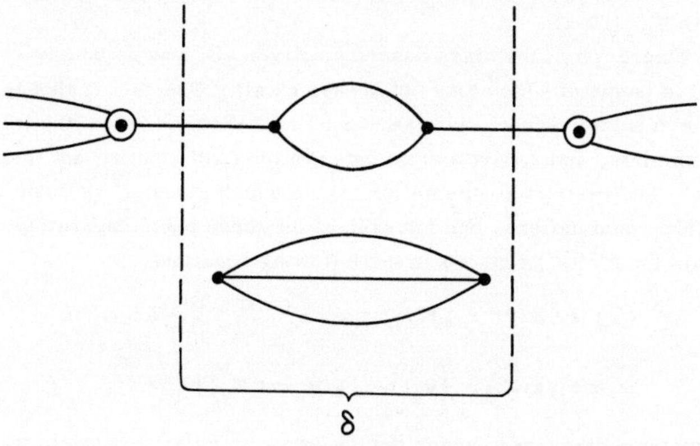

Fig. 10-1
Partial diagram δ of the type appearing in Eq. (10-2) for $S_z(\vec{\kappa})$.

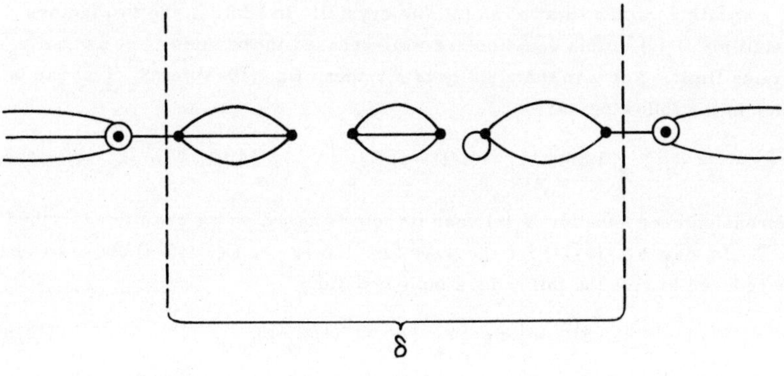

Fig. 10-2
Partial diagram δ of the type appearing in Eq. (10-2) for $S_z(\vec{\kappa})$.

The desired contribution to $S_z(\vec{\kappa})$ is obtained by limiting the summation over

δ in Eq. (10-2) to diagrams belonging to a certain class. That class consists of all the diagrams which contain the vacuum state at least once as an intermediate state. It includes the diagram δ in Fig. 10-2, for instance, but not that in Fig. 10-1. The resulting contribution to $S_z(\vec{\kappa})$ will be called $S_z^{(0)}(\vec{\kappa})$, and the corresponding contribution to the scattering function $S_0(\vec{\kappa}, \omega)$ will be called $S_0^{(0)}(\vec{\kappa}, \omega)$, in anticipation of agreement with Eq. (10-1).

Each diagram δ in the class described above will now be considered as made up of three parts (some of which may not always exist). One part is that to the right of the first intermediate vacuum state, a second is that to the left of the last intermediate vacuum state, and a third is that between the first and the last intermediate vacuum states. The restricted summation over δ which gives $S_z^{(0)}(\vec{\kappa})$ can then be rewritten as three summations, one for each of the three parts separately. With this the formula for $S_z^{(0)}(\vec{\kappa})$ reduces to the following equation:

$$S_z^{(0)}(\vec{\kappa}) = \langle \psi_0 | T_{-\kappa} [1+(1/H_0-z)\Sigma_{\delta_0} \{V_z\}_{\delta_0}] | 0 \rangle D_z(0)$$
$$\times \langle 0 | [1+\Sigma_{\delta'_0} \{V_z\}_{\delta'_0} (1/H_0-z) T_\kappa] | \psi_0 \rangle. \qquad (10\text{-}3)$$

Here δ_0 designates a diagram in which the vacuum occurs only as the initial state and δ'_0 designates a diagram in which the vacuum occurs only as a final state. The reasoning which leads to this equation is quite similar to that which leads to Eq. (8-2) for $R_z|0\rangle$.

As shown in earlier sections, the quantity $D_z(0)$ in Eq. (10-3) has a simple pole at z equals x_0 in the limit of an infinite crystal. In addition the two factors which multiply $D_z(0)$ in this equation are well-behaved in the vicinity of z equal x_0 in the same limit. For z in the vicinity of x_0, then, Eq. (10-3) for $S_z^{(0)}(\vec{\kappa})$ can be rewritten in the following way:

$$S_z^{(0)}(\vec{\kappa}) = | \langle \psi_0 | T_{-\kappa} \lim_{z \to x_0 \pm i0} [1+(1/H_0-z)\Sigma_{\delta_0} \{V_z\}_{\delta_0}] | 0 \rangle |^2 (e^n/x_0-z). \quad (10\text{-}4)$$

The expression used here for $D_z(0)$ near its pole is based on the results described in Sec. 7. In view Eq. (8-21) for the wave function $|\psi_0\rangle$, Eq. (10-4) above can be further reduced to give the following simple equation:

$$S_z^{(0)} = | \langle \psi_0 | T_\kappa | \psi_0 \rangle |^2 (1/x_0-z). \qquad (10\text{-}5)$$

As shown by the results above, the auxiliary function $S_z^{(0)}(\vec{\kappa})$ actually does have a simple pole at x_0. Because of this, the corresponding part of the scattering function, $S_0^{(0)}(\vec{\kappa}\, \omega)$, is given exactly by Eq. (10-1), which describes the spectrum for elastic scattering. The contributions to $S_z^{(0)}(\vec{\kappa})$ which were isolated and studied above are therefore exactly the ones which were desired.

The method of isolating relevant contributions to $S_z^{(0)}(\vec{\kappa})$ has been presented above because it turns out to work as well for the peaks in the inelastic spectrum as it does for the single peak which is the elastic spectrum. This will be discussed extensively after consideration of certain details of the elastic spectrum which follow from Eq. (10-1).

The matrix element $<\psi_o|T_\kappa|\psi_o>$ which occurs in Eq. (10-1) for $S_o^{(0)}(\vec{\kappa}\,\omega)$ can be evaluated by diagram analysis using the techniques discussed in Sec. 9. In the present case each diagram has a neutron vertex as its only vertex. According to the discussion in Sec. 9, the contribution from each of these diagrams includes a factor $\Delta(\vec{\kappa}+\vec{q})$, where $\vec{q}$ is the total wave vector of the state following the vertex minus that of the state preceding the vertex. Since $|\psi_o>$ has a wave vector of zero or $2\pi\vec{\tau}$, however, each of these total wave vectors $\vec{q}$ is equal to some vector $2\pi\vec{\tau}$. Each factor $\Delta(\vec{\kappa}+\vec{q})$ is therefore equivalent to a factor $\Delta(\vec{\kappa})$, and the latter factor can be taken as occuring in all of the contributions to the desired matrix element. This explains the occurence of the factor $\Delta(\vec{\kappa})$ in the following equation:

$$<\psi_o|T_\kappa|\psi_o> = (8\pi^3/v_o)\Delta(\vec{\kappa})[\Sigma_n <\psi_o|\exp(i\vec{\kappa}\cdot\vec{u}_{on})|\psi_o> \exp(i\vec{\kappa}\cdot\vec{R}_{on})]. \tag{10-6}$$

The equation itself is obtained by carrying out the diagram analysis in detail.

On the basis of the equation given above for the matrix element of T_κ, Eq. (10-1) for the elastic scattering function takes the following form:

$$S_o^{(0)}(\vec{\kappa},\omega) = N_o(8\pi^3/v_o)\Delta(\vec{\kappa})\Delta(\omega)$$
$$\times\ |\Sigma_n \exp(i\vec{\kappa}\cdot\vec{R}_{on}) <\psi_o|\exp i\vec{\kappa}\cdot\vec{u}_{on}|\psi_o>|^2. \tag{10-7}$$

The two deltas in this equation yield the Bragg conditions for elastic scattering which were written out in Eq. (9-14). Their occurence here is proof that the Bragg conditions apply whether or not anharmonic forces are neglected. The matrix element of $\exp(i\vec{\kappa}\cdot\vec{u}_{on})$ which appears in Eq. (10-7) is the Debye-Waller factor at O°K corrected for anharmonic effects, and the whole term in the absolute value signs is the structure factor at O°K corrected for anharmonic effects. In elastic scattering, then, the anharmonic forces can only effect the scattering intensity.

For the peaks in the inelastic scattering spectrum there is no simple method of treatment corresponding to the straightforward treatment of elastic scattering by which Eq. (10-1) was first obtained above. According to harmonic theory, the inelastic peaks are associated with excitations of the crystal from its ground state to one-phonon states. When anharmonic forces are included, however, the concept of a one-phonon state is no longer valid, and the inelastic peaks therefore cannot be obtained by establishing a correspondence between the excited states $|\psi_\nu>$ and one-phonon states. The ground state of a crystal is unique in having a meaning whether or not the harmonic approximation is made, and it is because of this that the straightforward treatment of elastic scattering is possible.

The breakdown of the concept of a one-phonon state is essentially a dissipative effect of the type discussed in Sec. 1. If a wave packet describing a single phonon is constructed, it decays into many phonons through the influence of anharmonic forces. In general the decay time for this process is sufficiently short that it affects most phonon phenomena of interest. The lack of a significant correspondence between one-phonon states and exact excited eigenstates is related to this effect.

The following treatment of the peaks for inelastic scattering is analogous to the alternate treatment of elastic scattering given earlier. A contribution to the auxiliary scattering function $S_z(\vec{\kappa})$ is isolated, and this is shown to yield a part of the scattering function $S_z(\vec{\kappa}, \omega)$ which describes the desired peaks. The particular contribution to $S_z(\vec{\kappa})$ which is isolated will be called $S_z^{(1)}(\vec{\kappa})$, and the part of the scattering function $S_o(\vec{\kappa}, \omega)$ which it yields will be called $S_o^{(1)}(\vec{\kappa}\, \omega)$.

The isolated contribution $S_z^{(1)}(\vec{\kappa})$ is obtained from Eq. (10-2) by restricting the summation over diagrams to include just diagrams which contain one or more one-phonon intermediate state. A sample diagram of this type is shown in Fig. 10-3. If it is assumed that the momentum transfer $\vec{\kappa}$ is different from any vector $2\pi\vec{\tau}$, the vacuum cannot occur as an intermediate state in any diagram for $S_z^{(1)}(\vec{\kappa})$. This is because the total wave vector of any intermediate state must equal $\vec{\kappa}$ module $2\pi\vec{\tau}$. The two isolated contributions $S_z^{(0)}(\vec{\kappa})$ and $S_z^{(1)}(\vec{\kappa})$ do not contain any common terms, therefore.

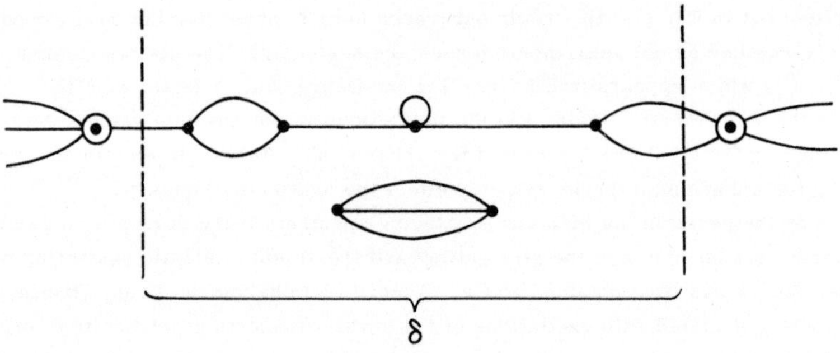

Fig. 10-3
Partial diagram δ of the type contributing to $S_z^{(1)}(\vec{\kappa})$

10. PEAKS IN THE ENERGY SPECTRUM OF NEUTRONS SCATTERED AT O°K

Each diagram δ contributing to $S_z^{(1)}(\vec{\kappa})$ will now be regarded as made up of three parts. One part is that to the right of the first intermediate one-phonon state, a second is that to the left of the last intermediate one-phonon state, and a third is that between these two states. Then, on the basis of reasoning similar to that which led to Eq. (10-3), the following equation for $S_z^{(1)}(\vec{\kappa})$ is obtained:

$$S_z^{(1)}(\vec{\kappa}) = \Sigma_{jj'} \Gamma_{qq'} < \psi_o | T_{-\kappa} [1+(1/H_o-z) \Sigma_{\delta_1} \{V_z\}_{\delta_1}] | \vec{q}j >$$

$$\times < \vec{q}j | R_z | \vec{q}'j' > < \vec{q}'j' | [1+\Sigma_{\delta_1'} \{V_z\}_{\delta'_1} (1/H_o-z)] T_{\kappa} | \psi_o >. \qquad (10\text{-}8)$$

Here δ_1 designates a diagram in which the only one-phonon state is the initial state $\vec{q}j$ and δ_1' designates a diagram in which the only one-phonon state is the final state q'j'.

The matrix element on the left of $< \vec{q}j | R_z | \vec{q}'j' >$ in Eq. (10-8) can now be written out in the following useful form:

$$< \psi_o | T_{-\kappa} [1+(1/H_o-z) \Sigma_{\delta_1} \{V_z\}_{\delta_1}] | \vec{q}j > = \Delta(\vec{q}-\vec{\kappa}) \theta_z(\vec{\kappa}, j) e^{-n/2}, \qquad (10\text{-}9)$$

where n is defined in Eq. (7-3). The factor $\Delta(\vec{q}-\vec{\kappa})$ which appears here can be justified easily by arguments which are now quite familiar. The remaining quantity $\theta_z(\vec{\kappa}, j)$ is essentially independent of the volume Ω in the limit of large Ω and it has no peaks of the type which are presently sought.

The matrix element on the right of $< \vec{q}j | R_z | \vec{q}'j' >$ in Eq. (10-8) is equal to the complex conjugate of that on the left if the indices $\vec{q}j$ and the variable z in the latter are changed to $\vec{q}'j'$ and z* respectively.

The remaining matrix element in Eq. (10-8), $< \vec{q}j | R_z | \vec{q}'j' >$, will now be written out in the following way:

$$< \vec{q}j | R_z | \vec{q}'j' > = \Delta(\vec{q}-\vec{q}') D_z(\vec{q}, j, j'), \qquad (10\text{-}10)$$

The justification for the factor $\Delta(\vec{q}-\vec{q}')$ in this equation should be obvious.

On the basis of Eqs. (10-8), (10-9) and (10-10), the isolated contribution $S_z^{(1)}(\vec{\kappa})$ is given by the following equation:

$$S_z^{(1)}(\vec{\kappa}) = (\Omega/8\pi^3) e^{-n} \Sigma_{jj'} \theta_z(\vec{\kappa}, j) [\theta_{z*}(\vec{\kappa}, j')]^* D_z(\vec{\kappa}, j, j'). \qquad (10\text{-}11)$$

The only factor in this equation which has yet to be discussed is $D_z(\vec{\kappa}, j, j')$, and this quantity turns out to contain the peaks which are sought.

Since $D_z(\vec{q}, j, j')$ is equal to a matrix element of the resolvent, to within a constant, it can be calculated formally by the diagram analysis of Sec. 6. The diagrams to be considered for this include both connected and disconnected diagrams. Consider the contribution to $D_z(\vec{q}, j, j')$ which is obtained by neglecting all disconnected diagrams. This contribution will be called $C(\vec{q}, j, j')$, and it is defined explicitly by the following equation:

$$C_z(\vec{q}, j, j')\,\Delta(\vec{q}-\vec{q}') = \Sigma_{\delta}^{\text{conn}} < \vec{q}j \left|\left\{R_z\right\}_\delta\right| \vec{q}'j' >. \quad (10\text{-}12)$$

With the introduction of this quantity, the following fairly simple equation for $D_z(\vec{q}, j, j')$ itself can be obtained:

$$D_z(\vec{q}, j, j') = (i/2\pi) \oint D_{z'}(0) C_{z-z'}(\vec{q}, j, j')dz', \quad (10\text{-}13)$$

where the contour of integration is the same as that for the convolution products in Sec. 8. This equation is useful because the properties of $D_z(0)$ are already well-known and the relevant properties of $C_z(\vec{q}, j, j')$ which are presently of interest are its singularities and near-singularities. In order to determine these by use of Eq. (10-13), it is only necessary to know the most singular parts of $D_z(0)$ and $C_z(\vec{q}, j, j')$. This is a property of convolution products which holds true whether the variable of integration is real or complex. The quantity $D_z(0)$ in Eq. (10-13) can therefore be replaced by the function $e^n/x_o - z$, which describes its pole. With this the following equation for $D_z(\vec{q}, j, j')$ in its most singular regions is obtained:

$$D_z(\vec{q}, j, j') \cong e^n C_{z-x_o}(\vec{q}, j, j'), \quad (10\text{-}14)$$

where use has been made of Cauchy's residue theorem.

On the basis of this result and Eq. (10-11), $S_z^{(1)}(\vec{\kappa})$ is given in its most singular regions by the following equation:

$$S_z^{(1)}(\vec{\kappa}) \cong (\Omega/8\pi^3)\,\Sigma_{jj'}\theta_z(\vec{\kappa}, j')\,[\theta_{z*}(\vec{\kappa}, j')]^*\; C_{z-x_o}(\vec{\kappa}, j, j'). \quad (10\text{-}15)$$

The quantity $C_z(\vec{q}, j, j')$ appearing here is essentially independent of the volume Ω in the limit of large Ω, as is the quantity $\theta_z(\vec{\kappa}, j)$. The quantity $S_z^{(1)}(\vec{\kappa})$ is therefore proportional to Ω in the limit of large Ω, as should be expected.

On the basis of the equation for $S_z^{(1)}(\vec{\kappa})$ given above, the corresponding partial scattering function $S_o^{(1)}(\vec{\kappa}, \omega)$ is given by the following equation:

$$S_o^{(1)}(\vec{\kappa}, \omega) \cong (\Omega/8\pi^3)\,\Sigma_{jj'}\theta_{x_o+\omega}(\vec{\kappa}j)[\theta_{x_o+\omega}(\vec{\kappa}j')]^*$$
$$\times\;(1/2\pi i)[C_{\omega+i0}(\vec{\kappa}jj') - C_{\omega-i0}(\vec{\kappa}jj')]\,. \quad (10\text{-}16)$$

In obtaining this it is assumed that the value of $\theta_z(\vec{\kappa}, \omega)$ is essentially the same whether z equals $x_0+\omega$ or $x_0+\omega\pm i0$. This assumption is valid as long as the width of each inelastic scattering peak is small compared to the value of ω at its center. This condition is prerequisite to the entire discussion, however, since the scattering peak is not distinguishable from the background if the condition is not fulfilled.

The problem now is to determine the most singular parts of the quantity $C_z(\vec{q}, j, j')$. In the case of a harmonic crystal this is easy. In this case R_z is just equal to $1/H_0-z$, and Eq. (10-12) then predicts the following exact result:

$$C_z(\vec{q}, j, j') = \delta_{jj'}/(\omega_{qj}-z). \tag{10-17}$$

When this is substituted into Eq. (10-16) for $S_0^{(1)}(\vec{\kappa}, \omega)$, the following equation is obtained:

$$S_0^{(1)}(\vec{\kappa}, \omega) \cong (\Omega/8\pi^3)\Sigma_j |\theta_{x_0+\omega}(\vec{\kappa}, j)|^2 \delta(\omega_{qj}-\omega). \tag{10-18}$$

In the case of a harmonic crystal, then, the partial scattering function $S_0^{(1)}(\vec{\kappa}\,\omega)$ does describe the peaks in the inelastic scattering spectrum. The remaining contributions to the total scattering function must then describe the smooth background.

When anharmonic forces exist but are small, $S_0^{(1)}(\vec{\kappa}\,\omega)$ is still expected to describe the scattering peaks, including the effects of the anharmonic forces. In this case the determination of the most singular parts of $C_z(\vec{q}, j, j')$ is facilitated by the introduction of a new quantity, $G_z(\vec{q}, j, j')$. This new quantity is defined by the following equation:

$$G_z(\vec{q}, j, j')\Delta(\vec{q}-\vec{q}\,') = \Sigma_{\delta_2} < \vec{q}j | \left\{ V_z \right\}_{\delta_2} | \vec{q}\,'j' >, \tag{10-19}$$

where δ_2 designates a connected diagram which has two or more phonons in each intermediate state. One diagram contributing to $G_z(\vec{q}, j, j')$ is illustrated in Fig. 10-4.

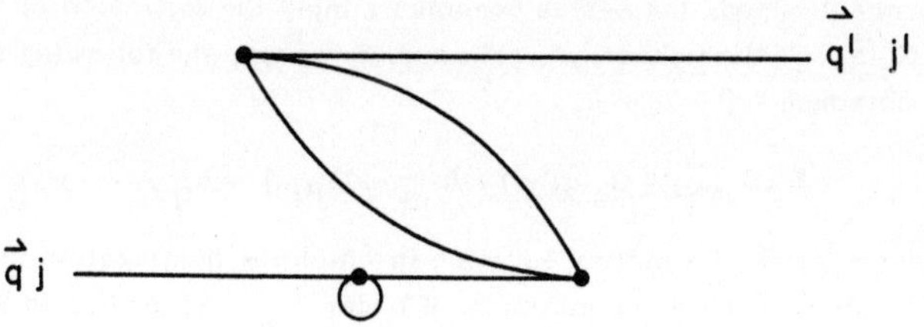

Fig. 10-4

Sample diagram contributing to Eq. (10-19) for $G_z(\vec{q}jj')$

The original quantity $C_z(\vec{q}, j, j')$ can be written out in terms of the new quantity $G_z(\vec{q}, j, j')$ in the following way:

$$C_z(\vec{q}jj') = \delta_{jj'}(1/\omega_{qj}-z) - (1/\omega_{qj}-z)G(\vec{q}jj')(1/\omega_{qj'}-z)$$

$$+ (1/\omega_{qj}-z)\Sigma_{j''}G(\vec{q}jj'')(1/\omega_{qj''}-z)G(\vec{q}j''j')(1/\omega_{qj'}-z)+\dots \quad (10\text{-}20)$$

This result is obtained by breaking each diagram for $C_z(\vec{q}jj')$ into parts which contain no intermediate states with less than two phonons. One diagram for $C_z(\vec{q}, j, j')$ is illustrated in Fig. 10-5, and the three appropriate parts of this diagram are separated by dashed lines. The term of order n in powers of G_z in Eq. (10-20) is just the sum of all the contributions to $C_z(\vec{q}jj')$ which come from diagrams having n parts. This approach to the determination of $C_z(\vec{q}jj')$ is analagous to a well-known method in the renormalization treatment of field theory.

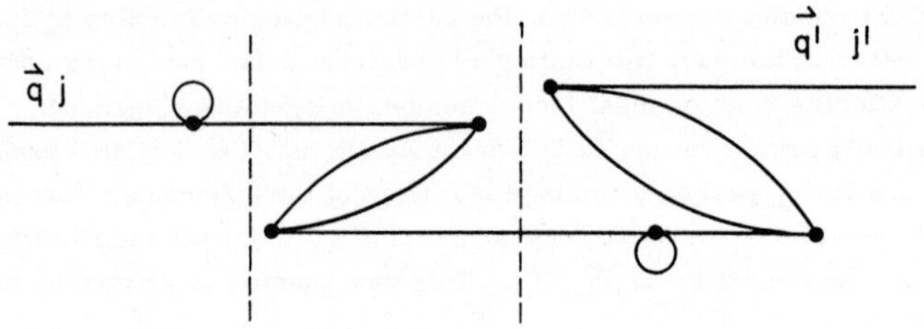

Fig. 10-5
Sample diagram contributing to $C_z(\vec{q}, j, j')$

The series given in Eq. (10-20) is poorly convergent when z is near any phonon energy ω_{qj}. For this reason the series must be treated in its entirety. If it were not for the polarization indices j and j', this would be a trivial matter. When these indices are dropped, the series becomes simply the expansion of $1/G_z(\vec{q}) + \omega - z$ in powers of $G_z(\vec{q})$. If the indices are retained, however, the following more complicated result is obtained:

$$\Sigma_{j'}C_z(\vec{q}jj')[G_z(\vec{q}j'j'') + (\omega_{qj'}-z)\delta_{j'j''}] = \delta_{jj''} \quad (10\text{-}21)$$

This can be considered as a matrix equation in which the polarization indices designate rows and columns of square matrices of order $3n_o$. According to Eq. (10-21), then, the matrix element $C_z(\vec{q}jj')$ is equal to the (j, j')'th element of the inverse of the matrix whose elements are given in the square brackets in Eq. (10-21). An element $C_z(\vec{q}jj')$ can therefore be determined quite easily if the appropriate elements $G_z(\vec{q}jj')$ are known.

10. PEAKS IN THE ENERGY SPECTRUM OF NEUTRONS SCATTERED AT O°K

Unlike the original quantity $C_z(\vec{q}jj')$, $G_z(\vec{q}jj')$ can be calculated by perturbation analysis, and good convergence is guaranteed for all values of z (except on the positive real axis). Contributions to $G_z(\vec{q}jj')$ can thus be ordered with respect to powers of (u/a), and only the largest contributions need to be calculated. The largest contribution, which is of order $(u/a)^2$, is calculated from the diagrams shown in Fig. 10-6. The results of this calculation will not be presented here, however. Like the quantity F_z discussed in Sec. 8, $G_z(\vec{q}jj')$ contains a cut along the positive real z axis in the limit of an infinite crystal.

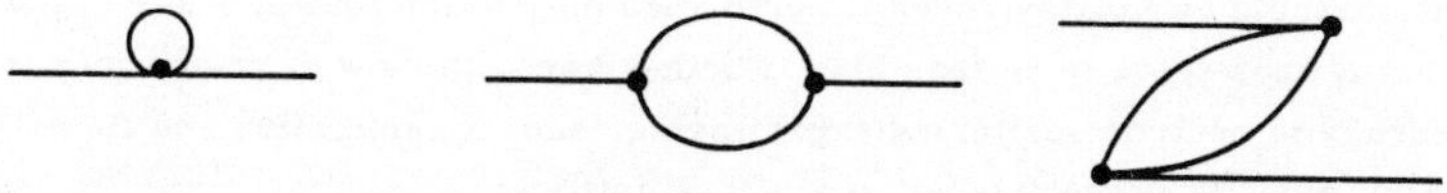

Fig. 10-6

Diagrams for lowest-order contribution to $G_z(\vec{q}, j, j')$

If the matrix $G_{\omega\pm i0}(\vec{q}jj')$ is Hermitian, it must have real eigenvalues. If this is the case, the quantities $C_{\omega\pm i0}(\vec{q}jj')$ determined from this matrix must have simple poles at various values of ω, which is supposed to be real. Such poles lead to delta-function singularities in the inelastic scattering spectrum, but these singularities are shifted relative to those predicted in the harmonic approximation. In general, however, the matrix $G_{\omega\pm i0}(\vec{q}jj')$ includes a small antihermitian part whose sign depends on the sign of ±i0. Because of this antihermitian part, $C_{\omega\pm i0}(\vec{q}jj')$ cannot have poles for real ω. The poles which would occur if the antihermitian part of $G_{\omega\pm i0}(\vec{q}jj')$ were neglected are thus broadened into finite peaks. These finite peaks then lead to finite peaks in the inelastic scattering spectrum, as can be shown by use of Eq. (10-16).

As a result of anharmonic forces, then, the inelastic scattering spectrum exhibits finite peaks rather than delta singularities. The widths of these peaks are determined primarily by the antihermitian parts of the quantities $G_{\omega\pm i0}(\vec{q}jj')$, and the shifts of these peaks from those predicted in the harmonic approximation are determined primarily by the hermitian parts. These two effects of broadening and shifting are really interdependent, however.

Before proceeding, it should be stressed that a direct perturbation analysis of $C_z(\vec{q}jj')$ itself does not yield the correct scattering spectrum. Such an analysis effectively requires cutting off the series given in Eq. (10-20), and that series can be very poorly convergent for certain values of z, as has already been stated. The desired scattering spectrum can be obtained to arbitrarily high accuracy by the procedure described above, however.

Under some circumstances, the anti-hermitian part of $G_{\omega\pm i0}(\vec{q}jj')$ can be extremely small. This happens when $\vec{q}$ is very small, for instance. When it does happen, it turns out to be possible to construct a perturbed one-phonon state which has physical meaning in that it has a very long lifetime. This was shown by Hugenholz for the case of a Fermi gas. If the antihermitian part of $G_{\omega \pm i0}(\vec{q}jj')$ is not extremely small, the lifetime of a perturbed one-phonon state may be much shorter than times of physical interest, and such a state then is not physically meaningful. Even when a perturbed one-phonon state can be constructed meaningfully, however, it turns out to be quite different from any unperturbed one-phonon state.

The general procedure outlined above for determining the peaks in the inelastic scattering spectrum has not yet been applied in an actual calculation. Such a calculation would be lengthy, even if performed only to the lowest order in powers of (u/a), but it does seem to be feasible. Furthermore, in view of recent increases in the accuracy of neutron scattering experiments, such a calculation and its extension to the case of finite temperatures is of actual interest.

The treatment of inelastic scattering which has been given here is specifically designed to yield information about just the peaks in the scattering spectrum. If the complete spectrum is to be calculated, however, it is better to use the appropriate results in Sec. 9 and then to determine $S_z(\vec{\kappa})$ by use of Feynman rather than Goldstone diagrams. Feynman diagrams are also more convenient than Goldstone diagrams for calculating the quantities $\theta_z(\vec{\kappa} j)$, which occur in Eq. (10-18). For such complete calculations, however, a simpler procedure still is to employ the methods of Sec. 11, in which the scattering at a non-zero temperature is discussed, and then to obtain the ground-state results by letting the temperature approach zero.

In some many-particle scattering problems it is possible to obtain information about the scattering peaks without using such complicated techniques as are used here. Intuitive arguments based on the exponential decay of one-particle states might meet with some success, for instance. Such simple techniques are complicated in the phonon case by the problem of polarization mixing, however, and, in any case, they can only be expected to give results which are valid to first order (in which the line-shift and line-broadening effects are independent). The present procedure has the advantages that it yields a closed formula, which can be evaluated to arbitrarily high accuracy (at least in principle), and that it is based directly and exclusively on the Schrödinger equation.

11. FREE ENERGY OF AN ANHARMONIC CRYSTAL

The free energy of a crystal is a more interesting quantity experimentally than the ground-state energy, since a crystal is only in its ground state at the inaccessable temperature of O°K. The free energy of an anharmonic crystal can be calculated by techniques which are closely related to those described in Secs. 7 and 8 for the groundstate energy, and such a calculation is outlined below.

The free energy of a system at a temperature T is related to the partition function of the system at that temperature in the following way:

$$F_\beta = -(1/\beta)\ln Z(\beta). \tag{11-1}$$

Here F_β is the free energy, $Z(\beta)$ is the partition function, $\ln$ is the natural logarithm, and β is $1/kT$, where k is Boltzmann's constant. The partition function itself is defined by the following equation:

$$Z(\beta) = \Sigma_\nu \exp(-\beta E_\nu), \tag{11-2}$$

in which ν runs over all states of the system and E_ν is the energy of the system in the state ν.

In the case of an anharmonic crystal the energies E_ν in Eq. (11-2) are not known. They are the exact eigenvalues of the Hamiltonian H which is given in Eq. (5-9), but, as was explained in Sec. 9, such exact eigenvalues cannot at present be calculated. In view of the summation over states which appears in Eq. (11-2), however, it is not actually necessary to know the individual eigenvalues. This is shown below.

Eq. (11-2) defining the partition function can be rewritten in the following way:

$$Z(\beta) = \Sigma_\nu \langle \psi_\nu | e^{-\beta H} | \psi_\nu \rangle = \mathrm{Sp}\left\{ e^{-\beta H} \right\}, \tag{11-3}$$

where $\mathrm{Sp}\left\{\mathrm{Op}\right\}$ designates the spur (or trace) of the operator Op. The partition function is therefore equal to the spur of the operator $e^{-\beta H}$ in the respresentation of the exact eigenfunctions $|\psi_\nu\rangle$ of the Hamiltonian H. The spur of a matrix is unchanged when the matrix undergoes a unitary transformation, however, and the partition function is therefore also equal to the spur of the operator $e^{-\beta H}$ in the representation of the eigenstates of the harmonic Hamiltonian. This is expressed in the following pair of equations:

$$Z(\beta) = \exp(-\beta\varepsilon_0 - \beta\varepsilon_{zp}) Z_\beta, \tag{11-4}$$

where

$$Z_\beta = \mathrm{Sp}\left\{\exp[-\beta(H_o+V)]\right\}$$
$$= \sum_{N=0}^{\infty} (1/N!)\, \Sigma(j_1, j_2, \ldots j_N) \int (\vec{q}_1, \vec{q}_2, \ldots \vec{q}_N)$$
$$\times \langle \vec{q}_N j_N, \ldots \vec{q}_2 j_2, \vec{q}_1 j_1 \,|\, \exp[-\beta(H_o+V)] \,|\, \vec{q}_1 j_1, \vec{q}_2 j_2, \ldots \vec{q}_N j_N \rangle . \quad (11\text{-}5)$$

To obtain these equations the Hamiltonian H which appears in Eq. (11-3) has been written out according to Eq. (5-9).

The matrix elements in Eq. (11-5) can be calculated by making a perturbation expansion of $\exp[-\beta(H_o+V)]$ in powers of V. This expansion is well known, and it takes the following form:

$$\exp[-\beta(H_o+V)] = \exp[-\beta H_o]$$
$$+ \sum_{n=1}^{\infty} (-1)^n \int_0^\beta d\beta_1 \int_0^{\beta_1} d\beta_2 \ldots \int_0^{\beta_{n-1}} d\beta_n \exp[-(\beta-\beta_1)H_o]\, V \exp[-(\beta_1-\beta_2)H_o]\, V \ldots V \exp[-\beta_n H_o] . \quad (11\text{-}6)$$

One way of obtaining this series is the following: first write $\exp[-\beta(H_o+V)]$ as the Fourier transform of the resolvent (using the contours of integration which were described in Sec. 8), then introduce the perturbation expansion of the resolvent, which is given in Eqs. (6-5) and (6-6), and, finally, take the Fourier transform of the result.

When the expansion of $\exp[-\beta(H_o+V)]$ given above is used in Eq. (11-5) for Z_β, the latter quantity can be evaluated by a form of diagram analysis which is quite similar to that used earlier in the calculation of the ground-state energy. Thus a term in Z_β which is of n'th order in V can be represented by diagrams containing n vertices each. The contribution to Z_β from a particular diagram must be calculated somewhat differently than before, of course. Different operators act on the intermediate states here, and also different coefficients as well as new integrations (over the β's) appear.

A sample diagram entering the calculation of Z_β is illustrated in Fig. 11-1. This diagram contributes to a term in Z_β which is of fifth order in V, and it comes from a matrix element

$$\langle \vec{q}_q j_q, \ldots \vec{q}_2 j_2, \vec{q}_1 j_1 \,|\, \exp[-\beta(H_o+V)] \,|\, \vec{q}_1 j_1, \vec{q}_2 j_2, \ldots \vec{q}_q j_q \rangle .$$

A number ν at the left or right of the diagram stands for the phonon $\vec{q}_\nu j_\nu$. The set of initial phonons is seen to be identical to the set of final phonons. The right-to-left order of the vertices in the diagram is important.

Two diagrams which differ from one another by interchanges of the roles of the phonons (the same interchanges on the right and left of the diagram) are taken

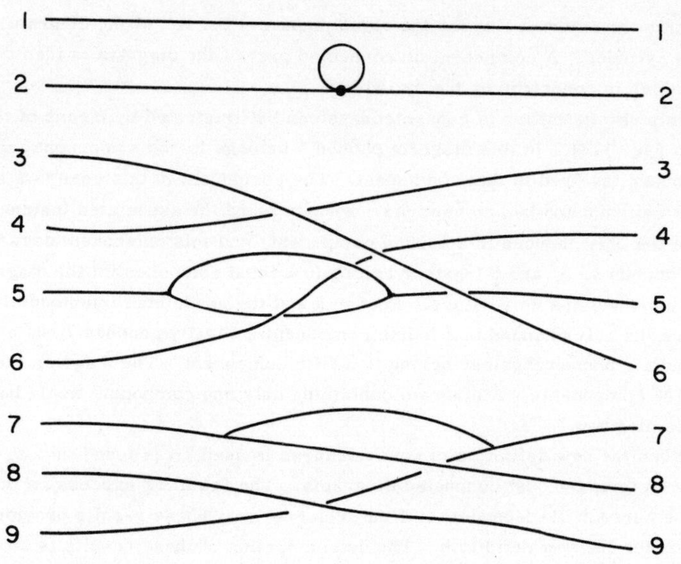

Fig. 11-1

Sample diagram contributing to Z_β

to be different diagrams. As an example, the two diagrams in Fig. 11-2 are taken to be different diagrams. This convention obviously affects the calculation of a contribution to Z_β.

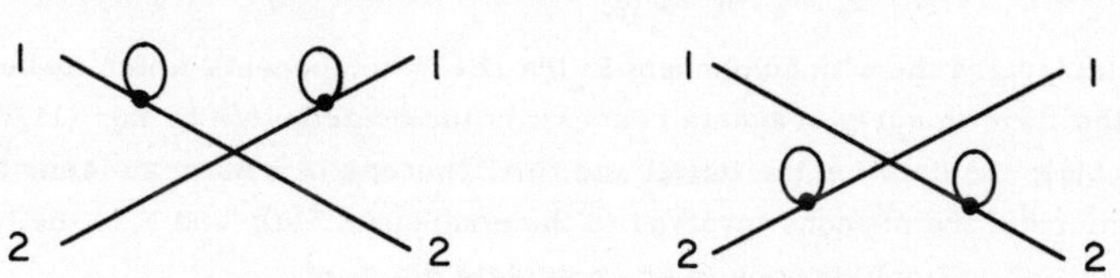

Fig. 11-2

Two different diagrams contributing to Z_β

At this point it is convenient to introduce a new definition of connectedness in a diagram. This new definition is justified by the simplifications to which it leads. A diagram such as appears in Fig. 11-1 is imagined to be rolled onto a cylinder in such a way that each external line at the right of the diagram joins continuously onto the external line for the same phonon at the left of the diagram on the back of the cylinder. A component or connected part of the diagram is then defined as a part which is connected on the cylinder.

This new definition of connectedness can be illustrated by means of the diagram in Fig. 11-1. In this diagram phonon 1 belongs to one component, and it is the only phonon involved in that component. The component in this case is a single loop on the cylinder and has no vertices. Phonon 2 and the associated instantaneous phonon are the only phonons in a second component, and this component does have a vertex. Phonons 3, 4, and 6 together belong to a third component of the diagram, and this component has no vertices. Phonon 5 and the associated intermediate phonons are the only phonons in a fourth component. Finally phonons 7, 8, and 9 and an intermediate phonon together belong to a fifth component. The diagram therefore contains five components. A diagram containing only one component would be called a connected diagram.

When the new definition of connectedness is used, it is found that Z_β can be written out in terms of just connected diagrams. The resulting expression then leads to the correct Ω-dependence of the free energy. These results provide the justification for the new definition. The demonstration of these results is outlined below.

Consider a set of diagrams which all contain the same components and which differ from one another only in the relative order of the vertices of the different components. Let the order of the vertices within a particular component be the same in each diagram. The sum of the contributions to Z_β from all the diagrams in such a set can be shown to equal the following expression:

$$(1/N!)\Sigma(j_1,\dots j_N)\int(\vec{q}_1,\dots\vec{q}_N)\Pi_{\delta(a)} <\dots|\Big\{\exp[-\beta(H_o+V)]\Big\}_{\delta(a)}|\dots> \quad (11\text{-}7)$$

Here $\delta(a)$ designates the a'th component in the set of components which makes up each diagram; the term in curly brackets represents the contribution to Eq. (11-6) from a component $\delta(a)$; the dots for the initial and final phonons in a matrix element represent the indices of the phonons involved in the component $\delta(a)$; and N is the total number of initial or final phonons in one complete diagram.

As an example of the application of the expression above, the appropriate set of diagrams which contains the diagram in Fig. 11-1 gives the following contribution to Z_β:

$$\begin{aligned}(1/9!)\Sigma(j_1\dots j_9)\int(\vec{q}_1\dots\vec{q}_9) &<1|\Big\{Op\Big\}_{\delta(1)}|1><2|\Big\{Op\Big\}_{\delta(2)}|2> \\ &\times<6,4,3|\Big\{Op\Big\}_{\delta(3)}|3,4,6><5|\Big\{Op\Big\}_{\delta(4)}|5> \\ &\times<9,8,7|\Big\{Op\Big\}_{\delta(5)}|7,8,9>.\end{aligned}$$

Here Op is taken to designate the operator $\exp[-\beta(H_0+V)]$, and the phonon indices $\vec{q}_\nu j_\nu$ are designated simply as ν.

Expression (11-7) is the total contribution to Z_β from the particular set of diagrams which was described above. Now consider another set of diagrams which is obtained from the original set by making a particular permutation of phonon indices on each of its diagrams (the same permutation on each diagram). This new set gives the same contribution to Z_β as the original set. The sum of the contributions to Z_β from all such related sets of diagrams is just the total contribution to Z_β from all the diagrams which can be constructed from a particular set of connected diagrams (in which the names of the phonons are irrelevant) used as components. This total contribution is just equal to expression (11-7) multiplied by a factor $N!/\pi_a n(a)!\,\pi_\beta n(\beta)!$, where $n(a)$ is the number of initial or final phonons in the component $\delta(a)$ and $n(\beta)$ is the number of components in the basic set which are identical and have the form β.

In view of the results above the quantity Z_β is given by the following equation:

$$Z_\beta = \Sigma\,(\text{sets of connected diagrams})\,[\,1/\pi_a n(a)!\ \pi_\beta n(\beta)!\,]$$
$$\times\ \pi_a \Sigma\,(j_1 \cdots j_{n(a)})\, \textstyle\int (\vec{q}_1 \cdots \vec{q}_{n(a)}) < a, \ldots 2, 1 | \left\{ \exp[-\beta(H_0+V)] \right\}_{\delta(a)} | 1, 2, \ldots a >. \qquad (11\text{-}8)$$

Here $\delta(a)$ designates one of the connected diagrams in a particular set, and different sets of connected diagrams are taken to differ by more than just the order of the diagrams.

The quantity Z_β can now be rewritten in simpler form by noting that the right side of Eq. (11-8) is the series expansion of an exponential. In view of this Z_β is given by the following equation:

$$Z_\beta = \exp\,[\,\Sigma_\delta^{conn}(1/n(\delta)!)\ \Sigma\,(j_1 \cdots j_{n(\delta)})\, \textstyle\int (\vec{q}_1 \cdots \vec{q}_{n(\delta)})$$
$$< n(\delta), \ldots 2, 1 | \left\{ \exp[-\beta(H_0+V)] \right\}_\delta | 1, 2, \ldots n(\delta) >]\,. \qquad (11\text{-}9)$$

Here $n(\delta)$ is the number of initial or final phonons in the connected diagram δ. This equation exhibits the reduction to connected diagrams which was sought.

The free energy of the crystal can be obtained from Z_β by use of Eqs. (11-1) and (11-4). On the basis of Eq. (11-9), then, the free energy of the crystal is given by the following equation:

$$F_\beta = \varepsilon_0 + \varepsilon_{zp} - (1/\beta)\Sigma_\delta^{conn}\,[\,1/n(\delta)!\,]\ \Sigma(j_1 \cdots j_{n(\delta)})$$
$$\times\ \textstyle\int (\vec{q}_1 \cdots \vec{q}_{n(\delta)}) < n(\delta), \ldots 2, 1 | \left\{ \exp[-\beta(H_0+V)] \right\}_\delta | 1, 2, \ldots n(\delta) >. \qquad (11\text{-}10)$$

It is thus given entirely in terms of contributions from connected diagrams. In the limit of large volume, Ω, each of these contributions is proportional to Ω. The free energy as given in Eq. (11-10) therefore has the proper volume-dependence for the extensive quantity that it is. In these respects the free energy is given by an equation which is similar to Eq. (7-1) for the ground-state energy, but it should be remembered that the definition of connectedness is now different than it was earlier.

At this point it is useful to consider the application of Eq. (11-10) in the harmonic approximation. This application suggests further simplifications which can be made in the general case. The free energy of a harmonic crystal is given by Eq. (11-10) with V set equal to zero. The diagrams which contribute to this free energy therefore contain no vertices. Three of the simplest of these diagrams are shown in Fig. 11-3, and the contributions from these diagrams are given by the following expressions (in the sequence of the diagrams):

$$-(1/\beta)\,\Delta(0)\,\Sigma_j \int_q \exp(-\beta\omega_{qj}) \qquad (11\text{-}11)$$

$$-(1/\beta)\,\Delta(0)\,(1/2!)\,\Sigma_j \int_q \exp(-2\beta\omega_{qj}) \qquad (11\text{-}12)$$

$$-(1/\beta)\,\Delta(0)\,(1/3!)\,\Sigma_j \int_q \exp(-3\beta\omega_{qj}) \qquad (11\text{-}13)$$

The one- and two-phonon diagrams in the figure are the only such diagrams, but there is another three-phonon diagram. This differs from the first three-phonon diagram only by a permutation of the phonon indices 2 and 3, and it therefore gives the same contribution to the free energy as the first.

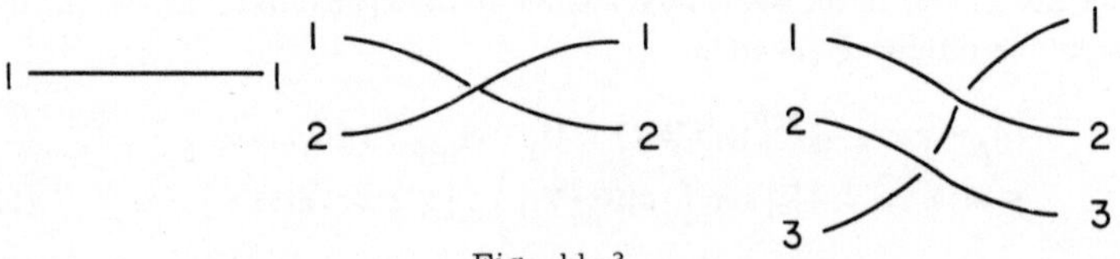

Fig. 11-3
Three diagrams contributing to F_β in the harmonic approximation

As suggested by the results above, the contribution to the harmonic free energy from a ν-phonon diagram turns out to be given by the following expression:

$$-(1/\beta)\,\Delta(0)\,(1/\nu!)\,\Sigma_j \int_q \exp(-\nu\beta\omega_{qj}).$$

There are $(\nu-1)!$ different ν-phonon diagrams, however, and each gives this same contribution. These different diagrams only differ by permutations of the phonon indices. The total contribution to the harmonic free energy from all ν-phonon diagrams is therefore equal to the expression above multiplied by a factor $(\nu-1)!$. From this it is apparent that the harmonic free energy is given by the following equation:

$$F_\beta = \varepsilon_o + \varepsilon_{zp} - (1/\beta)\,\Delta(0)\,\Sigma_j \textstyle\int_q [\Sigma_\nu (1/\nu) \exp(-\nu\beta\omega_{qj})]. \qquad (11\text{-}14)$$

The summation over ν in this equation can be performed analytically, and the equation then takes the following form:

$$F_\beta(0) = \varepsilon_o + \varepsilon_{zp} + \beta(\Omega/8\pi^3)\,\Sigma_j \textstyle\int_q \ln[1-\exp(-\beta\omega_{qj})], \qquad (11\text{-}15)$$

where $\Delta(0)$ has been replaced by its value, $\Omega/8\pi^3$. This is the familiar equation for the free energy of a harmonic crystal.

The foregoing treatment of a harmonic crystal suggests that there might be further analytic summations which can be performed in Eq. (11-10) in the general case. As will be seen below, there are such summations, and they are closely related to the summation which occurs in the harmonic case.

In the general case the operator $\exp[-\beta(H_o+V)]$ in Eq. (11-10) is supposed to be expanded in powers of V as in Eq. (11-6). The right side of the former equation therefore contains one term which is simply the free energy of the harmonic crystal. To show this explicitly, Eq. (11-10) will be rewritten as follows:

$$F_\beta = F_\beta(0) - (1/\beta)\Sigma_\delta^{\text{conn, vertex}} (1/n_\delta!)\,\Sigma(j_1,\dots j_{n(\delta)})$$
$$\times \textstyle\int (\vec{q}_1 \dots \vec{q}_{n(\delta)}) < n(\delta),\dots 2,1 | \left\{\exp[-\beta(H_o+V)]\right\}_\delta | 1,2,\dots n(\delta)>, \qquad (11\text{-}16)$$

where $F_\beta(0)$ is given by Eq. (11-15) and where the notation on the summation sign is meant to restrict the summation to connected diagrams which contain at least one vertex.

Before proceeding further it is necessary to introduce some new definitions. Consider a diagram which contributes to F_β in Eq. (11-16) and which, in its cylindrical form, contains no loops. A loop is a line which goes completely around the cylinder (not necessarily closing on itself) without encountering a vertex. Such a diagram will be called a reduced diagram. A two-phonon example of a reduced diagram is illustrated in Fig. 11-4. A reduced diagram will be understood to be connected and to have at least one vertex.

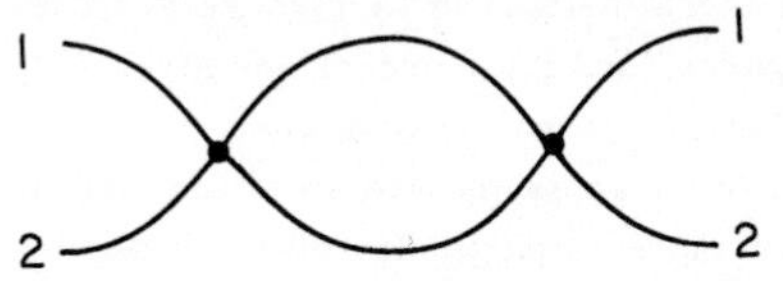

Fig. 11-4 Example of a reduced diagram contributing to F_β

Now consider a connected diagram which is obtained from some reduced diagram by breaking one or more lines on the back of the cylinder and reconnecting the ends by means of loops. Lines at the back of the cylinder will be called external lines, and the loops which are inserted in any external line will be said to constitute an external helix. To illustrate these concepts, the diagram in Fig. 11-5 is obtained from the reduced diagram in Fig. 11-4 by breaking the external line 2-2 and inserting a helix with two loops. The part of the new diagram which is called the external helix is enclosed in dashed lines in the figure. The helix involves three phonon indices (to be read from either side of the diagram). The number of phonon indices involved in a helix will be called the order of the helix. The lowest order possible for an external helix is therefore two, since a helix must contain at least one complete loop.

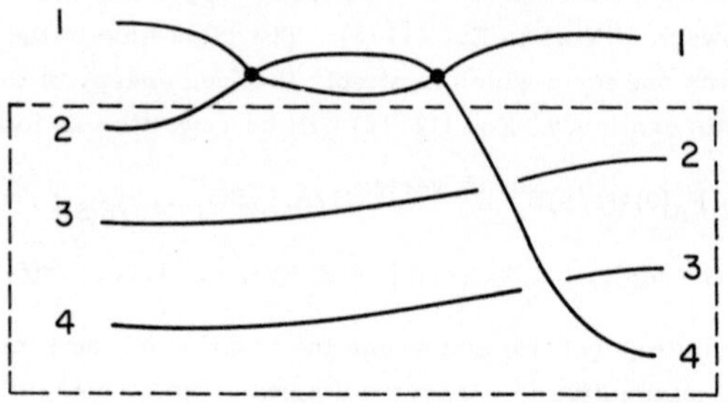

Fig. 11-5
Example of a diagram with an external helix of order three

Also consider a connected diagram which is obtained from some reduced diagram or some diagram with external helices by breaking one or more lines between vertices on the front of the cylinder and reconnecting the ends by means of helices. Lines between vertices on the front of the cylinder will be called internal lines, and the helices inserted in them will be called internal helices. To illustrate these concepts, the three diagrams in Figs. 11-6, 11-7 and 11-8 are obtained from the reduced diagram in Fig. 11-4 by adding internal helices in various ways. The helices are enclosed in dashed lines in the figures, and their orders are given in the figure headings. The lowest order possible for an internal helix is one.

Together the types of diagrams considered above include all of the diagrams which contribute to F_β in Eq. (11-16). Furthermore, a particular diagram which has internal and external helices can be obtained from one and only one reduced diagram by the processes which have been described.

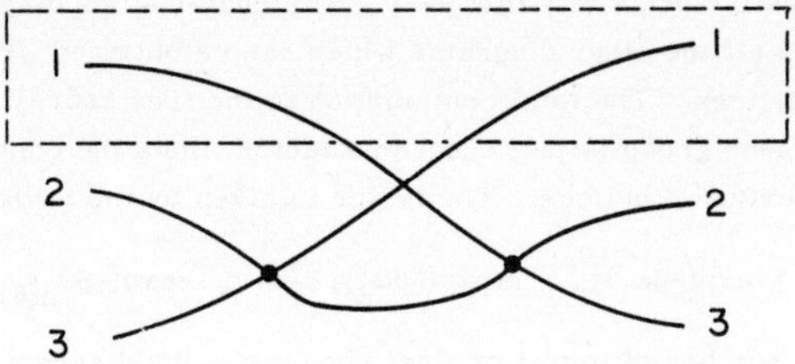

Fig. 11-6

Example of a diagram with an internal helix of order one

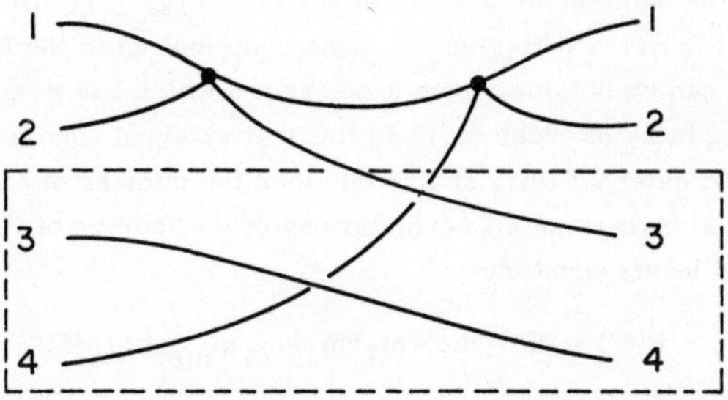

Fig. 11-7

Example of a diagram with an internal helix of order two

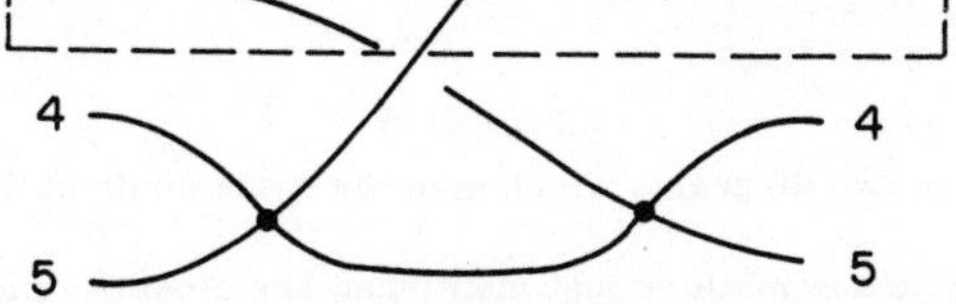

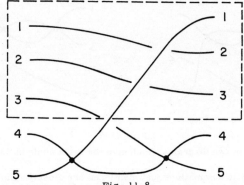

Fig. 11-8

Example of a diagram with an internal helix of order three

The set of diagrams which contribute to Eq. (11-16) for F_β can now be broken into groups in such a way that each group contains one diagram with no external helices and all the other diagrams which can be obtained from the first by adding external helices. The total contribution to the free energy from all of the diagrams in one such group is just equal to a factor times the contribution from the diagram with no external helices. The factor is given by the following expression:

$$[1-\exp(-\beta\omega_1)]^{-1}[1-\exp(-\beta\omega_2)]^{-1}\ldots[1-\exp(-\beta\omega_{n(\delta)})]^{-1}, \qquad (11\text{-}17)$$

where $n(\delta)$ is the number of initial or final phonons in the diagram with no external helices.

The proof of the foregoing result depends on the following fact: diagrams which differ from one another only by permutations of the indices of their external phonons all give the same contribution to the free energy. To illustrate this, the two diagrams in Fig. 11-9 both give the same contribution to the free energy. If a given diagram δ' can be obtained from a diagram δ which has no external helices by adding an external helix of order m_1+1 to its first external line, another of order m_2+1 to its second external line, and so on, then the number of diagrams which can be obtained from δ' by making all permutations of the indices of its external phonons is given by the following equation:

$$P(\delta') = P(\delta)[n(\delta)+m_1+m_2+\ldots m_{n(\delta)}]!/n(\delta)! \qquad (11\text{-}18)$$

Here $P(\delta)$ is the corresponding number for the diagram δ, and $n(\delta)$ is the number of external phonons in δ. With this equation for $P(\delta)$ the derivation of the factor (11-17) is a straightforward matter of performing simple analytic summations.

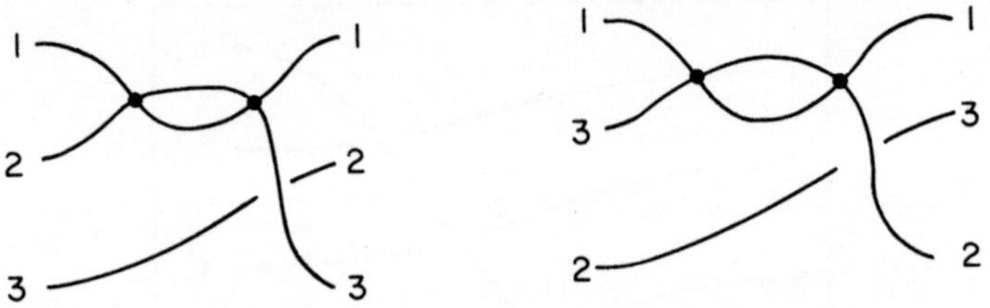

Fig. 11-9

Example of two diagrams which give the same contribution to F_β

The analytic summations just mentioned are closely related to the summation which occurs in the treatment of the harmonic crystal. This becomes apparent when the diagrams in the harmonic case are described as being given by a simple loop and all the other diagrams which can be obtained from such a loop by adding external helices.

On the basis of the result above, then, the summation over diagrams in Eq. (11-16) can be restricted to diagrams with no external helices. To account for the diagrams which are omitted, however, the contribution from each diagram which is retained must be taken to include an appropriate factor (11-17) inside the summation over external phonons.

The resulting equation for the free energy can be still further reduced, it turns out, since the set of diagrams retained above can again be broken into groups which yield analytic summations. Each of these new groups contains one reduced diagram and all of the diagrams which can be obtained from it by adding internal helices. The total contribution to the free energy from all of the diagrams in one of these groups is just equal to the contribution from the appropriate reduced diagram with an extra factor of $[1-\exp(-\beta\omega_{qj})]^{-1}$ for each of its internal phonons $\vec{q}j$. The extra factors must appear inside the summations over the internal phonons, of course. This result follows from considerations similar to those discussed above.

To summarize all of these results, the summation over diagrams in Eq. (11-16) can be restricted to just reduced diagrams if an appropriate modification is made to the contribution from each diagram. The modification consists of introducing a factor $[1-\exp(-\beta\omega_{qj})]^{-1}$ for each internal and external phonon in the diagram. For this modification each external phonon is to be counted only once, even though it appears on both sides of the diagram.

The simplified version of Eq. (11-16) just described can be written out compactly in the following way:

$$F_\beta = F_\beta(0) - (1/\beta)\Sigma_\delta^{\text{reduced}}(1/n(\delta)!)\Sigma(j_1, \ldots j_{n(\delta)})$$

$$\times \int (\vec{q}_1, \ldots \vec{q}_{n(\delta)}) \langle n(\delta), \ldots 2, 1 | \left\{ \exp[-\beta(H_o+V_\beta)] \right\}_\delta | 1, 2, \ldots n(\delta) \rangle. \qquad (11\text{-}19)$$

Here the operator V_β replaces the operator V which occurs in Eq. (11-16). The new operator V_β is defined from Eqs. (5-12) and (5-13) for V by making the following replacements: each creation operator A^*_{qj} in V becomes $A^*_{qj}[1-\exp(-\beta\omega_{qj})]^{-1/2}$, and each annihilation operator A_{qj} in V becomes $A_{qj}[1-\exp(-\beta\omega_{qj})]^{-1/2}$. These replacements can be seen to yield the required correction factor $[1-\exp(-\beta\omega_{qj})]^{-1}$ for each phonon line in a diagram, because each phonon line corresponds to the product of a creation and an annihilation operator with the same phonon indices. To be more specific, each internal phonon line in a diagram corresponds to a product $A_{qj}A^*_{qj}$, and each external phonon line corresponds to a product $A^*_{qj}A_{qj}$.

The last statement above brings up a subtlety which arises in the use of just reduced diagrams. As a result of the exclusion of diagrams with helices, a diagram like that in Fig. 11-10 must be taken to represent only those terms in V or V_β in which each annihilation A_{qj} occurs on the right of the corresponding creation A^*_{qj} ($\vec{q}j$ being an external phonon), and a diagram like that in Fig. 11-11 must be taken to represent only those terms in V or V_β in which each annihilation A_{qj} occurs on the left of the corresponding creation A^*_{qj} ($\vec{q}j$ being an internal phonon).

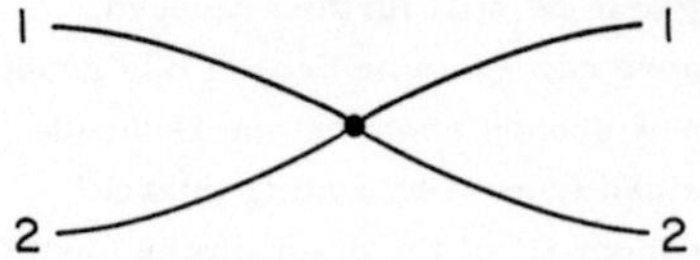

Fig. 11-10 Reduced diagram contributing to F_β

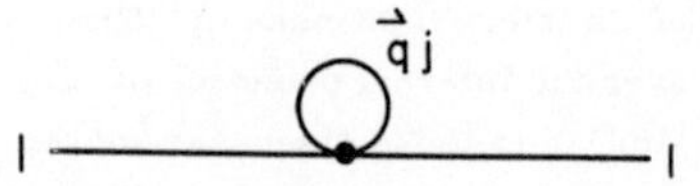

Fig. 11-11 Reduced diagram contributing to F_β

The replacement of V by V_β in Eq. (11-16) can be given a useful physical interpretation, as will now be shown. For particles such as phonons which obey Bose statistics, the average number of particles with an energy ω_{qj} at a temperature T (in the absence of interactions) is given by the following equation:

$$<n_{qj}> = 1/[\exp(\beta\omega_{qj})-1]$$

or

$$<n_{qj}> = \exp(-\beta\omega_{qj})[1-\exp(-\beta\omega_{qj})]^{-1}.$$

From the second form of this number the following relation is obtained:

$$[1-\exp(-\beta\omega_{qj})]^{-1} = <n_{qj}+1> \tag{11-20}$$

Now on the basis of Eq. (5-18) an operator $A_{qj}A^*_{qj}$ acting on a state with n_{qj} phonons and an operator $A^*_{qj}A_{qj}$ acting on a state with $(n_{qj}+1)$ phonons both bring down the same factor $(n_{qj}+1)$. If each state in a particular diagram for F_β contained an equilibrium distribution of thermal phonons in addition to the phonons explicitly shown, then, each operator $A_{qj}A^*_{qj}$ for an internal line and each operator $A^*_{qj}A_{qj}$ for an external line would bring down an extra factor $<n_{qj}+1>$. According to Eq. (11-20), however, this extra factor $<n_{qj}+1>$ is identical to the corresponding correction factor which is obtained by replacing V by V_β. The replacement of V by V_β in Eq. (11-16) can therefore be thought of as a correction for the presence of thermal phonons.

The physical interpretation just described should not be taken too literally, however. In the exponential operator whose matrix element appears in Eq. (11-18), the operator (H_o+V_β) has replaced the Hamiltonian operator (H_o+V) which appeared in earlier versions of the equation, but this should not be taken to mean that (H_o+V_β) is a new Hamiltonian for the system. It is only an effective Hamiltonian, and, as with all effective Hamiltonians, its use is only justified under very restricted conditions. In the present case these restricted conditions involve the use of just reduced diagrams.

With the limitation to reduced diagrams which has been achieved in Eq. (11-18), only a finite number of diagrams are required for a calculation of F_β to a given finite order in powers of u/a. For example, all the diagrams which contribute to the first-order term in F_β are illustrated in Fig. 11-12. The diagrams in a given column of the figure all give the same contribution to F_β to within a numerical factor, however. The first diagram in a column is a vacuum diagram, and the other diagrams in the same column are obtained from the first by breaking various internal lines and making them external lines. Since there are three columns of diagrams, there are just three independent first-order contributions to F_β to evaluate. If the crystal under study has a Bravais lattice (one atom per unit cell), however, the middle column of diagrams in the figure gives no contribution, and there are only two independent contributions to evaluate.

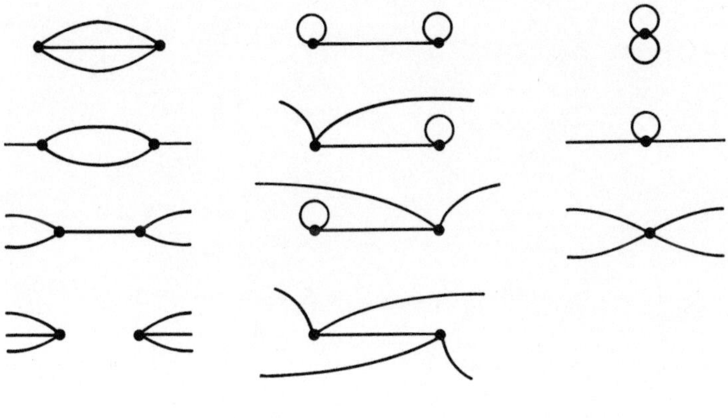

Fig. 11-12
Reduced diagrams for the first-order term in F_β

An actual calculation of F_β to first order would be quite straightforward, but it would also be lengthy. This is due to the complicated spectra of the frequencies ω_{qj} which occur for real crystals. A calculation based on a Debye frequency spectrum would be more feasible than an exact calculation, however, and it should yield results of the correct order of magnitude. A calculation based on the limiting form of Eq. (11-18) at high temperature (small β) would also be reasible.

Equations for F_β in various limiting cases have been developed by other methods by Bloch and DeDominicis (1958). These equations are in forms which also may be useful for actual calculations. In addition they show that the free energy F_β approaches the Goldstone ground-state energy in the limit of zero temperature, as it should. It should be mentioned that Montroll and Ward have given a treatment of the electron gas (1958) which is quite analagous to the treatment of the phonon system given here.

Altogether, the use of diagrams in quantum statistical mechanics has become fairly common in recent years. Papers by Massuraba (1955), Watson (1956), and Riesenfeld and Watson (1957) provide the early examples of this. Diagrams were also used in classical statistical mechanics, especially in the work of Mayer on the free energy of a classical gas.

12. SCATTERING OF NEUTRONS BY A CRYSTAL AT AN ARBITRARY TEMPERATURE

As mentioned in Sec. 9, the scattering of neutrons by a crystal at an arbitrary temperature involves anharmonic effects which should be susceptible to experimental study. The principle effect of this sort is the shift with temperature of the peaks in an inelastic scattering spectrum. Although this shift is small, it should be measurable, and experiments for this are already underway.

The theoretical discussion of this scattering in the present section is only given in brief outline. A detailed treatment will be published in the literature. For the sake of simplicity the discussion here is based on the same assumptions as were described in Sec. 9, where the scattering at O°K was treated.

The differential cross-section for scattering at a temperature T is given by the following equation:

$$d^2\sigma_T/d\Omega\, d\epsilon = a^2(|\vec{k}|/|\vec{k}_0|)S_T(\vec{\kappa}, \omega). \tag{12-1}$$

This only differs from Eq. (9-1) in that the scattering function $S_T(\vec{\kappa}\ \omega)$ is now given by the following equation, which is appropriate to the temperature T:

$$S_T(\vec{\kappa}, \omega) = Z(\beta)^{-1}\Sigma_{\nu_0} \exp(-\beta E_{\nu_0})$$
$$\times \Sigma_\nu | < \psi_\nu | T_\kappa | \psi_{\nu_0} > |^2 \delta(\omega + E_{\nu_0} - E_\nu). \tag{12-2}$$

Here $Z(\beta)$ is the partition function for the crystal and is defined in Eq. (11-2), ψ_{ν_0} is an initial state of the crystal, ψ_ν is a final state, and the factor $\exp(-\beta E_{\nu_0})/Z(\beta)$ gives the statistical weight of the initial states. The states ψ_{ν_0} and ψ_ν are eigenstates of the Hamiltonian H which is given in Eq. (5-9), and the corresponding eigenvalues are E_{ν_0} and E_ν respectively.

For reasons explained in Sec. 9 it is desirable to rewrite Eq. (12-2) in a form which does not explicitly involve the excited states of the crystal. This cannot be done in just the same way as it was in Sec. 9, however, because both the initial and final states can be excited in the present case. Instead, a trick will be used here which has been used previously in neutron scattering problems (Van Hove, 1954 a, b, and references there quoted). This trick makes use of the following relation:

$$\delta(x) = (1/2\pi) \lim_{t' \to \infty} \int_{-t'}^{t'} e^{-itx} dt. \tag{12-3}$$

When the delta function in Eq. (12-2) is replaced by use of this relation, the equation takes the following form:

$$S_T(\vec{\kappa}, \omega) = [1/2\pi Z(\beta)] \int_{-\infty}^{\infty} dt\, e^{-it\omega} \Big\{ \Sigma_{\nu\,\nu_0} \exp[-(\beta + it)E_{\nu_0}]$$
$$\times < \psi_{\nu_0} | T_{-\kappa} | \psi_\nu > \exp(itE_\nu) < \psi_\nu | T_\kappa | \psi_{\nu_0} > \Big\}, \tag{12-4}$$

where the limit on t' has been applied. Although it will not be verified here, the dummy variable t in this equation has the significance of time.

Eq. (12-4) gives the scattering function in a useful form because the term in curly brackets is just the spur of the operator

$$\exp\,[-(\beta+it)H]\,T_{-\kappa}\exp\,(itH)T_{\kappa} \tag{12-5}$$

in the representation of the actual eigenstates of the crystal. The equation can therefore be rewritten in the following way:

$$S_T(\vec{\kappa},\omega) = [1/2\pi Z(\beta)]\int_{-\infty}^{\infty} e^{-it\omega}dt\ \mathrm{Sp}\left\{\exp\,[-(\beta+it)H]\,T_{-\kappa}\exp\,(itH)T_{\kappa}\right\}. \tag{12-6}$$

Since the spur can be written out in a basis other than that of the exact eigenstates, Eq. (12-6) exhibits the desired property of not explicitly involving the exact excited eigenstates.

For present purposes the spur in Eq. (12-6) should be written out in the basis of phonon states. The resulting equation can then be treated by the techniques described in Sec. 11, where the spur of another operator was treated. As the first step in this treatment, H and Z(β) in Eq. (12-6) should be replaced by use of Eqs. (5-9) and (11-4) respectively. Eq. (12-6) then takes the following form:

$$S_T(\vec{\kappa},\omega) = (1/2\pi Z_\beta)\int_{-\infty}^{\infty} e^{it\omega}dt\ \mathrm{Sp}\left\{\exp\,[-(\beta+it)(H_o+V)]\right.$$
$$\left.\times\ T_{-\kappa}\exp\,[it(H_o+V)]\,T_{\kappa}\right\}. \tag{12-7}$$

As the next step the exponential operators in the curly brackets above should be expanded in powers of the operator V. One such expansion is given in Eq. (11-6). The resulting equation for $S_T(\vec{\kappa}\omega)$ can then be analyzed in terms of diagrams which are essentially the same as those used in the analysis of F_β in Sec. 11. In the present case, of course, each diagram must contain two neutron vertices in addition to the ordinary vertices (at least if $\vec{\kappa}$ is different from $2\pi\vec{\tau}$) but in other respects each diagram can be drawn like a diagram for F_β. The diagrams can be interpreted as cylinders, and the concept of connectedness which was defined for cylindrical diagrams can be invoked again.

A diagram in the present problem can contain components which do not involve neutron vertices as well as components which do. Consider a diagram which contains only components with neutron vertices, and consider all the other diagrams which can be constructed from the first by adding components without neutron vertices. The sum of the contributions to $S_T(\vec{\kappa},\omega)$ from all of these related diagrams turns out to equal just the contribution of the first diagram times a factor Z_β. This factor cancels the Z_β in the denominator of Eq. (12-7), and the equation becomes:

12. SCATTERING OF NEUTRONS BY A CRYSTAL AT AN ARBITRARY TEMPERATURE

$$S_T(\vec{\kappa}\omega) = (1/2\pi) \int_{-\infty}^{\infty} dt\, e^{-it\omega}$$

$$\times \Sigma_\delta^{\text{neutron}} \text{Sp} \left\{ \exp\left[-(\beta+it)(H_o+V)\right] T_{-\kappa} \exp\left[it(H_o+V)\right] T_\kappa \right\}_\delta . \quad (12\text{-}8)$$

Here the superscript on the summation sign means that the summation is restricted to diagrams which contain only components with neutron vertices. It is to be understood that the spur in this equation is expressed in the basis of phonon states.

The diagrams which occur in Eq. (12-8) are of two types. The first type contains a single component which involves both of the neutron vertices, and the second type contains two components, each of which contains one of the neutron vertices. As it turns out, the inelastic scattering spectrum is obtained if the summation is restricted to just the first type of diagram (one component), and the elastic spectrum is obtained if the summation is restricted to just the second type of diagram (two components). The elastic and inelastic spectra are discussed separately below.

As in the case of scattering at O°K, the elastic spectrum can be obtained in a straightforward way by requiring that the final state of the crystal, $\langle \psi_\nu |$, be identical to the initial state, $|\psi_o\rangle$. When this is done, Eq. (12-2) for the scattering function takes the following form:

$$S_T^{(0)}(\vec{\kappa}\omega) = Z(\beta)^{-1} \Sigma_\nu \exp(-\beta E_\nu) | \langle \psi_\nu | T_\kappa | \psi_\nu \rangle |^2 \delta(\omega). \quad (12\text{-}9)$$

In the present case of non-zero temperature, then, the straightforward procedure leads to a rather strange result. This result involves the canonical average at a temperature T of the square of a diagonal matrix element instead of the canonical average of a matrix element itself.

When the elastic spectrum is investigated by means of diagram analysis along the lines sketched above, however, the following equation for the scattering function is obtained:

$$S_T^{(0)}(\vec{\kappa}\omega) = | Z(\beta)^{-1} \Sigma_\nu \exp(-\beta E_\nu) \langle \psi_\nu | T_\kappa | \psi_\nu \rangle |^2 \delta(\omega). \quad (12\text{-}10)$$

This equation involves the more reasonable form of canonical average, and it is also much more suitable for calculations than Eq. (1 -9) in the case of an anharmonic crystal.

In inelastic scattering, only the most singular parts of the spectrum are of interest. The reasons for this were given in Sec. 9. These most-singular parts can be obtained by themselves from Eq. (12-8) if the summation in that equation is further restricted to just one-component diagrams which involve at least one phonon line and which would become disconnected diagrams if one of the phonon lines were broken. This result is essentially the same as that for the scattering at O°K. On examination of they types of diagrams which are involved, however, it is seen that there is a new feature in the present case. One of the types is illustrated schematically in Fig. 12-1. Each shaded region in the figure represents a system of phonon lines and vertices, including a neutron vertex (which is indicated). Each of these regions may be very complicated. A second type of diagram is illustrated schematically in a similar way in Fig. 12-2. The first type of diagram occurs whether the temperature is zero or non-zero, as examination of Fig. 10-3 will show. The second type of diagram does not occur when the temperature is zero, however, and it is the new feature in the present case.

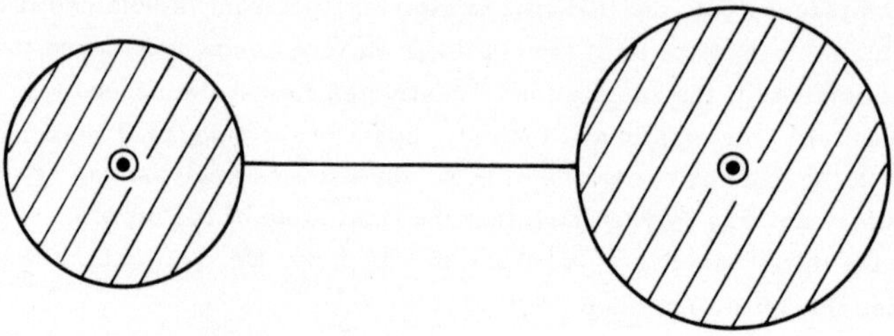

Fig. 12-1

Schematic representation of one type of diagram contributing to the most singular part of $S_T(\vec{K}\omega)$ in the case of inelastic scattering

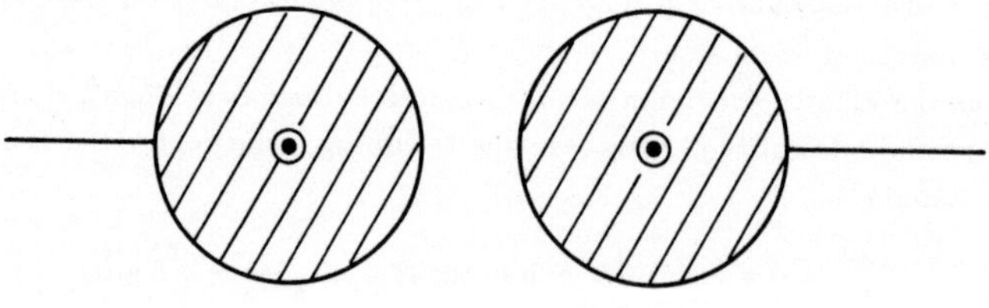

Fig. 12-2

Schematic representation of a second type of diagram contributing to the most singular part of $S_T(\vec{K}\omega)$ in the case of inelastic scattering

It is quite easy to see why a new type of diagram should occur at a non-zero temperature. At O°K the crystal is initially in its ground state, and the neutrons can only excite phonons. At a non-zero temperature, however, the crystal initially has a thermal distribution of phonons, and the neutrons can destroy some initial phonons as well as excite new ones. The type of diagram in Fig. 12-1 corresponds to the creation of a phonon by a neutron, and the type in Fig. 12-2 corresponds to the destruction of a phonon. This interpretation is particularly apparent in the case of a harmonic crystal, when the types of diagrams shown in Figs. 12-1 and 12-2 reduce to the simple diagrams in Figs. 12-3 and 12-4 and the diagrams which differ from these by the insertion of helices.

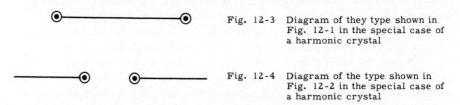

Fig. 12-3 Diagram of they type shown in Fig. 12-1 in the special case of a harmonic crystal

Fig. 12-4 Diagram of the type shown in Fig. 12-2 in the special case of a harmonic crystal

This is as far as the discussion of neutron scattering at a non-zero temperature will be carried here. The analysis is presently being worked out in further detail. Since the shifts of the inelastic scattering peaks with changing temperature are expected to be measurable, these shifts constitute one of the main objects of the investigation. In view of the experimental situation, the time really seems ripe for a quantitative calculation of these shifts. Such a calculation is bound to be lengthy, but it does seem feasible. The approach described above does lead to closed formulae for the quantities which would have to be calculated, and the formulae only involve a small number of diagrams, at least in the lowest order.

The problem considered in the present section provides a further example of the separation of extensive and intensive effects which was mentioned as a difficulty in Sec. 1. As a result of the concept of connectedness which has been used here, a factor $Z(\beta)$ has been extracted from the numerator of Eq. (12-2) to cancel the same factor in the denominator. By this means an apparent dependence of the scattering cross-section on the bulk properties of the crystal has been eliminated.

13. CONCLUSION

In the course of the treatments of the various problems in the preceding sections, a new perturbation theory has been presented. This perturbation theory is suitable for any system containing a very large number of interacting particles, and it therefore has applications in many problems besides those which have been treated here. The perturbation theory is closely related to techniques which are commonly used in field theory, and, in fact, it was largely inspired by those techniques.

The new, many-particle perturbation theory can be said to reconcile perturbation theory with thermodynamics. One of the cornerstones of thermodynamics is the assumption that in the limit of a very large system there are certain average quantities of the system which have very simple behaviors. These average quantities are the working variables of thermodynamics. These quantities are readily calculated by the new, many-particle perturbation theory, whereas they are very hard to calculate by standard perturbation theory, due to the difficulty of finding formulae which exhibit the expected simple behaviors.

For the system of interacting phonons which is the special topic of this report, the work to date has been entirely formal. In view of the present theoretical and experimental situations, however, quantitative calculations are highly desirable. In particular, a quantitative calculation of the thermal shifts of the neutron scattering peaks would be of real interest. Quantitative calculations have been performed in analogous problems in field theory, and they have led to good results. A phonon calculation is expected to be even harder than one of the field theory calculations, however. In the phonon problem there is no Lorentz invariance to simplify the work, and there are the added difficulties of polarization mixing, finite space groups, and the like. Despite these difficulties, a significant quantitative calculation in the phonon problem does seem to be feasible.

REFERENCES

H. Bethe, Phys. Rev. 103, 1353 (1956).

C. Bloch and C. DeDominicis, Nuc. Phys. 7, 459 (1958).

N. N. Bogolyubov, J. Phys. U. S. S. R. 11, 23 (1947).

M. Born and K. Huang, Dynamical Theory of Crystal Lattices, (Oxford, 1954).

K. A. Brueckner and C. A. Levinson, Phys. Rev. 97, 1344, (1955).

K. A. Brueckner and K. Sawada, Phys. Rev. 106, 1117 (1957); 106, 1128 (1957).

R. P. Feynman, Phys. Rev. 76, 749 (1949).

W. R. Frazer and L. Van Hove, Physica 24, 137 (1958).

J. Goldstone, Proc. Roy. Soc., A239, 267 (1957).

K. Huang and C. N. Yang, Phys. Rev. 105, 767 (1957).

N. M. Hugenholtz, Physica 23, 481 (1957a); Physica 23, 533 (1957b).

N. M. Hugenholtz and L. Van Hove, Physica 24, 363 (1958).

G. Liebfried, Hbk. d. Phys. 7, Part 1, 104 (1955).

T. Massuraba, Prog. Theor. Phys. 14, 357 (1955).

E. W. Montroll and J. C. Ward, Phys. of Fluids 1, 55 (1958).

G. Placzek and L. Van Hove, Phys. Rev. 93, 1207 (1954).

W. B. Riesenfeld and K. M. Watson, Phys. Rev. 108, 518 (1957).

A. Sjölander, Ark. f. Phys. 7, 375 (1954).

L. Van Hove, Phys. Rev. 95, 249 (1954a); Phys. Rev. 95, 1374 (1954b); Physica 21, 517 (1955a); Physica 21, 901 (1955b); Physica 22, 343 (1956); Physica 23, 441 (1957).

K. Watson, Phys. Rev. 103, 489 (1956).

G. C. Wick, Rev. Mod. Phys. 27, 339 (1955).

PHYSICAL REVIEW VOLUME 93, NUMBER 6 MARCH 15, 1954

Crystal Dynamics and Inelastic Scattering of Neutrons

G. PLACZEK AND L. VAN HOVE
Institute for Advanced Study, Princeton, New Jersey

(Received December 10, 1953)

A general discussion is given for the angular and energy distribution of neutrons inelastically scattered by a crystal, with special emphasis on those features of the distribution in which the dynamical properties of the crystal manifest themselves most immediately. The direct relationship between the energy changes in scattering and the dispersion law of the crystal vibrations is analyzed. While for x-rays, due to the extremely small relative size of these energy changes, the dispersion law has to be inferred indirectly from intensity measurements, it is shown that the very much larger relative magnitude of energy transfers in the case of slow neutrons opens the possibility of direct determination of the frequency-wave vector relationship and the frequency-distribution function of the crystal vibrations by energy measurements on scattered neutrons. The general properties of the outgoing neutron distribution in momentum space which are relevant for this purpose are derived by first considering the particularly instructive limiting case of neutrons initially at rest and subsequently generalizing the results to incident neutrons of arbitrary energy.

I. INTRODUCTION

THE diffraction of neutrons by crystals has been in recent years the object of an increasing number of investigations and has been recognized as a promising tool for crystallographic research.[1] Considerable work has been done on elastic scattering, the coherent part of which exhibits Bragg reflections in full analogy with x-rays, and on transmission measurements, dealing with total cross sections. The influence of crystal dynamics on neutron scattering was discussed by various authors[2–14a] and quantitative calculations of total cross sections were carried out on the basis of a greatly simplified model for the crystal elastic vibrations, the familiar Debye model, in which the velocity of sound waves (phonons) is assumed independent of wavelength, direction, and polarization.

From its success in describing specific heats, the Debye model is known to be a fair approximation for effects which involve the average of a smooth function over all crystal vibrations. It gives, therefore, at least for cubic crystals, a reliable estimate of the Debye-Waller factor affecting Bragg reflections of neutrons and x-rays and can be expected to provide a good orientation as to the magnitude and energy dependence of total inelastic neutron cross sections for the incoherent[15] part of the scattering. For other effects, however, in particular for the angular and energy distribution of inelastically scattered neutrons, the details of the vibration spectrum play a much more important role and the theoretical discussion has to take them into account. It is the aim of the present investigation to show how they manifest themselves in this distribution.

The analogous problem for the inelastic scattering of x-rays has been the object of detailed theoretical and experimental study[16–23] with the purpose of determining from scattering data the actual vibrational spectrum of the crystal, i.e., the exact relation $\omega=\omega_j(\mathbf{q})$ between frequency ω, wave vector $\mathbf{q}$, and polarization j of a plane wave vibration (phonon). This function manifests itself directly in the wavelength shift of x-rays scattered by one-phonon processes. Because of its extremely small relative size, however, this shift is not readily accessible to measurement, and hence the function $\omega_j(\mathbf{q})$ has to be inferred from measurements of the scattered intensity.

Because of the different relation between energy and momentum the energy balance is entirely altered in the case of slow neutrons. While this is generally true, it may be exemplified more concretely by considering the important particular case of coherent one-phonon processes. For an incident wavelength of the order of the lattice constant the absolute energy changes in a

[1] For surveys see: J. M. Cassels, Progr. Nuclear Phys. **1**, 185 (1950); D. J. Hughes, *Pile Neutron Research* (Addison-Wesley Publishing Company, Cambridge, 1953); G. E. Bacon and K. Lonsdale, Repts. Progr. in Phys. **16**, 1 (1953).
[2] G. C. Wick, Physik. Z. **38**, 403, 689 (1937).
[3] I. Pomeranchuk, Physik. Z. Sowjetunion **13**, 65 (1938).
[4] Halpern, Hamermesh, and Johnson, Phys. Rev. **59**, 981 (1941).
[5] R. Seeger and E. Teller, Phys. Rev. **62**, 37 (1942).
[6] R. Weinstock, Phys. Rev. **65**, 1 (1944).
[7] A. Akhiezer and I. Pomeranchuk, J. Phys. (U.S.S.R.) **11**, 167 (1947).
[8] Placzek, Nijboer, and Van Hove, Phys. Rev. **82**, 392 (1951).
[9] J. M. Cassels, Proc. Roy. Soc. (London) **A208**, 527 (1951).
[10] D. A. Kleinman, thesis, Brown University, 1951 (unpublished) and abstracts in Phys. Rev. **81**, 326 (1951); **86**, 622 (1952); **90**, 355 (1953).
[11] I. Waller and P. O. Fröman, Arkiv. Fysik **4**, 183 (1951).
[12] P. O. Fröman, Arkiv. Fysik **4**, 191 (1951); **5**, 53 (1952).
[13] G. Placzek, Phys. Rev. **86**, 377 (1952).
[14] G. L. Squires, Proc. Roy. Soc. (London) **A212**, 192 (1952).
[14a] G. Placzek, Phys. Rev. **93**, 897 (1954).

[15] Using the same terminology as Hughes, reference 1, we call coherent the interferent part of the slow neutron scattering, and incoherent the noninterferent part due to spin and isotope disorder. The existence of these two types of scattering has been discussed first by Wick (reference 2). Both types comprise elastic as well as inelastic processes.
[16] J. Laval, Bull. soc. franç. minéral. **64**, 1 (1941).
[17] K. Lonsdale, Repts. Progr. in Phys. **9**, 256 (1943).
[18] M. Born, Repts. Progr. in Phys. **9**, 294 (1943).
[19] W. H. Zachariasen, *Theory of X-Ray Diffraction in Crystals* (John Wiley and Sons, Inc., New York, 1945).
[20] P. Olmer, Acta Cryst. **1**, 57 (1948); Bull. soc. franç. minéral. **71**, 144 (1948).
[21] H. Curien, thèse, Paris, 1952; Acta Cryst. **5**, 393 (1952).
[22] H. Cole and B. E. Warren, J. Appl. Phys. **23**, 335 (1952).
[23] H. Cole, J. Appl. Phys. **24**, 482 (1953).

general direction are, for neutrons, not radically different from those for x-rays, being in both cases of the order of average phonon energies. For neutrons, however, the energy corresponding to such an incident wavelength is of the same order of magnitude and the relative change in energy or wavelength is therefore of order one, which considerably reduces the difficulty of its direct measurement.

As the incident wavelength increases, the contrast between the x-ray and neutron cases becomes even more pronounced. For x-rays, in the case of a Bravais lattice, the absolute energy change in a given scattering direction becomes proportional to the incident energy, with a relative change of the order of the ratio of sound velocity to light velocity. For neutrons, on the other hand, the absolute energy changes in a given scattering direction do not systematically decrease with increasing incident wavelength; in fact, they ultimately become independent of it, tending to finite values. Thus, a limiting case is approached for which the incident energy and momentum can be put equal to zero both in the conservation laws which determine the energy shift, and in the transition probabilities. Physically, this is the case of a neutron initially at rest which takes up energy and momentum by absorbing a phonon. For finite incident wavelength this description will be adequate if the outgoing wavelength is small compared to the incoming one. Under this condition the transition probability is approximately constant, and hence the scattering cross section becomes proportional to the wavelength. The actual wavelength beyond which the condition is satisfied depends on the scattering direction and on crystal structure, but it often lies in the accessible region of the subthermal neutron spectrum in which transmission experiments are already quite common. Scattering experiments in this region[24] still present a certain intensity problem and may be easier at somewhat shorter wavelengths, which, as we shall see, have to be used anyhow if one wishes to determine the function $\omega_j(\mathbf{q})$ for all $\mathbf{q}$.

In the above remarks we have been concerned with coherent one-phonon scattering only. The energy distribution of neutrons incoherently scattered by one-phonon processes is also of considerable interest in connection with crystal dynamics, especially for cubic crystals, for which, as will be shown later, it is directly connected with the frequency-distribution function of the crystal. For multiphonon processes, coherent as well as incoherent, the relation between neutron scattering and dynamical properties of the crystal is much more complicated, except for the limiting of high incident energies.[13] For the purpose of the determination of the frequency spectrum of the crystal from scattering data these processes are therefore of less interest, and for this reason we shall concentrate on one-phonon processes.

One has, however, to inquire under what conditions one-phonon scattering can be experimentally separated from multiphonon processes. For a single crystal, one-phonon coherent scattering is distinguishable from all other processes by its energy distribution in each outgoing direction, which will be seen to comprise a finite number of discrete energy values, appearing as sharp peaks above the continuous background of one-phonon incoherent and multiphonon scattering. No such direct distinction is possible between neutrons scattered in one-phonon incoherent and multiphonon processes. While the contribution of the latter to the cross section is always decisive at high incident energies and often appreciable even in the limiting case of zero incident energy,[25] it would, however, seem quite feasible to carry out scattering experiments under conditions (moderately low temperature and incident energy and high nuclear mass) which make multiphonon effects either entirely negligible or reduce them to the size of a manageable correction, thus allowing the isolation of the incoherent one-phonon processes.

In the following sections, we discuss the angular and energy distribution of neutrons scattered by one-phonon processes, both coherent and incoherent. Sections II and III deal with the limiting case of infinite incident wavelength. Apart from its direct interest, this case illustrates with particular clarity the essential aspects of the problem. The complications arising for finite incident wavelength are of a purely formal nature and are taken care of in Sec. IV.

Regarding the crystal structure, we consider for convenience a Bravais lattice, with one nucleus per cell. For a lattice with more particles per cell, our discussion has to be supplemented by consideration of a structure factor and of optical branches in the frequency spectrum. With minor modifications, our treatment can also be extended to neutron scattering by spin waves in ferromagnetic crystals, a problem already studied by Moorhouse[26] from a slightly different point of view.

II. ANGULAR AND ENERGY DISTRIBUTION FOR INFINITE INCIDENT WAVELENGTH

In the limiting case of infinite incident wavelength, energy can only be transferred from the crystal to the neutron, and inelastic scattering is therefore possible only if the crystal is at a nonvanishing temperature. In one-phonon scattering, a phonon initially excited in the crystal is absorbed by the neutron initially at rest which picks up its energy. Energy conservation is expressed by

$$k^2=(2m/\hbar)\omega_j(\mathbf{q}), \qquad (1)$$

where m and $\mathbf{k}$ are the mass and final wave vector of the neutron; $\mathbf{q}$, j, and $\hbar\omega_j(\mathbf{q})$ are the wave vector, polarization index ($j=1, 2, 3$ for a Bravais lattice), and energy of the absorbed phonon.

Equation (1) holds for both coherent and incoherent

[24] P. Egelstaff, Nature **168**, 290 (1951).

[25] For estimates see Squires, reference 14.

[26] R. G. Moorhouse, Proc. Phys. Soc. (London) **64**, 1097 (1951).

scattering. For the latter it is the only condition relating the phonon variables to the momentum $\hbar\mathbf{k}$ transferred to the neutron; Eq. (1) has then only to be supplemented by an intensity formula given in Sec. III. For coherent scattering, the interference between waves scattered by the various nuclei imposes a further relation

$$\mathbf{k}=\mathbf{q}+2\pi\boldsymbol{\tau}, \tag{2}$$

where $\boldsymbol{\tau}$ is an arbitrary vector of the reciprocal lattice.[7] It is well known that the wave vector $\mathbf{q}$ of a lattice vibration is only defined apart from 2π times an arbitrary reciprocal lattice vector $\boldsymbol{\tau}$; the frequency $\omega_j(\mathbf{q})$ is accordingly a periodic function of $\mathbf{q}$,

$$\omega_j(\mathbf{q}+2\pi\boldsymbol{\tau})=\omega_j(\mathbf{q}). \tag{3}$$

To a phonon of wave vector $\mathbf{q}+2\pi\boldsymbol{\tau}$ can be attributed a momentum $\hbar(\mathbf{q}+2\pi\boldsymbol{\tau})$, and in this sense Eq. (2) is conventionally regarded as expressing momentum conservation.[27]

The conservation laws determine the main features of the angular and energy distribution of scattered neutrons. To show this, we shall use the following properties of the $\omega_j(\mathbf{q})$ function, valid for any Bravais lattice: for each $j=1, 2, 3$, $\omega_j(\mathbf{q})$ is a continuous function with the periodicity (3) of the reciprocal lattice; for $\mathbf{q}$ approaching $2\pi\boldsymbol{\tau}$, it has the form

$$\omega_j(\mathbf{q})=c_j(\boldsymbol{\xi}/\xi)\xi;\quad \boldsymbol{\xi}=\mathbf{q}-2\pi\boldsymbol{\tau}, \tag{4}$$

where $c_j(\boldsymbol{\xi}/\xi)$, the sound velocity for long wavelengths in the direction $\boldsymbol{\xi}/\xi$, can be calculated from the elastic constants.[28]

For incoherent scattering, the energy equation (1) shows that the length of $\mathbf{k}$ is restricted to the interval

$$0\leqslant k\leqslant k_{\max}=(2m\omega_{\max}/\hbar)^{\frac{1}{2}}, \tag{5}$$

where $\omega_{\max}$ is the maximum of $\omega_j(\mathbf{q})$ for all $\mathbf{q}$ and j; the direction of $\mathbf{k}$ is unrestricted. Equation (5) defines in $\mathbf{k}$ space a sphere Σ of radius $k_{\max}$ and center $\mathbf{k}=0$. Any vector with endpoint inside or on Σ is a possible value for the outgoing neutron wave vector. Hence, neutrons are scattered in all directions, with energies ranging continuously from 0 to $\hbar\omega_{\max}$. This conclusion holds for single crystals as well as for powders.

The restrictions affecting $\mathbf{k}$ are more severe for coherent scattering. Combining Eqs. (1), (2), (3) one obtains them in the simple form

$$k^2=(2m/\hbar)\omega_j(\mathbf{k}). \tag{6}$$

For each j, (6) defines in $\mathbf{k}$ space a surface S_j, which may be composed of several disconnected parts. The surfaces S_1, S_2, S_3 in general cross each other, and the set of all three will be called S. We suppose the origin $\mathbf{k}=0$ not to be counted as a point of S. For neutrons scattered coherently with absorption of one phonon, the outgoing wave vector is thus restricted to have its endpoint on S.

In order to discuss the general properties of the surface S, let us call lattice vectors in $\mathbf{k}$ space the reciprocal lattice vectors $\boldsymbol{\tau}$ multiplied by 2π, and let us speak accordingly of lattice points and cells in $\mathbf{k}$ space. We state

(i) The surface S is entirely contained in the sphere Σ.

(ii) Each radius of the sphere Σ crosses S at least once and in general a finite number of times not smaller than 3.

(iii) Each connected region of $\mathbf{k}$ space inside Σ which contains a lattice point $2\pi\boldsymbol{\tau}\neq 0$ and a point $\mathbf{k}_1$, where $\omega_j(\mathbf{k}_1)=\omega_{\max}$ for some j, is crossed by S; in particular, S crosses any cell of $\mathbf{k}$ space, centered at a lattice point $2\pi\boldsymbol{\tau}\neq 0$ and fully contained in Σ.

Property (i) is obvious. To establish (ii), we notice first that, S being a two-dimensional surface, if a radius of Σ crosses it at all, it will in general do so a finite number of times. To show that every radius crosses S, consider

$$\varphi_j(\mathbf{k})=k^2-(2m/\hbar)\omega_j(\mathbf{k})$$

as a function of k for fixed direction of $\mathbf{k}$ and fixed j: for small k, Eq. (4) gives

$$\varphi_j(\mathbf{k})=k^2-(2m/\hbar)c_j(\mathbf{k}/k)\cdot k<0,$$

whereas, for $k=k_{\max}$,

$$\varphi_j(\mathbf{k})=k_{\max}{}^2-(2m/\hbar)\omega_j(\mathbf{k})=(2m/\hbar)[\omega_{\max}-\omega_j(\mathbf{k})]\geqslant 0.$$

Since the function is continuous, it must vanish for at least one value k_j of k, giving a point on S. For general directions of $\mathbf{k}$, the three k_j's will be different. Property (iii) is established by a similar continuity argument, considering $\varphi_j(\mathbf{k})$ for the polarization j which gives $\omega_j(\mathbf{k}_1)=\omega_{\max}$, along a path in $\mathbf{k}$ space from $2\pi\boldsymbol{\tau}$ to $\mathbf{k}_1$.

The physical meaning of property (i) is quite trivial: it states that the outgoing neutron energy never exceeds the maximum phonon energy $\hbar\omega_{\max}$. Property (ii) determines the main features of the angular and energy distribution for coherent one-phonon scattering by a single crystal: neutrons are scattered in every direction and for each direction the outgoing energy has a finite number of discrete values, in general three or more. Measurement of outgoing energy as function of direction determines the surface S and thus yields $\omega_j(\mathbf{k})$.[29] This type of scattering is, therefore, particularly well fitted to give information on the crystal vibrations.

As mentioned in the introduction, the discrete nature of their energy spectrum allows an experimental separation of neutrons scattered in one-phonon coherent processes. It is, indeed, easily established that in

[27] The momentum $\hbar\mathbf{q}$ thus attributed to a vibration is not to be confused with the momentum of the crystal considered as a system of particles, and Eq. (2) has nothing in common with momentum conservation in the sense of particle dynamics.

[28] H. A. Jahn, Proc. Roy. Soc. (London) **A179**, 320 (1941).

[29] In order to measure in this way $\omega_j(\mathbf{q})$ for every $\mathbf{q}$ and j, one has to use neutrons with nonvanishing initial momentum. See Eqs. (17) and (18) below.

multiphonon coherent processes, as well as in incoherent inelastic scattering, the final wave vector $\mathbf{k}$ depends on three or more parameters, giving in each direction an outgoing energy which ranges continuously over one or more finite intervals. The latter type of energy distribution is also obtained for coherent one-phonon scattering by a powder, as is shown by averaging over orientations the energy distribution for a single crystal. In this respect, powders are less convenient than single crystals for study of the elastic vibrations by means of neutron scattering.

Returning to one-phonon coherent scattering by a single crystal, we have still to consider the implications of property (iii) above. (iii) is of interest particularly when the sphere Σ contains a rather large number of lattice points of $\mathbf{k}$ space. It then shows that the surface S is distributed in Σ with a certain uniformity, since it passes through every cell inside Σ, except possibly the cell centered at the origin. In every direction, the discrete values of the outgoing wave vector $\mathbf{k}$ will be distributed over the interval $0\leqslant k\leqslant k_{\max}$ with a corresponding amount of uniformity.

While such conclusions are bound to be rather vague, it is instructive to compare the size of the sphere Σ with the size of the lattice cell in $\mathbf{k}$ space. The ratio of their volumes is

$$\frac{(4\pi/3)k_{\max}^3}{(2\pi)^3/v_0}=\frac{v_0}{6\pi^2}\left(\frac{2m\omega_{\max}}{h}\right)^{\frac{3}{2}}=F, \tag{7}$$

where v_0 is the volume per particle in the crystal.

The parameter F plays an important role in determining the general shape of the surface S. When F is very small compared to 1, the sphere Σ is entirely in the region where the approximation (4) applies with $\boldsymbol{\tau}=0$. Equation (6) reduces to

$$k=(2m/h)c_j(\mathbf{k}/k),\quad (j=1,2,3). \tag{8a}$$

Hence, S is formed of three closed surfaces around the origin of $\mathbf{k}$ space, intersecting each other and fully contained in the lattice cell of center $\mathbf{k}=0$. For slightly larger F, S can be expected to have the same general shape, but Eq. (8a) will have to be completed with correction terms of relative order $F^{\frac{1}{3}}$, $F^{\frac{2}{3}}$, $\cdots$. For $F\gg1$ on the other hand, the shape of S is again simple in the region of $\mathbf{k}$ space where k is small compared to $k_{\max}$. S is there composed of three closed surfaces around each lattice point $2\pi\boldsymbol{\tau}\neq0$, of approximate equation

$$\xi=4\pi^2h\tau^2[2mc_j(\boldsymbol{\xi}/\xi)]^{-1}+\cdots,\quad (j=1,2,3),$$
$$\boldsymbol{\xi}=\mathbf{k}-2\pi\boldsymbol{\tau}, \tag{8b}$$

with correction terms of relative order $F^{-\frac{1}{3}}$, $F^{-\frac{2}{3}}$, $\cdots$. In the region where k is comparable to $k_{\max}$, S behaves quite differently: it runs continuously from cell to cell in $\mathbf{k}$ space.

For actual crystals F seems to be larger than one, but in general not large enough for (8b) to apply. This is thus the case intermediate between those considered above. Here even the general shape of S cannot be predicted without a fairly accurate knowledge of the $\omega_j(\mathbf{q})$ function. Conversely this case would appear to be all the more favorable for the determination of the $\omega_j(\mathbf{q})$ function from the measured shape of the surface S.

The calculation of F for an actual substance requires the knowledge of $\omega_{\max}$, which is accurately available only for a very few crystals. It is, however, only the order of magnitude of F which is of interest, and this is easily obtained by remarking that the order of magnitude of $\omega_{\max}$ is given by the Debye temperature θ

$$\omega_{\max}\simeq k_B\theta/h,$$

(k_B = Boltzmann constant).[30] The approximate value of F thus obtained, defined by

$$F_D=\frac{v_0}{6\pi^2}\frac{(2mk_B\theta)^{\frac{3}{2}}}{h^3}, \tag{9}$$

is given in Table I for a few substances.

III. INTENSITY FORMULAS FOR LONG INCIDENT WAVELENGTH

The discussion of Sec. II has to be supplemented by the consideration of the scattered intensity per unit angular and energy range. This intensity is simply expressed in terms of the differential cross section $d\sigma/d\mathbf{k}$ per unit volume in $\mathbf{k}$ space.

We consider a single crystal and measure the coherent cross section per nucleus in units of $\langle a\rangle_{\mathrm{Av}}^2$ and the incoherent cross section per nucleus in units of $\langle a^2\rangle_{\mathrm{Av}}-\langle a\rangle_{\mathrm{Av}}^2$. a is the spin- and isotope-dependent scattering length. The units are, respectively, the coherent and incoherent scattering cross sections of the bound nucleus per unit solid angle. With the aid of standard methods[7] it is then found that

$$\frac{d\sigma_1^{\mathrm{inc}}}{d\mathbf{k}}=\frac{2}{Mk_0}\exp[-\langle(\mathbf{k}\cdot\mathbf{u})^2\rangle_{\mathrm{Av}}]\frac{v_0}{(2\pi)^3}\sum_j\int d\mathbf{q}$$
$$\times\frac{[\mathbf{k}\cdot\mathbf{e}_j(\mathbf{q})]^2}{k^2}\frac{\delta[k^2-2mh^{-1}\omega_j(\mathbf{q})]}{\exp[\beta\omega_j(\mathbf{q})]-1}, \tag{10}$$

$$\frac{d\sigma_1^{\mathrm{coh}}}{d\mathbf{k}}=\frac{2}{Mk_0}\exp[-\langle(\mathbf{k}\cdot\mathbf{u})^2\rangle_{\mathrm{Av}}]\sum_j\frac{[\mathbf{k}\cdot\mathbf{e}_j(\mathbf{k})]^2}{k^2}$$
$$\cdot\frac{\delta[k^2-2mh^{-1}\omega_j(\mathbf{k})]}{\exp[\beta\omega_j(\mathbf{k})]-1}. \tag{11}$$

The suffix 1 in σ_1^{inc} and σ_1^{coh} refers to one-phonon scattering. M is the ratio of nuclear to neutron mass. In the Debye-Waller factor $\exp[-\langle(\mathbf{k}\cdot\mathbf{u})^2\rangle_{\mathrm{Av}}]$, $\mathbf{u}$ is the displacement vector of any nucleus in the crystal from its equilibrium position, and the average is taken over

[30] For tungsten, calculations by P. C. Fine [Phys. Rev. 56, 355 (1939)] give $h\omega_{\max}/k_B=336°$, as compared to $\theta=373°$ from the elastic constants and $\theta=310°$ from specific heats.

the thermal equilibrium distribution. $\mathbf{e}_j(\mathbf{q})$ is the polarization vector of the phonon defined by j and $\mathbf{q}$, β is the reciprocal temperature multiplied by $\hbar k_B^{-1}$. The integration over $\mathbf{q}$ in (10) extends over one cell in $\mathbf{k}$ space. The argument of the δ function in (11) gives directly the Eq. (6) of the surface S discussed in the previous section and the functions $\mathbf{e}_j(\mathbf{k})$ as well as $\omega_j(\mathbf{k})$ are defined for all $\mathbf{k}$ through the periodicity condition corresponding to (3).

The cross sections (10) and (11) correspond to transition probabilities for a neutron initially at rest, in conformity with the limiting case discussed in the previous section. The incident momentum $\hbar k_0$ thus appears only in the factor relating transition probability to cross section. This limiting case applies if $k \gg k_0$. For coherent scattering, as follows from our discussion of the surface S, k has a nonvanishing minimum, and hence (11) holds for all outgoing energies as soon as $k_0 \ll k_{\min}$. For incoherent scattering, on the other hand, there is no such minimum. However small k_0 may be, therefore, the limiting case will not apply in the small region of the outgoing energy spectrum where k is not large compared to k_0. Here (10) must be replaced by the general expression (15).

Equation (10) can be considerably simplified for cubic crystals. As is well known, a quadratic form $\Sigma_{xy}A_{xy}k_xk_y$ invariant under the operations of any of the cubic point groups is a multiple of $\Sigma_x k_x^2$, i.e., $A_{xy}=A\delta_{xy}$ (δ_{xy}=Kronecker symbol). For cubic crystals, this fact implies, firstly,[19]

$$\langle(\mathbf{k}\cdot\mathbf{u})^2\rangle_{\mathrm{Av}}=k^2\langle u_0^2\rangle_{\mathrm{Av}},$$

where u_0 is the component of $\mathbf{u}$ in an arbitrary direction. The Debye-Waller factor is thus independent of the direction of $\mathbf{k}$. Secondly,

$$\sum_j \int d\mathbf{q}\, e_j^x(\mathbf{q})e_j^y(\mathbf{q})\frac{\delta[k^2-2m\hbar^{-1}\omega_j(\mathbf{q})]}{\exp[\beta\omega_j(\mathbf{q})]-1}=A\delta_{xy},$$

with

$$A=\frac{1}{3}\sum_j \int d\mathbf{q}\frac{\delta[k^2-2m\hbar^{-1}\omega_j(\mathbf{q})]}{\exp[\beta\omega_j(\mathbf{q})]-1}.$$

Introducing the frequency distribution function $g(\omega)$, defined as the number of normal vibrations per unit frequency interval, divided by the total number of vibrations,

$$g(\omega)d\omega=\frac{1}{3}\frac{v_0}{(2\pi)^3}\sum_j \int_{\omega\leqslant\omega_j(\mathbf{q})\leqslant\omega+d\omega} d\mathbf{q},$$

$$g(\omega)=0 \quad \text{for} \quad \omega>\omega_{\max},$$

we find:

$$\frac{d\sigma_1^{\mathrm{inc}}}{d\mathbf{k}}=\frac{2}{Mk_0}\exp[-k^2\langle u_0^2\rangle_{\mathrm{Av}}] \times\int_0^{\omega_{\max}}\frac{\delta(k^2-2m\hbar^{-1}\omega)}{\exp(\beta\omega)-1}g(\omega)d\omega,$$

TABLE I. The parameter F_D.

Substance	Lattice type	$10^{24}\ v_0$ in cm³	θ in °K	F_D
Pb	cu face-cent.	30.0	88	3.6
W	cu body-cent.	15.7	310	12
Fe	cu body-cent.	11.7	462	17
Al	cu face-cent.	16.5	398	19

or

$$\frac{d\sigma_1^{\mathrm{inc}}}{d\mathbf{k}}=\frac{\hbar}{Mmk_0}\exp[-k^2\langle u_0^2\rangle_{\mathrm{Av}}]\frac{g(\hbar k^2/2m)}{\exp(\beta\hbar k^2/2m)-1}. \tag{12}$$

For cubic crystals the one-phonon incoherent scattering has thus, for small k_0, an energy distribution independent of direction and simply expressed in terms of the frequency distribution $g(\omega)$ of the crystal.

It has been shown elsewhere[31] that the $g(\omega)$ function of a general crystal contains a finite number of singularities resulting from the periodic structure; they are singular points ω_c in the neighborhood of which $g(\omega)$ has one of the two forms

$$g(\omega)=g(\omega_c)+\left\{\begin{matrix} A|\omega-\omega_c|^{\frac{1}{2}}+O(\omega-\omega_c) & \text{for } \omega<\omega_c \\ O(\omega-\omega_c) & \text{for } \omega>\omega_c\end{matrix}\right\}, \tag{13}$$

or the same with $\omega<\omega_c$ and $\omega>\omega_c$ interchanged. The constant A can have either sign; it is usually negative for $\omega_c<\omega_{\max}$ and positive for $\omega_c=\omega_{\max}$ [$\omega_{\max}$ is in general a singular point of $g(\omega)$]. The symbol $O(\omega-\omega_c)$ denotes a rest term of order $|\omega-\omega_c|$ for $\omega\to\omega_c$. The singular frequencies ω_c are simply related to the $\omega_j(\mathbf{q})$ function of the crystal: apart from exceptional cases, they are the values of $\omega_j(\mathbf{q})$ at the points where grad $\omega_j(\mathbf{q})=0$, (j=1, 2, 3).[31] We shall call them the singular frequencies of the crystal. The general shape of the energy distribution $(2mk/\hbar^2)(d\sigma_1^{\mathrm{inc}}/d\mathbf{k})$ (for fixed direction of $\mathbf{k}$) can be predicted from the behavior of $g(\omega)$ and a typical distribution is given in Fig. 1. Its singularities are of the same analytical type as (13), ω being replaced by k or the energy $E=\hbar^2k^2/2m$.[32]

Apart from (10), the inelastic incoherent cross section contains terms due to multiphonon processes. In general they depend on the direction of $\mathbf{k}$, but the energy distribution in each direction can be shown to be continuously differentiable. The energy distribution in each direction for inelastic incoherent scattering by a cubic

[31] L. Van Hove, Phys. Rev. **89**, 1189 (1953); in the formulas on p. 1191 of this paper $(\nu-\nu_c)^{\frac{1}{2}}$ must be replaced by $|\nu-\nu_c|^{\frac{1}{2}}$. The vector $\mathbf{q}$ there used is our present vector $\mathbf{q}$ divided by 2π. The frequency distribution of a simple cubic crystal has been calculated with its correct singularities by G. F. Newell, J. Chem. Phys. **21**, 1877. See also H. B. Rosenstock and G. F. Newell, J. Chem. Phys. **21**, 1607 (1953); H. B. Rosenstock and H. M. Rosenstock, J. Chem. Phys. **21**, 1608 (1953).

[32] All our statements concerning singularities in the $g(\omega)$ function and in energy distributions of scattered neutrons hold for general values of the force constants of the crystal. The origin and nature of possible exceptions have been discussed by Van Hove (reference 31).

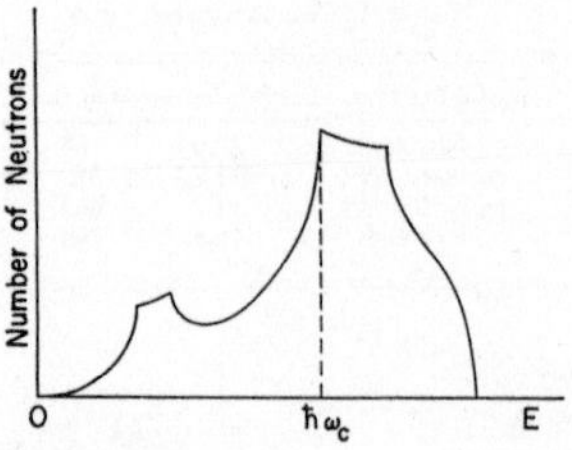

FIG. 1. Schematic shape of the energy distribution of scattered neutrons for long incident wavelength in the case of one-phonon incoherent scattering. E is the outgoing neutron energy, and ω_c a singular frequency of the crystal.

crystal has, therefore, still the shape illustrated in Fig. 1; its singularities in the first derivative are all due to one-phonon processes and are the same in all directions.

For noncubic crystals, the one-phonon incoherent cross section cannot be expressed in terms of the frequency distribution $g(\omega)$ of the crystal. The polarization terms of Eq. (10) cannot be eliminated, and the energy distribution of scattered neutrons varies with direction. In each direction, however, it has the shape illustrated in Fig. 1 and its singularities, unaffected by multiphonon processes occur, as for cubic crystals, at neutron energies E_c independent of direction and related by $E_c = \hbar\omega_c$ to the singular frequencies of the crystal.[33] As mentioned later, the singular frequencies of the crystal do not show up in coherent cross sections. Incoherent scattering of neutrons, for crystals where it is appreciable, seems to be the simplest phenomenon singling out these frequencies, which are important in determining the analytical singularities of the frequency distribution of the crystal.

The foregoing discussion was concerned with single crystals. For inelastic scattering by a powder, according to (12) nothing is changed for a cubic crystal, whereas Eq. (10) must be averaged over orientations in the noncubic cases. As we have seen, however, the singularities in the energy distribution occur at energies independent of direction and are thus retained in the averaging; consequently, the qualitative behavior shown in Fig. 1 remains unchanged.

Turning now to coherent scattering, we note that in one-phonon processes, the neutrons scattered in a given direction have a discrete energy spectrum, corresponding to outgoing wave vectors $\mathbf{k}_1, \mathbf{k}_2, \cdots$. From (11) the cross section per unit solid angle for the outgoing beam of energy $\hbar^2 k_i^2/2m$ is

$$\left(\frac{d\sigma_1^{\mathrm{coh}}}{d\Omega}\right)_{k_i} = \frac{2}{Mk_0} \exp[-\langle(\mathbf{k}_i\cdot\mathbf{u})^2\rangle_{\mathrm{Av}}] \cdot \frac{[\mathbf{k}_i\cdot\mathbf{e}_j(\mathbf{k}_i)]^2}{\{\exp[\beta\omega_j(\mathbf{k}_i)]-1\}\cdot|2k_i-2m\hbar^{-1}d\omega_j/dk|}, \quad (14)$$

where j is the polarization index for which $k_i^2 = 2m\hbar^{-1}\omega_j(\mathbf{k}_i)$, and the derivative of $\omega_j(\mathbf{k})$ is taken at $\mathbf{k} = \mathbf{k}_i$, for fixed orientation of $\mathbf{k}$. For a powder, Eq. (14) must be averaged over all crystal orientations, producing in each direction an outgoing energy distribution continuous over finite intervals.

As mentioned before, multiphonon coherent scattering by a single crystal gives in each direction a continuous energy distribution of outgoing neutrons. Without entering into its detailed discussion, we shall mention that the energy distribution contains again, in general, singularities of type (13), produced by two-phonon processes. In this case the singularities occur at energies unrelated to the singular frequencies of the crystal and varying with the outgoing direction considered. They are thereby distinguishable from the singularities resulting from one-phonon incoherent scattering (which occur at the same energies in all directions), and for a powder they disappear by directional averaging.

To summarize the results obtained in the previous sections, we shall now briefly recall the main properties derived for the angular and energy distribution of inelastically scattered neutrons by single crystals in the limit of long incident wavelengths. In each outgoing direction the energy distribution of scattered neutrons contains a discrete part, resulting from one-phonon coherent scattering, and a continuous part produced by incoherent and multiphonon coherent scattering. The discrete part gives direct information on the crystal vibrations: the outgoing momentum $\mathbf{k}$ verifies Eq. (6) for some j. The continuous part has singularities of the analytical type (13) (with ω replaced by outgoing energy), the shape of which is illustrated in Fig. 1. Some of these singularities occur at energies E_c independent of direction: they are produced by incoherent one-phonon scattering and $\hbar^{-1}E_c$ are the singular frequencies of the crystal. The other singularities, which occur at energies varying with direction, originate from two-phonon coherent scattering.

IV. EXTENSION TO ARBITRARY INCIDENT WAVELENGTHS

The previous considerations are easily extended to the inelastic scattering of neutrons of arbitrary initial momentum $\hbar\mathbf{k}_0$. The only important change is the occurrence of scattering with energy transfer from the neutron to the crystal. Apart from this fact, we shall see that all essential features of the angular and energy distribution are retained. As the discussion runs entirely parallel to that presented in Secs. II and III, we shall make it very brief and restrict ourselves to scattering by a single crystal.

Considering first one-phonon incoherent scattering, we find for the case of energy gain by the neutron that the final wave vector $\mathbf{k}$ has in every direction a length ranging from k_0 to $(k_0^2+2m\hbar^{-1}\omega_{\max})^{\frac{1}{2}}$, whereas for energy loss by the neutron, k ranges from k_0 down

[33] L. Van Hove (to be published).

to 0 if $k_0^2 \leqslant 2m\hbar^{-1}\omega_{\max}$, or to $(k_0^2-2m\hbar^{-1}\omega_{\max})^{\frac{1}{2}}$, if $k_0^2>2m\hbar^{-1}\omega_{\max}$. The differential cross sections are

$$\frac{d\sigma_1^{\text{inc}}}{d\mathbf{k}}=\frac{2}{Mk_0}\exp[-\langle(\boldsymbol{\kappa}\cdot\mathbf{u})^2\rangle_{\text{Av}}]\frac{v_0}{(2\pi)^3}\sum_j\int d\mathbf{q}$$
$$\times\frac{[\boldsymbol{\kappa}\cdot\mathbf{e}_j(\mathbf{q})]^2}{|k^2-k_0^2|}\times\left[\frac{1}{\exp[\beta\omega_j(\mathbf{q})]-1}+\tfrac{1}{2}(1\mp1)\right]$$
$$\cdot\delta[k^2-k_0^2\mp2m\hbar^{-1}\omega_j(\mathbf{q})]. \quad (15)$$

The upper (lower) signs correspond to scattering with energy gain (loss) by the neutron, i.e., to $k>k_0$ ($k<k_0$). The integration is extended over one cell in $\mathbf{k}$ space. $\hbar\boldsymbol{\kappa}$, with $\boldsymbol{\kappa}=\mathbf{k}-\mathbf{k}_0$, is the momentum transfer.

For cubic crystals, Eq. (15) can be simplified with the help of the frequency distribution function $g(\omega)$:

$$\frac{d\sigma_1^{\text{inc}}}{d\mathbf{k}}=\frac{\hbar}{Mmk_0}\exp[-\kappa^2\langle u_0^2\rangle_{\text{Av}}]\times\frac{\kappa^2}{|k^2-k_0^2|}$$
$$\times\left(\frac{1}{\exp(\beta\hbar|k^2-k_0^2|/2m)-1}+\tfrac{1}{2}(1\mp1)\right)$$
$$\times g(\hbar|k^2-k_0^2|/2m). \quad (16)$$

For cubic as well as noncubic crystals, the energy distribution in each outgoing direction has singularities of the type shown in Fig. 1 and Eq. (13) (ω being replaced by the neutron energy), occurring at energies

$$\hbar^2k^2/2m=(\hbar^2k_0^2/2m)\pm\hbar\omega_c,$$

where the ω_c are the singular frequencies of the crystal. Multiphonon incoherent scattering produces no such singularities.

For coherent scattering the situation is again similar to that prevailing in the limiting case of $k_0=0$. For one-phonon processes with energy gain by the neutron, momentum and energy conservation are expressed by the single equation

$$k^2-k_0^2=(2m/\hbar)\omega_j(\mathbf{k}-\mathbf{k}_0), \quad j=1, 2, 3, \quad (17)$$

the obvious generalization of Eq. (6). Equation (17) defines in $\mathbf{k}$ space a surface located between the spheres of radii k_0 and $(k_0^2+2m\hbar^{-1}\omega_{\max})^{\frac{1}{2}}$, centered at the origin. Each radius of the large sphere intersects the surface at least once, in general a finite number of times, and each cell of $\mathbf{k}$ space contained between the two spheres is crossed by the surface [compare properties (i), (ii), (iii) in Sec. II]. Some points of the surface may, however, correspond to a vanishing energy transfer: they give rise to elastic coherent scattering. If we include them, the main feature of the angular and energy distribution is, therefore, retained: neutrons are scattered in each direction with a discrete energy spectrum.

The situation is slightly more complicated for one-phonon coherent scattering with energy loss by the neutron, which is governed by the equation

$$k_0^2-k^2=(2m/\hbar)\omega_j(\mathbf{k}-\mathbf{k}_0). \quad (18)$$

This equation has no solution, and the type of scattering considered is thus impossible when k_0 is smaller than a minimum value $k_0^{(1)}$; it is only for k_0 larger than a value $k_0^{(2)}>k_0^{(1)}$ that neutrons are scattered in *every* direction. Both for $k_0>k_0^{(2)}$ and $k_0<k_0^{(2)}$ the scattered neutrons have a discrete energy spectrum in each outgoing direction. The actual values of $k_0^{(1)}$ and $k_0^{(2)}$ depend on the details of the $\omega_j(\mathbf{q})$ function. It is, however, generally true that

$$k_0^{(1)}\leqslant\pi\tau_0, \quad (19)$$
$$k_0^{(2)}\leqslant(2m\hbar^{-1}\omega_{\max})^{\frac{1}{2}}, \quad (20)$$

where τ_0 is a reciprocal lattice vector of minimum length.[34]

The differential cross section for one-phonon coherent scattering is

$$\frac{d\sigma_1^{\text{coh}}}{d\mathbf{k}}=\frac{2}{Mk_0}\exp[-\langle(\boldsymbol{\kappa}\cdot\mathbf{u})^2\rangle_{\text{Av}}]\sum_j\frac{[\boldsymbol{\kappa}\cdot\mathbf{e}_j(\boldsymbol{\kappa})]^2}{|k^2-k_0^2|}$$
$$\times\left[\frac{1}{\exp[\beta\omega_j(\boldsymbol{\kappa})]-1}+\tfrac{1}{2}(1\mp1)\right]$$
$$\times\delta[k^2-k_0^2\mp2m\hbar^{-1}\omega_j(\boldsymbol{\kappa})], \quad (21)$$

with the same use of double signs as in Eq. (15). An expression similar to (14) is easily deduced from Eq. (21).

There exists for one-phonon coherent scattering a special case deserving a discussion of its own: it is the case when $\mathbf{k}_0$ approximately verifies the Bragg condition

$$|\mathbf{k}_0+2\pi\boldsymbol{\tau}|^2\simeq k_0^2.$$

Inelastic scattering with $\boldsymbol{\kappa}$ nearly equal to $2\pi\boldsymbol{\tau}$ and with small energy transfer is then taking place, with a large differential cross section increasing proportionally to $(k^2-k_0^2)^{-2}\sim|\boldsymbol{\kappa}-2\pi\boldsymbol{\tau}|^{-2}$ when the Bragg condition is approached. This is seen from Eq. (21) by using

$$\exp[\beta\omega_j(\boldsymbol{\kappa})-1]\simeq\beta\omega_j(\boldsymbol{\kappa})=\frac{\beta\hbar}{2m}|k^2-k_0^2|$$
$$\simeq\beta c_j\left(\frac{\boldsymbol{\kappa}-2\pi\boldsymbol{\tau}}{|\boldsymbol{\kappa}-2\pi\boldsymbol{\tau}|}\right)|\boldsymbol{\kappa}-2\pi\boldsymbol{\tau}|$$

The nature of the conservation laws for this special case was discussed by Seeger and Teller;[5] Waller and Fröman[11] gave a detailed treatment of the differential cross section.[34a]

[34] The condition $k_0\geqslant\pi\tau_0$ insures the possibility of the type of scattering under discussion for some but not all orientations of the crystal. It can be written $\lambda_0\leqslant\lambda_B$ where λ_0 is the incident wavelength and $\lambda_B=(2\tau_0)^{-1}$ the Bragg cut-off wavelength. It was first given by Wick (reference 2). The inequality (20) applies to an arbitrary orientation of the crystal.

[34a] *Note added in proof.*—See also the recent paper by R. D. Lowde, Proc. Roy. Soc. (London) **A221**, 206 (1954).

Regarding multiphonon coherent scattering, the general situation is again the same as in the case of long incident wavelength: in each outgoing direction the scattered neutrons have a continuous energy spectrum, with singularities resulting from two-phonon processes and occurring at energies which vary with direction.

It has been the main purpose of this paper to put in evidence the direct relationship between the energy changes of neutrons scattered by a crystal and the dispersion law of the crystal vibrations as expressed by the $\omega_j(\mathbf{q})$ and $g(\omega)$ functions. We hope to have shown that energy measurements on scattered neutrons provide a new approach to the problem of determining these functions from scattering data. While the few experimental data so far available[24,35,36] do not as yet permit an analysis along these lines, the foregoing discussion indicates that further experimental work in this field would be of considerable interest.

[35] B. N. Brockhouse and D. G. Hurst, Phys. Rev. **88**, 542 (1952).

[36] R. D. Lowde, Proc. Phys. Soc. (London) **A65**, 857 (1952) and reference (34a).

PHYSICAL REVIEW VOLUME 95, NUMBER 1 JULY 1, 1954

Correlations in Space and Time and Born Approximation Scattering in Systems of Interacting Particles

Léon Van Hove
Institute for Advanced Study, Princeton, New Jersey
(Received March 16, 1954)

A natural time-dependent generalization is given for the well-known pair distribution function $g(\mathbf{r})$ of systems of interacting particles. The pair distribution in space and time thus defined, denoted by $G(\mathbf{r},t)$, gives rise to a very simple and entirely general expression for the angular and energy distribution of Born approximation scattering by the system. This expression is the natural extension of the familiar Zernike-Prins formula to scattering in which the energy transfers are not negligible compared to the energy of the scattered particle. It is therefore of particular interest for scattering of slow neutrons by general systems of interacting particles: G is then the proper function in terms of which to analyze the scattering data.

After defining the G function and expressing the Born approximation scattering formula in terms of it, the paper studies its general properties and indicates its role for neutron scattering. The qualitative behavior of G for liquids and dense gases is then described and the long-range part exhibited by the function near the critical point is calculated. The explicit expression of G for crystals and for ideal quantum gases is briefly derived and discussed.

I. INTRODUCTION

In two special cases, the first Born approximation for the scattering of x-rays or particles by a system S of interacting particles is known to express the differential cross section in terms of simple density distribution functions for the particles of S.

(i) If S is in a pure quantum state and if this state does not change in the scattering process, the latter is elastic and the differential cross section is expressible in terms of the density distribution $\rho(\mathbf{r})$ for one particle of the system (supposed for simplicity to be composed of identical particles). This applies for example to the elastic scattering of x-rays or electrons by the electrons of an atom.[1,2]

(ii) If the energy transfers occurring in the scattering process are negligible compared to the energy of the scattered photon or particle, the momentum transfer is essentially unique for each scattering angle and the differential cross section per unit angle is expressible in terms of the pair distribution function $g(\mathbf{r})$ of S, which describes the average density distribution as seen from a particle of the system. This is the so-called static approximation which applies, for example, to the sum of elastic and inelastic scattering of x-rays and electrons by the electrons of an atom,[3,4] as well as to that part of the scattering of x-rays by solids, liquids, and gases which leaves the atomic quantum states unchanged.[5,6]

The purpose of the present paper is to show that in Born approximation the scattering cross section is always expressible in terms of a suitably generalized pair distribution function $G(\mathbf{r},t)$ depending on a space vector $\mathbf{r}$ and a time interval t, and to study this function in some detail for a number of systems. For scattering theory this would be of rather academic interest in connection with x-ray scattering, for which the conditions of case (ii) above are usually well fulfilled. The same holds for electrons, for which, however, the Born approximation is of much more limited applicability than for x-rays. For slow neutrons, on the contrary, (wavelength $\gtrsim$1A) now used in a rapidly growing variety of scattering experiments,[7] the energy transfers are usually comparable to or larger than the incident energy, whereas the first Born approximation holds quite well provided the neutron-nucleus interaction is described by means of the Fermi pseudopotential. The need has thus arisen for an improvement of the static approximation for scattering by general systems, and correction terms valid at relatively high neutron energies have been calculated by Placzek and by Wick.[8] We present here a general solution to this problem, applicable at all neutron energies, by describing the Born approximation scattering in terms of the time-dependent pair-distribution function G.

Furthermore, the fact that G has often, even for complicated systems, a number of qualitative properties which are easy to visualize, makes it in many cases a practical tool for the discussion of scattering experiments. Its use for the analysis and interpretation of experimental data has been illustrated elsewhere on the case of slow neutron scattering by ferromagnetic crystals.[9]

The generalized pair-distribution function $G(\mathbf{r},t)$, to which neutron scattering gives direct experimental access, turns out to be a very natural extension of the conventional $g(\mathbf{r})$ function. Independently of its use in scattering theory, it is of genuine interest from the general standpoint of statistical mechanics. Its physical

[1] I. Waller, Z. Physik **51**, 213 (1928).
[2] N. F. Mott, Proc. Roy. Soc. (London) **A127**, 658 (1930).
[3] I. Waller and D. R. Hartree, Proc. Roy. Soc. (London) **A124**, 119 (1929).
[4] P. M. Morse, Physik. Z. **33**, 443 (1932).
[5] I. Waller, dissertation, Uppsala, 1925 (unpublished).
[6] F. Zernike and J. Prins, Z. Physik **41**, 184 (1927); P. Debye and H. Memke, Ergeb. Tech. Röntgenk. **II** (1931).
[7] See, e.g., D. J. Hughes, *Pile Neutron Research* (Addison-Wesley Publishing Company, Cambridge, 1953).
[8] G. Placzek, Phys. Rev. **86**, 377 (1952); G. C. Wick, Phys. Rev. **94**, 1228 (1954).
[9] L. Van Hove, Phys. Rev. **93**, 268 (1954).

meaning is particularly simple in the absence of quantum effects: $G(\mathbf{r},t)$ is then, for the system under consideration, the average density distribution at a time $t'+t$ as seen from a point where a particle passed at time t'. This definition has to be slightly modified for a quantum system, in view of the noncommutativity of the operators representing particle positions at different times. In all cases $G(\mathbf{r},t)$ describes the correlation between the presence of a particle in position $\mathbf{r}'+\mathbf{r}$ at time $t'+t$ and the presence of a particle in position $\mathbf{r}'$ at time t', averaged over $\mathbf{r}'$. It essentially reduces to $g(\mathbf{r})$ for $t=0$.

The concept of time-dependent correlations has already been used in connection with neutron scattering by crystals in unpublished work by Glauber.[10]

The choice of a proper definition of the pair distribution $G(\mathbf{r},t)$ for general quantum-mechanical systems requires some care since it deals with correlations between noncommuting quantities. We will be led to it conveniently by starting from the Born scattering formula and following a natural extension of the well-known procedure to introduce the $g(\mathbf{r})$ function in the static approximation. This is done in the next section, where a number of general properties of $G(\mathbf{r},t)$ are also derived.

The use of the pair distribution G to describe neutron scattering data is indicated in Sec. III. This distribution is the proper function in terms of which to analyze the angular and energy distribution of neutrons scattered by general systems of nuclei, in exactly the same way as the $g(\mathbf{r})$ function is the proper function with which to analyze angular distributions in x-ray scattering. In full analogy with the x-ray case, it is expected to be useful mainly for systems too complicated to allow an explicit calculation of either the scattering or the pair distribution. Liquids and dense gases are clearly the principal examples of such systems.

The advantage of using pair distribution functions for the analysis of scattering data is their simple and intuitively clear physical meaning, which makes their qualitative behavior rather easy to visualize. It is therefore of importance to form as complete a picture of this behavior as possible, and, in absence of sufficient experimental data, it is indicated to discuss systems for which the pair distribution function can be entirely or partly calculated. In the present paper we treat mainly liquids and dense gases, for which the general shape of G is easy to guess and its long-range part near the critical point can be calculated (Sec. IV). We also consider more briefly crystals (Sec. V) and the ideal quantum gases (Sec. VI).

With the experimental data available so far, the best example of the usefulness of pair distributions in space and time for the analysis of scattering data is provided by the case of magnetic scattering of neutrons by ferromagnetic crystals.[11] A short account of the analysis has already been published.[9] The full discussion will appear as a separate paper.

[10] R. J. Glauber (private communication); Phys. Rev. **87**, 189 (1952); Phys. Rev. **94**, 751 (1954), and forthcoming paper.

II. THE PAIR DISTRIBUTION IN SPACE AND TIME

A. Definition

The correct definition of $G(\mathbf{r},t)$ for a general quantum-mechanical system is best inferred from the Born approximation scattering formula. The nature of the scattered particle and the details of the scattering law are, of course, largely irrelevant for this purpose. We will assume that the scattered particle is nonrelativistic and interacts with the particles of the system S through a potential $V(r)$ depending on distance only. For simplicity S is supposed to be composed of one single type of particle. The differential scattering cross section per unit solid angle and unit interval of outgoing energy ϵ of the scattered particle is given in the first Born approximation by

$$\frac{d^2\sigma}{d\Omega d\epsilon}=\frac{m^3}{2\pi^2\hbar^6}\frac{k}{k_0}W(\kappa)\sum_{n_0}p_{n_0}\sum_{n}\left|\left[\sum_{j=1}^{N}\exp(i\boldsymbol{\kappa}\cdot\mathbf{r}_j)\right]_{n_0}^{n}\right|^2 \cdot\delta\left\{k^2-k_0^2+\frac{2m}{\hbar^2}(E_n-E_{n_0})\right\}, \quad (1)$$

where m, $\mathbf{k}_0$, and $\mathbf{k}=\mathbf{k}_0-\boldsymbol{\kappa}$ are the mass and the initial and final wave vectors of the scattered particle. The operators $\mathbf{r}_j$ represent the position vectors of the N particles of the scattering system S, whose initial and final quantum states are labeled by n_0, n and have energies E_{n_0}, E_n, respectively. The bracket $[\cdots]_{n_0}^{n}$ denotes a matrix element and p_{n_0} is the statistical weight of the initial state n_0 (usually the Boltmann factor divided by the sum of states). The function $W(\kappa)$ is defined by

$$W(\kappa)=\left\{\int\exp(i\boldsymbol{\kappa}\cdot\mathbf{r})V(r)d\mathbf{r}\right\}^2.$$

If, besides the momentum transfer $\hbar\boldsymbol{\kappa}$, we introduce the energy transfer

$$\hbar\omega=\hbar^2(k_0^2-k^2)/2m,$$

Eq. (1) can be written

$$\frac{d^2\sigma}{d\Omega d\epsilon}=A\,\mathcal{S}(\boldsymbol{\kappa},\omega), \quad (2)$$

$$A=\frac{m^2}{4\pi^2\hbar^5}\frac{k}{k_0}W(\kappa), \quad (3)$$

$$\mathcal{S}(\boldsymbol{\kappa},\omega)=\sum_{n_0}p_{n_0}\sum_{n}\left|\left[\sum_{j=1}^{N}\exp(i\boldsymbol{\kappa}\cdot\mathbf{r}_j)\right]_{n_0}^{n}\right|^2 \cdot\delta\left\{\omega+\frac{E_{n_0}-E_n}{\hbar}\right\}, \quad (4)$$

[11] H. Palevsky and D. J. Hughes, Phys. Rev. **92**, 202 (1953); G. L. Squires (to be published). We are indebted to these authors for communication of their results before publication.

where, for given momentum and energy transfers, $\mathcal{S}(\boldsymbol{\kappa},\omega)$ is independent of the mass and energy of the scattered particle as well as of the interaction potential, whereas A depends only on the properties of the individual particles of S. This separation of two factors in the differential cross section is quite general; it is an immediate consequence of the use of momentum and energy transfers as independent variables.

It is now an easy matter to express in terms of a pair distribution the function $\mathcal{S}(\boldsymbol{\kappa},\omega)$ which, in the first Born approximation, contains the scattering properties of the system S. If it is remembered that in the static approximation [case (ii) of the introduction] the differential cross section per unit solid angle,

$$\frac{d\sigma}{d\Omega}=\int\frac{d^2\sigma}{d\Omega d\epsilon}d\epsilon, \tag{5}$$

is essentially, as a function of $\boldsymbol{\kappa}$, the Fourier transform over $\mathbf{r}$ of the $g(\mathbf{r})$ function, it is natural to expect $\mathcal{S}(\boldsymbol{\kappa},\omega)$ to be essentially the Fourier transform over $\mathbf{r}$ and t of the pair distribution in space and time $G(\mathbf{r},t)$. We therefore define the latter through the equivalent equations:

$$\mathcal{S}(\boldsymbol{\kappa},\omega)=(2\pi)^{-1}N\int\exp[i(\boldsymbol{\kappa}\cdot\mathbf{r}-\omega t)]\cdot G(\mathbf{r},t)d\mathbf{r}dt, \tag{6}$$

or

$$G(\mathbf{r},t)=(2\pi)^{-3}N^{-1}\int\exp[i(\omega t-\boldsymbol{\kappa}\cdot\mathbf{r})]\cdot\mathcal{S}(\boldsymbol{\kappa},\omega)d\boldsymbol{\kappa}d\omega. \tag{7}$$

The coefficient $(2\pi)^{-1}N$ in (6) is introduced for convenience. It makes $G(\mathbf{r},t)$ independent of N and asymptotically equal to the number density for the large systems of statistical mechanics, in which the limit $N\to\infty$ is to be taken. From Eqs. (4) and (7) one gets, successively,

$$G(\mathbf{r},t)=(2\pi)^{-3}N^{-1}\sum_{n0}p_{n0}\sum_{n}\sum_{l,j=1}^{N}\int d\boldsymbol{\kappa}\exp(-i\boldsymbol{\kappa}\cdot\mathbf{r})\cdot[\exp(-i\boldsymbol{\kappa}\cdot\mathbf{r}_l)]_n{}^{n0}\cdot\exp(iE_nt/\hbar)\cdot[\exp(i\boldsymbol{\kappa}\cdot\mathbf{r}_j)]_{n0}{}^{n}\cdot\exp(-iE_{n0}t/\hbar), \tag{8}$$

$$G(\mathbf{r},t)=(2\pi)^{-3}N^{-1}\sum_{l,j=1}^{N}\int d\boldsymbol{\kappa}\exp(-i\boldsymbol{\kappa}\cdot\mathbf{r})\cdot\langle\exp\{-i\boldsymbol{\kappa}\cdot\mathbf{r}_l(0)\}\cdot\exp\{i\boldsymbol{\kappa}\cdot\mathbf{r}_j(t)\}\rangle.$$

The last formula contains the Heisenberg operator $\mathbf{r}_j(t)$, defined for all j and t by

$$\mathbf{r}_j(t)=\exp(itH/\hbar)\mathbf{r}_j\exp(-itH/\hbar),$$

where H is the Hamiltonian of the system.[12] The bracket $\langle\cdots\rangle$ stands for the average of the expectation value of the enclosed operator:

$$\langle\cdots\rangle=\sum_{n0}p_{n0}[\cdots]_{n0}{}^{n0}. \tag{9}$$

With the help of the convolution formula for the Fourier transform of an (ordered) product, we obtain finally the expression

$$G(\mathbf{r},t)=N^{-1}\left\langle\sum_{l,j=1}^{N}\int d\mathbf{r}'\cdot\delta(\mathbf{r}+\mathbf{r}_l(0)-\mathbf{r}')\delta(\mathbf{r}'-\mathbf{r}_j(t))\right\rangle, \tag{10}$$

which defines $G(\mathbf{r},t)$ entirely in terms of space and time variables, with the proper ordering of the operators belonging to different times.

For $t=0$, all operators commute and the integration can be carried out, leading to

$$G(\mathbf{r},0)=N^{-1}\langle\sum_{l,j=1}^{N}\delta(\mathbf{r}+\mathbf{r}_l(0)-r_j(0))\rangle,$$

or

$$G(\mathbf{r},0)=\delta(\mathbf{r})+N^{-1}\sum_{l\neq j}\langle\delta(\mathbf{r}+\mathbf{r}_l-\mathbf{r}_j)\rangle=\delta(\mathbf{r})+g(\mathbf{r}), \tag{11}$$

according to the familiar definition of the conventional pair distribution $g(\mathbf{r})$. Similarly, in the scattering formula, if the incident energy is sufficiently large compared to the energy transfers, the momentum transfer for a given scattering angle is independent of the outgoing energy, and the differential cross section per unit solid angle becomes

$$\frac{d\sigma}{d\Omega}=\int\frac{d^2\sigma}{d\Omega d\epsilon}d\epsilon=\hbar A\int\mathcal{S}(\boldsymbol{\kappa},\omega)d\omega$$

$$=\hbar AN\int\exp(i\boldsymbol{\kappa}\cdot\mathbf{r})\delta(t)G(\mathbf{r},t)d\mathbf{r}dt$$

$$=[m/(2\pi\hbar^2)]^2NW(\kappa)\left\{1+\int\exp(i\boldsymbol{\kappa}\cdot\mathbf{r})g(\mathbf{r})d\mathbf{r}\right\},$$

the familiar formula in the static approximation. Just as measurement of $d\sigma/d\Omega$ provides an experimental determination of $g(\mathbf{r})$ in the latter approximation, the pair distribution in space and time $G(\mathbf{r},t)$ is experimentally accessible through measurements of $d^2\sigma/d\Omega d\epsilon$.

B. General Properties

We will now discuss a few immediate properties of the pair distribution in space and time. $G(\mathbf{r},t)$, which is in general complex, has the Hermitian symmetry,

$$G(-\mathbf{r},-t)=\{G(\mathbf{r},t)\}^*, \tag{12}$$

[12] The introduction of a time variable to eliminate the δ function in Eq. (1) and the subsequent consideration of time-dependent operators have become familiar in scattering theory. See, e.g., A. Akhiezer and I. Pomeranchuk, J. Phys. (U.S.S.R.) 11, 167 (1947); G. C. Wick, reference 8.

easily derived as follows: from (10),

$$\{G(\mathbf{r},t)\}^* = N^{-1}\Big\langle \sum_{l,j} \int d\mathbf{r}'\delta(\mathbf{r}'-\mathbf{r}_j(t))\delta(\mathbf{r}+\mathbf{r}_l(0)-\mathbf{r}')\Big\rangle$$

$$= N^{-1}\Big\langle \sum_{l,j} \int d\mathbf{r}''\delta(\mathbf{r}-\mathbf{r}_j(t)+\mathbf{r}'')\delta(\mathbf{r}_l(0)-\mathbf{r}'')\Big\rangle$$

$$= N^{-1}\Big\langle \sum_{l,j} \int d\mathbf{r}''\delta(\mathbf{r}-\mathbf{r}_j(0)+\mathbf{r}'') \times\delta(\mathbf{r}_l(-t)-\mathbf{r}'')\Big\rangle$$

$$= G(-\mathbf{r}, -t).$$

In the second step the integration variable is $\mathbf{r}''=\mathbf{r}'-\mathbf{r}$; the third step uses the invariance of the expectation value under the unitary transformation $\exp(itH/\hbar)$, whereas the last is based on the even character of the δ function. Property equation (12) is equivalent with the fact that $\mathcal{S}(\boldsymbol{\kappa},\omega)$ is a real-valued function.

Complex values of $G(\mathbf{r},t)$ reflect quantum properties of the system. Indeed, under classical conditions, the operators in (10) reduce to commuting c numbers and G takes the real, positive value:

$$G(\mathbf{r},t) = N^{-1}\langle \sum_{l,j} \delta(\mathbf{r}+\mathbf{r}_l(0)-\mathbf{r}_j(t))\rangle.$$

As announced in the introduction, it is seen to describe the average density distribution at time $t'+t$ as seen from a point which was occupied by a particle at time t'; this distribution is independent of t', here given the value 0.

When quantum effects are present,—they are for any actual system in certain ranges of r and t values—, G is complex and the simple physical interpretation given above cannot hold in view of the noncommutativity of particle positions at different times. How this noncommutativity enters into the expression of G can best be seen by introducing suitable density operators. Let us consider in space a volume element ΔV centered at point $\mathbf{r}$ and define the Heisenberg operator $\Delta P(\mathbf{r},t)$ satisfying $\Delta P(\mathbf{r},t)\psi=\psi$ for all states ψ of the system for which, with probability one, at least one particle is in ΔV at time t, and $\Delta P(\mathbf{r},t)\psi=0$ for all states such that, with probability one, no particle is in ΔV at time t. One has, in the limit of infinitesimal ΔV,

$$\Delta P(\mathbf{r},t)/\Delta V = \sum_j \delta(\mathbf{r}-\mathbf{r}_j(t)),$$

and thus, taking identical volume elements around each point,

$$G(\mathbf{r},t) = N^{-1}\Delta V^{-2}\int d\mathbf{r}''\langle \Delta P(\mathbf{r}'',0)\cdot\Delta P(\mathbf{r}''+\mathbf{r},t)\rangle. \quad (13)$$

For a system homogeneous in space (like a gas or a liquid), enclosed in a volume $V=N/\rho$, we get the very simple formula:

$$G(\mathbf{r},t) = \rho^{-1}\Delta V^{-2}\langle \Delta P(\mathbf{r}'',0)\cdot\Delta P(\mathbf{r}''+\mathbf{r},t)\rangle, \quad (14)$$

where $\mathbf{r}''$ is an arbitrary point in V. From Eq. (13) or (14) follows immediately that the real part of G is related to the average value of the symmetrized product,

$$\tfrac{1}{2}\{\Delta P(\mathbf{r}'',0)\cdot\Delta P(\mathbf{r}''+\mathbf{r},t)+\Delta P(\mathbf{r}''+\mathbf{r},t)\cdot\Delta P(\mathbf{r}'',0)\},$$

and is therefore the natural extension to quantum systems of the classical, real-valued, pair distribution function in space and time, whereas the imaginary part reduces essentially to the average value of the commutator of $\Delta P(\mathbf{r}'',0)$ and $\Delta P(\mathbf{r}''+\mathbf{r},t)$.

In the case of systems for which the symmetric or antisymmetric character of the wave function is of little importance, and which can thus be regarded as composed of distinguishable particles (Boltzmann statistics), the G function splits naturally into a part G_s describing the correlation between positions of one and the same particle at different times, and a part G_d referring to pairs of distinct particles (the subscripts stand for "self" and "distinct," respectively). They are defined as follows:

$$G_s(\mathbf{r},t) = N^{-1}\Big\langle \sum_{j=1}^{N} \int d\mathbf{r}'\cdot\delta(\mathbf{r}+\mathbf{r}_j(0)-\mathbf{r}') \times\delta(\mathbf{r}'-\mathbf{r}_j(t))\Big\rangle, \quad (15)$$

$$G_d(\mathbf{r},t) = N^{-1}\Big\langle \sum_{j\neq l=1}^{N} \int d\mathbf{r}'\cdot\delta(\mathbf{r}+\mathbf{r}_l(0)-\mathbf{r}') \times\delta(\mathbf{r}'-\mathbf{r}_j(t))\Big\rangle. \quad (16)$$

They verify separately the symmetry condition (12) and equations of type Eq. (13) with density operators $\Delta P_j/\Delta V$ defined for individual particles. For $t=0$, they reduce to

$$G_s(\mathbf{r},0)=\delta(\mathbf{r}),\quad G_d(\mathbf{r},0)=g(\mathbf{r}). \quad (17)$$

For the systems of large numbers of particles studied in statistical mechanics, solids, liquids, or gases, the pair distribution $G(\mathbf{r},t)$, in the definition [Eqs. (9) and (10)] of which the statistical weights p_{n0} must be given the Boltmann value

$$p_{n0}=Z^{-1}\exp(-\beta E_{n0}),\quad Z=\sum_{n0}\exp(-\beta E_{n0}) \quad (18)$$

(β^{-1} = temperature T multiplied by Boltzmann constant k_B), has especially simple asymptotic expressions for large r or $|t|$. For such systems, the particles in regions widely separated in space are statistically independent, and so are the properties of the system at two widely distant times. For sufficiently large r or large $|t|$, we can thus write asymptotically

$$\langle \sum_{l,j=1}^{N} \delta(\mathbf{r}+\mathbf{r}(0)-\mathbf{r}')\delta(\mathbf{r}'-\mathbf{r}_j(t))\rangle \simeq \rho(\mathbf{r}'-\mathbf{r})\rho(\mathbf{r}'),$$

where

$$\rho(\mathbf{r}')=\langle\sum_{j=1}^{N}\delta(\mathbf{r}'-\mathbf{r}_j(t))\rangle \tag{19}$$

is the average density at point $\mathbf{r}'$, independent of the time t. Hence, from Eq. (10), we can write the asymptotic formula

$$G(\mathbf{r},t)\simeq N^{-1}\int d\mathbf{r}'\cdot\rho(\mathbf{r}'-\mathbf{r})\rho(\mathbf{r}'), \tag{20}$$

the right-hand side of which is the often considered autocorrelated density.[13] In particular, for an homogeneous system, $\rho(\mathbf{r}')$ is a constant, the number density $\rho=N/V$ (V volume of the system), and Eq. (20) reduces to

$$G(\mathbf{r},t)\simeq\rho. \tag{21}$$

It is the difference between G and its asymptotic value (20) which represents the correlation between pairs of particles. The instantaneous part of this correlation is contained in $G(\mathbf{r},0)=\delta(\mathbf{r})+g(\mathbf{r})$ and is well known from the study of the familiar $g(\mathbf{r})$ function. The interest of G for $t\neq 0$ is to describe in addition its time dependence: if we consider a given, fixed point of space through which a particle passes at time 0, the density distribution of the system is disturbed around this point not only at time 0, but before and afterwards. The average time variation of this disturbance is represented by the G function. As formally expressed by Eq. (20), the disturbance is negligible far from the fixed point at all times, and everywhere in the system long before and long after time 0. Except in the case of long-range order or under critical conditions, to be discussed later on, the size and duration of the disturbance are characterized by a length R_0 and a time T_0 of microscopic dimensions such that Eq. (20) holds for all t if $r\gg R_0$ and for all r if $|t|\gg T_0$. R_0 is the *range* of the pair correlation, T_0 its *relaxation time*. To establish from first principles the existence of R_0 and T_0, and, *a fortiori*, to calculate G in terms of intermolecular forces, are difficult problems of statistical mechanics, unsolved except in very special cases. The relaxation time T_0 in particular is obviously related to the irreversible return of a locally perturbed system to equilibrium, and thus depends on the ergodic properties of the system. Such problems will not be touched upon here. We hope to have shown, however, that quite apart from its interest for scattering theory, the pair distribution in space and time is an important extension of the conventional $g(\mathbf{r})$ function from the standpoint of general statistical mechanics.

The separation of G into its asymptotic value and a correlation term G',

$$G'(\mathbf{r},t)=G(\mathbf{r},t)-N^{-1}\int d\mathbf{r}'\cdot\rho(\mathbf{r}'-\mathbf{r})\rho(\mathbf{r}'), \tag{22}$$

has also a simple significance for scattering. Insertion in (6) gives

$$\mathcal{S}(\boldsymbol{\kappa},\omega)=\delta(\omega)\cdot\left|\int \exp(i\boldsymbol{\kappa}\cdot\mathbf{r})\cdot\rho(\mathbf{r})d\mathbf{r}\right|^2 + (2\pi)^{-1}N\int \exp[i(\boldsymbol{\kappa}\cdot\mathbf{r}-\omega t)]\cdot G'(\mathbf{r},t)d\mathbf{r}dt. \tag{23}$$

The first term of the right-hand side represents elastic scattering ($\omega=0$); for an homogeneous system of large dimensions it reduces to $N\rho\delta(\omega)\delta(\boldsymbol{\kappa})$, i.e., to forward elastic scattering, which in the first Born approximation is indistinguishable from the unscattered beam. The second term represents inelastic scattering: since G' tends to zero for r and $|t|\to\infty$, the energy distribution has no peak of form $\delta(\omega)$ in any scattering direction, nor has its angular distribution any peak of form $\delta(\boldsymbol{\kappa})$ in the forward direction. In some cases, however, the convergence of G' to zero may be slow. This will then produce, through the Fourier transform in the last term of (23), singularities of weaker type in the angular and energy distribution of inelastically scattered particles. A simple example of this situation is provided by slow neutron scattering in crystals and will be discussed in Sec. V.

The range R_0 and relaxation time T_0 determine the orders of magnitude $\hbar/R_0$, $\hbar/T_0$ of average momentum and energy transfers in those scattering processes which are appreciably affected by the collective properties of the system S. Let us consider incident particles with momentum of order $\hbar/R_0$, and let us determine under which condition the values of G for $|t|\sim T_0$ make an important contribution to the scattering. The condition is that the angle of scattering depends appreciably on both momentum and energy transfers [if it depends essentially on momentum transfer alone, the static approximation applies and the scattering depends on $G(\mathbf{r},0)$ only]. It requires that the spread $\hbar\Delta k$ in the length $\hbar k$ of the final momentum, due to energy transfers of order $\hbar/T_0$, is at least comparable to the momentum transfers $\hbar/R_0$. Since $\Delta k\sim(vR_0)^{-1}$, where v is the velocity of the incident particle, the condition is $v\lesssim R_0/T_0$ or $T_1\gtrsim T_0$, where T_1 is the time R_0/v in which the incident particle travels over a correlation range. In the latter form, the physical meaning of the condition is obvious: the time variation of G affects the total scattering and angular distribution only for a particle spending at least a time of order T_0 over a correlation length R_0. If on the contrary $T_1\ll T_0$, the scattering is not affected by the values of G for $|t|\sim T_0$. Apart from the distribution of outgoing energies, it is then entirely determined by the value of G for $|t|\ll T_0$, and the static approximation gives a good description of the

[13] For large $|t|$, Eq. (20) is valid also for systems with a small number of particles if the initial state is a pure quantum state, nondegenerate in energy. The asymptotic convergence for $|t|\to\infty$ may then, however, hold only in the mean, as is the case for a harmonic oscillator.

effect of collective properties of S on the scattering, in the sense that $d\sigma/d\Omega$ can be calculated by replacing $G(\mathbf{r},t)$ by $G_{id}(\mathbf{r},t)+G(\mathbf{r},0)-G_{id}(\mathbf{r},0)$, where G_{id} is the pair distribution function for an ideal gas of same density and temperature as S.

For incident particles of wavelength $\sim R_0$, the ratio T_1/T_0 is essentially equal to the ratio of average energy transfer to incident energy. A very crude estimate of R_0 and T_0 for actual substances, solids or liquids at average temperatures, gives $R_0\sim 10^{-8}$ cm, $T_0\sim 10^{-13}$ sec, and thus $T_1/T_0\sim 10^5/v$ if the incident velocity v is measured in cm sec^{-1}. This gives $T_1/T_0\sim 10^{-6}$ for photons of arbitrary wavelength, and $T_1/T_0\sim 1$ for neutrons of wavelength around 1 A or somewhat larger, i.e., exactly of the right order R_0 for which collective effects on scattering are most conveniently observed. For electrons of wavelength around 1 A, one finds $T_1/T_0\sim 10^{-4}$.

Before closing this section, we mention an extension of the $G(\mathbf{r},t)$ function to systems of identical particles with spin, to be used later in connection with spin-dependent scattering. If a_j is an operator depending on the spin of the jth particle, the same for each particle, a spin-dependent pair correlation is defined by

$$\Gamma(\mathbf{r},t)=N^{-1}\Big\langle\sum_{l,j=1}^{N}\int d\mathbf{r}'\cdot a_l(0)\delta(\mathbf{r}+\mathbf{r}_l(0)-\mathbf{r}') \times a_j(t)\delta(\mathbf{r}'-\mathbf{r}_j(t))\Big\rangle, \quad (24)$$

in terms of the Heisenberg operators,

$$a_j(t)=\exp(itH/\hbar)a_j\exp(-itH/\hbar).$$

For a system of Boltzmann particles with spin-independent Hamiltonian H and for the thermal distribution (18), there is no correlation between spins nor between spins and positions. Using the definitions (15) and (16) we then find

$$\Gamma(\mathbf{r},t)=\langle a^2\rangle_{\mathrm{Av}}G_s(\mathbf{r},t)+\langle a\rangle_{\mathrm{Av}}^2G_d(\mathbf{r},t), \quad (25)$$

where a is any of the a_j's and $\langle\cdots\rangle_{\mathrm{Av}}$ denotes an average over the spin states of the corresponding particle. Correlations involving the spins can be produced either by the symmetry requirements of the wave functions (Bose-Einstein and Fermi-Dirac particles) or by spin interactions. The first case is illustrated in Sec. VI. The second case occurs in ferromagnetic substances and will be discussed in a separate paper.

The extension of the foregoing considerations to systems composed of different types of particles is straightforward and will not be given here.

III. NUCLEAR SCATTERING OF SLOW NEUTRONS

As mentioned before, it is for the scattering of slow neutrons that use of the pair distributions in space and time is of most practical interest. We consider in the present section scattering due to the nuclear interaction between neutrons and the nuclei of the scattering system S. If the true interaction is replaced by the corresponding Fermi pseudopotential,

$$V(r)=(2\pi a\hbar^2/m)\delta(r),$$

where m is the neutron mass and a the scattering length of the nuclei assumed all identical, the Born approximation formula can be applied.[14] Equations (2), (3), and (6) give then, for the cross section of S,

$$\frac{d^2\sigma}{d\Omega d\epsilon}=\frac{a^2N}{2\pi\hbar}\frac{k}{k_0}\int\exp[i(\boldsymbol{\kappa}\cdot\mathbf{r}-\omega t)]\cdot G(\mathbf{r},t)d\mathbf{r}dt. \quad (26)$$

If the nuclei of S have a nonvanishing spin, this equation assumes a to be spin independent. For nuclei with a spin-dependent scattering length, or for nuclei belonging to different isotopes (the mass differences being neglected), Eq. (26) is simply replaced by

$$\frac{d^2\sigma}{d\Omega d\epsilon}=\frac{N}{2\pi\hbar}\cdot\frac{k}{k_0}\int\exp[i(\boldsymbol{\kappa}\cdot\mathbf{r}-\omega t)]\cdot\Gamma(\mathbf{r},t)d\mathbf{r}dt,$$

with the spin- or isotope-dependent scattering lengths a_j to be used in the definition (24) of Γ.[14] In most cases the nuclei can be treated as Boltzmann particles and the spin or isotope disorder can be considered perfect, so that Eq. (25) applies, and, remembering $G=G_s+G_d$, we obtain

$$\frac{d^2\sigma}{d\Omega d\epsilon}=\frac{d^2\sigma_{\mathrm{coh}}}{d\Omega d\epsilon}+\frac{d^2\sigma_{\mathrm{inc}}}{d\Omega d\epsilon}, \quad (27)$$

$$\frac{d^2\sigma_{\mathrm{coh}}}{d\Omega d\epsilon}=\frac{\langle a\rangle_{\mathrm{Av}}^2N}{2\pi\hbar}\frac{k}{k_0}\int\exp[i(\boldsymbol{\kappa}\cdot\mathbf{r}-\omega t)]\cdot G(\mathbf{r},t)d\mathbf{r}dt, \quad (28)$$

$$\frac{d^2\sigma_{\mathrm{inc}}}{d\Omega d\epsilon}=\frac{\{\langle a^2\rangle_{\mathrm{Av}}-\langle a\rangle_{\mathrm{Av}}^2\}N}{2\pi\hbar}\frac{k}{k_0}\int\exp[i(\boldsymbol{\kappa}\cdot\mathbf{r}-\omega t)] \cdot G_s(\mathbf{r},t)d\mathbf{r}dt. \quad (29)$$

Equations (28) and (29) are the so-called coherent and incoherent scattering cross sections.

The separation Eq. (23) of elastic and inelastic scattering applies to Eq. (28). A similar separation can be performed for Eq. (29) by considering the limit of G_s for $|t|\rightarrow\infty$. In the static approximation we get, as in Sec. II,

$$d\sigma_{\mathrm{coh}}/d\Omega=\langle a\rangle_{\mathrm{Av}}^2N\left\{1+\int\exp(i\boldsymbol{\kappa}\cdot\mathbf{r})g(\mathbf{r})d\mathbf{r}\right\}, \quad (30)$$

$$d\sigma_{\mathrm{inc}}/d\Omega=\{\langle a^2\rangle_{\mathrm{Av}}-\langle a\rangle_{\mathrm{Av}}^2\}N. \quad (31)$$

The incoherent cross section no longer depends on the structure of S. Equation (30), identical to the Zernike-

[14] The relevant information on slow neutron scattering will be found, for example, in J. M. Cassels, Progr. Nuclear Phys. 1, 185 (1950).

Prins formula for x-ray scattering, has often been used before in connection with slow neutrons.[15–19]

The physical interest of Eqs. (28) and (29) is entirely similar to that of the familiar Eq. (30). It mainly concerns systems for which a complete calculation of pair distributions in terms of elementary forces cannot be carried out. Indeed, whenever an explicit calculation is possible, it leads to the differential cross sections as directly as to the pair distributions. For more complicated systems, however, like liquids or dense gases, the pair distributions, dealing with two-particle configurations in space and time, are much easier to visualize than the cross sections, and a qualitative prediction of their behavior is almost always possible, thus providing great help in understanding the main features of the scattering. For such systems, on the other hand, the pair distribution is the proper quantity in terms of which to interpret the scattering data, and since it contains very important information on the local structure of the system, its experimental determination is desirable. Equations (28), (29) provide the basis for such a determination.

Complete measurements of $d^2\sigma/d\Omega d\epsilon$, i.e., of the angular and energy distribution of scattered neutrons, will provide a direct determination of G or G_s by inversion of a 4-dimensional Fourier integral (2-dimensional for isotropic systems). At present, for intensity reasons, energy distributions of scattered neutrons are still difficult to observe, even when they spread over wide ranges. Progress will, however, undoubtedly be made in this direction[20] and it is to be hoped that complete sets of experimental values for $d^2\sigma/d\Omega d\epsilon$ will eventually become available.

A simpler but much less direct and less satisfactory approach to the experimental study of G or G_s can be made by measuring transmissions (i.e., total cross sections) or angular distributions in their dependence on the incident wavelength λ_0. For angular distributions, the contribution to the scattering of values of G or G_s with $t\neq 0$ will manifest itself through the fact that the differential cross section

$$\int (d^2\sigma/d\Omega d\epsilon) f(\epsilon) d\epsilon, \tag{32}$$

where $f(\epsilon)$ is determined by the detector used, does no longer depend on λ_0 and on the scattering angle θ through the single combination $\lambda_0^{-1}\sin(\theta/2)$, as it does in the static approximation with $f(\epsilon)$ constant. Since a quantity like Eq. (32) has a complicated functional expression in G or G_s, the analysis of its experimental values is bound to be much more difficult than it would be for $d^2\sigma/d\Omega d\epsilon$, and the choice of a detailed procedure would require careful consideration.

The next sections deal with the properties of G and G_s for special systems. Their aim is to form a more accurate picture of the behavior to be expected for these functions and to illustrate the correspondence between some of their properties and simple features of the angular and energy distributions obtained in scattering.

IV. LIQUIDS AND DENSE GASES

The discussion of pair distributions in space and time for liquids and dense gases presents the same difficulties as the corresponding discussion for the instantaneous pair distribution $g(\mathbf{r})$. Although the general behavior of the distribution functions can easily and safely be guessed, no reliable method has yet been found to calculate them in terms of the intermolecular forces.[21] We will therefore limit ourselves to a description of their most immediate properties.

Except for the case of substances of light atomic mass taken at very low temperatures, like liquid helium for example, the particles in a liquid or a dense gas have a mean de Broglie wavelength $\lambda_B=\hbar(2Mk_BT)^{-\frac{1}{2}}$ small compared to the distance between particles or, what amounts to the same, to the range of interatomic forces. M is the mass of the particles in the system. Under these conditions, the distinction between $G_s(r,t)$ and $G_d(r,t)=G-G_s$ is possible and these functions, which are independent of the direction of $\mathbf{r}$, verify, as already mentioned,

$$G_s(r,0)=\delta(\mathbf{r}),\quad G_d(r,0)=g(r), \tag{33}$$

$$\lim_{r'\to\infty} G_s(r',t)=\lim_{|t'|\to\infty} G_s(r,t')=0, \tag{34}$$

$$\lim_{r'\to\infty} G_d(r',t)=\lim_{|t'|\to\infty} G_d(r,t')=\rho, \tag{35}$$

where ρ is the number density. Except in the neighborhood of the critical point, the convergence in Eqs. (34) and (35) takes place over a length R_0 of the order of intermolecular distances and a time T_0 of the order of the time needed by an average particle of the system to travel over a distance R_0. T_0 is essentially identical with the Debye relaxation time.

Under the same condition of a mean de Broglie wavelength small compared to interatomic distances ($\lambda_B\ll R_0$), no quantum effects will manifest themselves in G_d, which deals with pairs of particles separated by distances of order R_0, and $G_d(r,t)$ is thus a real-valued, positive function, even in t. The situation is slightly dif-

---

[15] O. Chamberlain, Phys. Rev. **77**, 305 (1950).
[16] Placzek, Nijboer, and Van Hove, Phys. Rev. **82**, 392 (1951).
[17] L. Goldstein, Phys. Rev. **84**, 466 (1951).
[18] P. C. Sharrah and G. P. Smith, J. Chem. Phys. **21**, 288 (1953).
[19] Henshaw, Hurst, and Pope, Phys. Rev. **92**, 1229 (1953).
[20] Crude information on energy distributions of neutrons scattered by solids has been obtained by P. Egelstaff, Nature **168**, 290 (1951); B. N. Brockhouse and D. G. Hurst, Phys. Rev. **88**, 542 (1952); R. D. Lowde, Proc. Roy. Soc. (London) **A221**, 206 (1954).

[21] The determination of pair distribution functions based on the superposition approximation of Kirkwood, J. Chem. Phys. **3**, 300 (1935), cannot be considered reliable for dense systems. It has been discussed for a gas of hard spheres by B. R. A. Nijboer and L. Van Hove, Phys. Rev. **85**, 777 (1952), and by B. R. A. Nijboer and R. Fieschi, Physica **19**, 545 (1953).

ferent for $G_s(r,t)$, which for very small times

$$|t|\sim\hbar/k_BT\sim(\lambda_B/R_0)T_0,$$

is entirely concentrated in the region $r\sim\lambda_B$ where quantum effects are appreciable. For small displacements of this order, however, the potential acting on a particle is practically constant, so that the ideal gas value can be adopted for G_s:

$$G_s(r,t)\simeq\{2\pi t(k_BTt-i\hbar)/M\}^{-3/2}\times\exp\{-Mr^2/[2t(k_BTt-i\hbar)]\}.$$

This holds for $|t|\ll T_0$. For larger times, the form of G_s is affected by the interatomic forces, but quantum effects become negligible, and G_s thus also becomes real-valued positive and even in t. Characteristic shapes of G_s and G_d are given in Fig. 1 for three ranges of t values: $|t|\ll T_0$ (the curve for G_s is to be understood as representing the real part of the function if $|t|\lesssim\hbar/k_BT$), $|t|\sim T_0$, and $|t|\gg T_0$.

For quantum liquids like liquid helium at low temperature the situation is, of course, entirely different. The distribution function G has complex values for all nonvanishing times. We will not try to make a guess at its theoretical shape but want to stress the interest of its experimental determination.

After these general considerations, let us return to the case of the so-called classical liquids ($\lambda_B\ll R_0$) which will now be studied in the neighborhood of the critical point. When critical conditions are approached, the

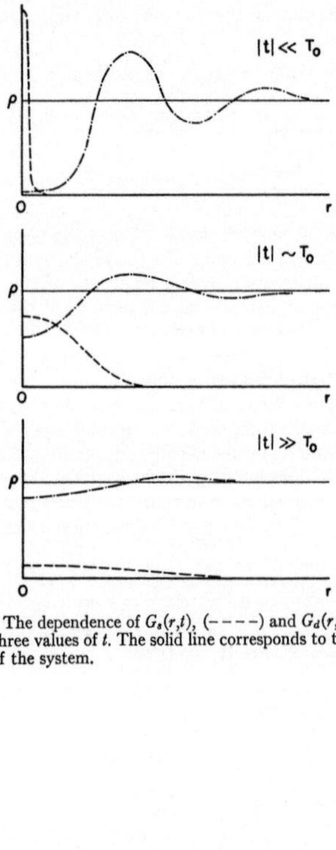

FIG. 1. The dependence of $G_s(r,t)$, (– – – –) and $G_d(r,t)$, (–·–·–) on r for three values of t. The solid line corresponds to the average density of the system.

qualitative behavior of G_s is not expected to be greatly modified. G_d, however, is known to exhibit long-range correlations resulting from the occurrence in the system of spontaneous density fluctuations of macroscopic size. In contrast with the short-range part of the pair distribution, these long-range phenomena can be explicitly studied, at least for temperatures T slightly above the critical temperature T_c, by the methods of macroscopic fluctuation theory. The applicability of such methods is actually not restricted to the neighborhood of the critical point. They make a general study possible for the scattering from macroscopic density fluctuations, by permitting the calculation of the value and the time dependence of the Fourier components of G_d:

$$\int\{G_d(r,t)-\rho\}\exp(i\boldsymbol{\kappa}\cdot\mathbf{r})d\mathbf{r},$$

for macroscopic κ^{-1}. This question, studied by Landau and Placzek for light scattering,[22] will not be treated in full generality in the present paper, where we limit ourselves to the more special case of critical fluctuations.

The behavior of $g(r)=G_d(r,0)$ near the critical point, for $T>T_c$ and for r large compared to the intermolecular distance, has been determined by Ornstein and Zernike.[23] It is given by

$$G_d(r,0)\simeq\rho+(4\pi r_0^2r)^{-1}e^{-\kappa_0r},\quad r\gg r_0, \tag{36}$$

where r_0 is a length slowly varying with temperature and density, of the order of the range of the forces, with value 1 at the critical point, and κ_0 is the reciprocal length

$$\kappa_0=r_0^{-1}(\rho k_BT\chi_T)^{-\frac{1}{2}}, \tag{37}$$

defined in terms of the isothermal compressibility $\chi_T=\rho^{-1}(\partial\rho/\partial p)_T$. Equation (36) holds for $r\gg r_0$, in the temperature and density region where $r_0\kappa_0\ll1$. Its derivation assumes the system monophasic. Through its dependence on χ_T, the range κ_0^{-1} of the pair correlation becomes infinite at the critical point, where Eq. (36) reduces to

$$G_d(r,0)\simeq\rho+(4\pi r_0^2r)^{-1},\quad r\gg r_0. \tag{38}$$

We have now to determine the time variation of G_d for $r\gg r_0$. The long-range part of the pair distribution $G_d(r,t)$ can be identified with the average shape at time t of the spontaneous macroscopic density fluctuations in the system, as seen from a point through which a particle passed at time 0. Following Onsager,[24] it is

[22] L. Landau and G. Placzek, Physik. Z. Sowjetunion **5**, 172 (1934). For a more detailed exposition, see J. Frenkel, *Kinetic Theory of Liquids* (Clarendon Press, Oxford, 1946), pp. 244 ff. The author is indebted to G. Placzek for illuminating discussions and communication of unpublished work on this subject.

[23] L. S. Ornstein and F. Zernike, Proc. Acad. Sci. Amsterdam **17**, 793 (1914); Physik. Z. **19**, 134 (1918). The length r_0 in our Eq. (36) is related by $6r_0^2=\epsilon^2$ to the length ϵ defined in the latter paper.

[24] L. Onsager, Phys. Rev. **37**, 405 (1931); **38**, 2265 (1931).

natural to assume that macroscopic variables which have taken nonequilibrium values as a consequence of spontaneous fluctuations have on the average in their return to equilibrium the same time variation as if their initial nonequilibrium values had been produced by suddenly released artificial constraints. This time variation is given by the well-known phenomenological laws of irreversible processes, in our case the Navier-Stokes equations for viscous flow supplemented by the continuity equation, and the equation for energy transport involving heat conduction.

Since we deal with fluctuations of small amplitude, all equations can be linearized and treated by Fourier analysis. We then find three independent plane-wave fluctuations of wave vector **k**: two corresponding to damped waves propagating with sound velocity in the directions of **k** and $-\mathbf{k}$, and one of nonpropagating nature, with a time dependence given by the factor

$$\exp(-\tfrac{1}{4}\Lambda_0 k^2 t), \tag{39}$$

with

$$\Lambda_0 = 4\kappa(\rho c_p)^{-1} = 4\kappa(\rho c_v)^{-1}(\chi_S/\chi_T). \tag{40}$$

κ is the coefficient of heat conduction, c_p and c_v are the specific heats per particle, at constant pressure and volume, respectively, and χ_S is the adiabatic compressibility

$$\chi_S = \rho^{-1}(\partial\rho/\partial p)_S$$

(S: entropy). As expected, the fluctuations of the two first modes are found to be adiabatic and the third mode is a fluctuation at constant pressure.[25]

When the critical point is approached, whereas fluctuations of the two first modes remain normal, the magnitude of the spontaneous fluctuations at constant pressure increases indefinitely. They alone thus contribute to the long-range part of the pair correlation, and the time dependence of G_d for $r \gg r_0$ and $t > 0$ can be obtained by multiplying each Fourier component of Eq. (36) by the corresponding factor (39), i.e., by calculating the convolution of Eq. (36) with the Fourier transform,

$$\frac{1}{(2\pi)^3}\int \exp(-\tfrac{1}{4}\Lambda_0 k^2 t)\exp(i\mathbf{k}\cdot\mathbf{r})d\mathbf{k} = (\pi\Lambda_0 t)^{-3/2}\exp\left(-\frac{|\mathbf{r}-\mathbf{r}'|^2}{\Lambda_0 t}\right),$$

of (39). One has thus, remembering that G_d is even in t,

$$G_d(r,t) \simeq \rho + (4\pi r_0^2)^{-1}(\pi\Lambda_0|t|)^{-3/2} \times \int \exp\left\{-\frac{|\mathbf{r}-\mathbf{r}'|^2}{\Lambda_0|t|} - \kappa_0 r'\right\}\frac{d\mathbf{r}'}{r'}. \tag{41}$$

Integration over the angles then gives

$$G_d(r,t) \simeq \rho + (4\pi r_0^2 r)^{-1}\Psi[\kappa_0(\Lambda_0|t|)^{\frac{1}{2}}, r(\Lambda_0|t|)^{-\frac{1}{2}}], \tag{42}$$

where the function Ψ of two dimensionless arguments is defined by

$$\Psi(v,w) = 2\pi^{-\frac{1}{2}}\exp(-w^2) \times \int_0^\infty \exp(-x^2 - vx)\sinh(2wx)dx. \tag{43}$$

It is easily expressed in terms of the error integral:

$$\Psi(v,w) = \exp(\tfrac{1}{4}v^2 - vw)\cdot\psi(\tfrac{1}{2}v - w) - \exp(\tfrac{1}{4}v^2 + vw)\cdot\psi(\tfrac{1}{2}v + w),$$

$$\psi(x) = \frac{1}{\pi^{\frac{1}{2}}}\int_x^\infty \exp(-y^2)dy.$$

The behavior of G_d for large r and for large and small $|t|$ is immediately obtained from

$$\Psi(v,w) \simeq \exp(-vw), \quad \text{for } w \gg 1,\ w \gg v; \tag{44}$$

$$\Psi(v,w) \simeq 4\pi^{-1/2}v^{-2}w\exp(-w^2), \quad \text{for } v \gg 1,\ v \gg w. \tag{45}$$

Equation (44) shows that the expression Eq. (42) reduces to Eq. (36) in the limit of $t \to 0$. Its strict validity is, however, restricted to values of $|t|$ large compared to the microscopic relaxation time T_0 considered before, since the phenomenological equations used in our derivation apply only to quantities averaged over a time interval large compared to the duration of microscopic fluctuations. This limitation accounts for the occurrence of a spurious discontinuity at $t = 0$ in the derivative of the right-hand side of (42) with respect to t; this derivative, if calculated correctly for t of microscopic order of magnitude, would be found continuous and equal to zero at $t = 0$. Apart from the condition $|t| \gg T_0$, the derivation of Eq. (42) requires of course $r_0\kappa_0 \ll 1$ and $r \gg r_0$ as for Eq. (36). It is, however, interesting that the latter condition can be abandoned for all times for which the expression (42) differs appreciably from its value (36) at $t = 0$. Indeed, it follows from (41) that whenever $|t| \gg \Lambda_0^{-1}r_0^2$ the value of $G_d(r,t)$ for all r, even of order r_0, is overwhelmingly determined by the values of $G_d(r,0)$ for $r \gg r_0$. If now $|t|$ is not large enough to satisfy this condition

$$|t| \lesssim \Lambda_0^{-1}r_0^2,$$

we get

$$v \lesssim \kappa_0 r_0 \ll 1, \quad w \gtrsim r/r_0.$$

Hence, for $r \gg r_0$, the asymptotic form (44) of Ψ can be used, and $G_d(r,t) \simeq G_d(r,0)$ for $r \gg r_0$. To present this conclusion differently, we can say that as $|t|$ increases, the time dependence of the long-range part of G_d sets in only for times[26]

$$|t| \gg \Lambda_0^{-1}r_0^2 \sim (\chi_T/\chi_S)T_0 \sim (\kappa_0 r_0)^{-2}T_0 \gg T_0,$$

[25] The foregoing analysis of spontaneous fluctuations has been carried out by L. Landau and G. Placzek (reference 22) to account for the occurrence of a triplet line in the fluctuation scattering of light by liquids, and to calculate the line widths.

[26] The following estimate is made by using values of κ, c_v, and χ_S calculated for rarefied gases, with the help of kinetic theory for κ.

at which the short-range part of the pair distribution has completely reduced to the instantaneous value of the local macroscopic density, the variation of which is correctly described by Eq. (42) for all r. It is finally to be remarked that Λ_0^{-1} increases indefinitely when the critical point is approached, corresponding to an increasingly slower time variation of the macroscopic part of the pair correlation.

The above discussion is valid for monophasic systems near the critical point, i.e., for gases at densities near the critical density ρ_c and temperatures slightly above the critical temperature T_c. The relevant condition for its applicability is that the dimensionless quantity,

$$\kappa_0 r_0 = (\rho k_B T \chi_T)^{-\frac{1}{2}},$$

be small compared to one, let's say of order 0.1 or smaller. A more concrete idea about the corresponding density and temperature ranges is obtained by using the approximate expression for χ_T given by the van der Waals equation of state. One finds that at the critical density or a density differing from it by less than some 5 percent, one must have $T - T_c \lesssim 0.005 T_c$.[23]

For temperatures approaching T_c from below, the system is no longer monophasic at densities near ρ_c and the previous treatment is then not strictly applicable. It seems, however, likely that the long-range part of the pair distribution and its time variation will not be radically different from what we have found them to be for T above T_c.

Let us now indicate a few consequences of the above discussion for the scattering of neutrons by liquids and dense gases, for neutron wavelengths of the order of the separation between particles or larger. Away from critical conditions and apart from the forward elastic peak, which is entirely coherent, the differential cross section $d^2\sigma/d\Omega d\epsilon$ is a smooth function of outgoing energy and angle of scattering, corresponding to average momentum and energy transfers or order $\hbar R_0^{-1}$ and $\hbar T_0^{-1}$, respectively. This applies to coherent and incoherent scattering alike, although the collective properties of the liquid will evidently affect the scattering to a greater extent in the coherent case. Qualitative shapes to be expected for the angular and energy distribution could easily be obtained from Fig. 1 by Fourier transformation.

When critical conditions are approached, whereas no rapid change is expected to occur for incoherent scattering, the occurrence of a tail of increasing range in the pair distribution G_d reflects itself in an increasing amount of coherent scattering characterized by small momentum and energy transfers. Using for the latter our customary notations $\hbar\boldsymbol{\kappa}$, $\hbar\omega$, we obtain by Fourier transformation of Eq. (41) over space and time [the Fourier transform over space gives the product of Eq. (39) by the Fourier transform of Eq. (36); one has then to make a Fourier transformation over time] the following expression,

$$\left(\frac{d^2\sigma_{\mathrm{coh}}}{d\Omega d\epsilon}\right)_{\mathrm{crit}} = \frac{4\langle a\rangle_{\mathrm{Av}}^2 N}{\pi\hbar}\cdot\frac{k}{k_0}\cdot\frac{1}{r_0^2(\kappa^2+\kappa_0^2)}\cdot\frac{\Lambda_0\kappa^2}{\Lambda_0^2\kappa^4+16\omega^2}, \qquad (46)$$

for the part of the differential cross section originating from long-range correlations. Near the critical point ($\kappa_0 r_0 \lesssim 0.1$), it is the main part of the cross section in the region $\kappa \ll r_0^{-1}$. From Eq. (46) this critical scattering is seen to have momentum and energy transfers of order $\kappa \sim \kappa_0$, $\omega \sim \Lambda_0\kappa_0^2/4$, respectively. Their relative magnitude compared to average momentum and energy transfers in noncritical scattering is easily estimated to be, very crudely,[26]

$$R_0\kappa_0 \sim (\rho k_B T \chi_T)^{-\frac{1}{2}},$$

$$\tfrac{1}{4} T_0 \Lambda_0 \kappa_0^2 \sim (R_0\kappa_0)^4 \sim (\rho k_B T \chi_T)^{-2}.$$

The most important feature revealed by this estimate is that in critical scattering, the energy transfers decrease very much faster than the momentum transfers when the critical point is approached, thus restoring the validity of the static approximation and causing the scattering to be not only more abundant than under normal conditions but also completely different in all its properties. The total cross section, for example, which under normal conditions is proportional to the incident neutron wavelength $2\pi/k_0$ as soon as the incident energy is small compared to $\hbar/T_0$,[27] has a completely different wavelength dependence in the immediate neighborhood of the critical point. Its main contribution comes then from the critical scattering represented by Eq. (46), which has to be integrated over outgoing energies and angles, with the result:

$$\sigma_{\mathrm{coh}} \simeq \frac{\pi\langle a\rangle_{\mathrm{Av}}^2 N}{(r_0 k_0)^2}\log\left(\frac{4k_0^2}{\kappa_0^2}+1\right). \qquad (47)$$

Application of Eq. (46) at the critical point itself, where κ_0 and Λ_0 vanish, would lead to an infinite value for the total cross section (47). As was shown by Placzek for the case of light scattering,[28] the occurrence of this spurious conclusion is due to the fact that our entire treatment of scattering assumes the range of the pair correlations to be small compared to the dimensions of the vessel containing the system. We indeed have always assumed the system large enough to make surface effects negligible. Application of Eqs. (46) and (47) therefore requires κ_0^{-1} to be small compared to the dimensions of the vessel. Practically this condition is violated only in a temperature interval of $\sim 10^{-12}$ degree around T_c, in which the scattering would depend on the size and shape of the vessel.

We will not in the present paper consider the case of rarefied gases. The natural way of treating it is by an

[27] This dependence on incident wavelength follows directly from the presence of the denominator k_0 in Eq. (28).

[28] G. Placzek, Physik. Z. 31, 1052 (1930).

expansion of G_s and G_d in powers of the density, entirely similar to the familiar expansion of the $g(r)$ function. The ideal Bose-Einstein and Fermi-Dirac gases will be considered in Sec. VI.

V. CRYSTALS

For crystals, the harmonic nature of the forces permits explicit calculations of the scattering cross sections and pair distributions. Such calculations have often been made for scattering.[29] We will here briefly derive the expressions for the $G(\mathbf{r},t)$ function, describing the correlations in position between any two particles of the crystal, and the $G_s(\mathbf{r},t)$ function, describing the correlation of a particle with itself. The calculation is most easily done by starting from Eq. (8), a fact generally valid for systems which have plane waves as independent modes of motion.

We restrict ourselves to a single crystal of infinite extension, with Bravais lattice (one atom per cell). The lattice vectors are denoted by $\mathbf{R}$, and the position vector of the particle with equilibrium position at $\mathbf{R}$ is written $\mathbf{R}+\mathbf{u}_R$.[30] Defining for each $\mathbf{R}$, including the origin $\mathbf{R}=0$ of the lattice, the pair distribution G_R for particles of equilibrium positions 0 and $\mathbf{R}$, we have

$$G=\sum_R G_R,\quad G_s=G_0. \tag{48}$$

From Eq. (8),

$$G_R(\mathbf{r},t)=(2\pi)^{-3}\int d\boldsymbol{\kappa}\cdot\exp\{-i\boldsymbol{\kappa}\cdot(\mathbf{r}-\mathbf{R})\}$$
$$\cdot\langle\exp\{-i\boldsymbol{\kappa}\cdot u_0(0)\}\cdot\exp\{i\boldsymbol{\kappa}\cdot\mathbf{u}_R(t)\}\rangle_T. \tag{49}$$

The Heisenberg operators are defined as usual. The subscript T indicates that the thermal distribution must be used in the definition (9) of the average.

We have first, since the commutator is a c number,

$$\langle\exp\{-i\boldsymbol{\kappa}\cdot\mathbf{u}_0(0)\}\cdot\exp\{i\boldsymbol{\kappa}\cdot\mathbf{u}_R(t)\}\rangle_T$$
$$=\langle\exp\{i\boldsymbol{\kappa}\cdot[\mathbf{u}_R(t)-\mathbf{u}_0(0)]\}\rangle_T.$$
$$\cdot\exp\{\tfrac{1}{2}[\boldsymbol{\kappa}\cdot\mathbf{u}_0(0),\ \boldsymbol{\kappa}\cdot\mathbf{u}_R(t)]\}. \tag{50}$$

Next, in view of the fact that

$$\boldsymbol{\kappa}\cdot\{\mathbf{u}_R(t)-\mathbf{u}_0(0)\}$$

is a linear combination of coordinates of independent harmonic oscillators and has thus a Gaussian probability distribution,[31] the first factor in the right-hand side of Eq. (50) has the value

$$\exp\{-\tfrac{1}{2}\langle[\boldsymbol{\kappa}\cdot(\mathbf{u}_R(t)-\mathbf{u}_0(0))]^2\rangle_T\}.$$

Replacing the commutator in the second factor by its average, we get

$$\langle\exp\{-i\boldsymbol{\kappa}\cdot\mathbf{u}_0(0)\}\cdot\exp\{i\boldsymbol{\kappa}\cdot\mathbf{u}_R(t)\}\rangle_T$$
$$=\exp\{-\sum_{\beta,\gamma}[M_{\beta\gamma}(0,0)-M_{\beta\gamma}(\mathbf{R},t)]\kappa_\beta\kappa_\gamma\}, \tag{51}$$

where $\beta,\gamma=x,\ y,\ z$ and

$$M_{\beta\gamma}(\mathbf{R},t)=M_{\gamma\beta}(\mathbf{R},t)=\langle u_0^\beta(0)u_R^\gamma(t)\rangle_T. \tag{52}$$

Inserting into (49), we get

$$G_R(\mathbf{r},t)=\{N(\mathbf{R},t)/8\pi^3\}^{\frac{1}{2}}$$
$$\times\exp\{-\tfrac{1}{2}\sum_{\beta,\gamma}N_{\beta\gamma}(\mathbf{R},t)(r_\beta-R_\beta)(r_\gamma-R_\gamma)\}, \tag{53}$$

with the 3×3 matrix $N_{\beta\gamma}(\mathbf{R},t)$ defined as the inverse of

$$2\{M_{\beta\gamma}(0,0)-M_{\beta\gamma}(\mathbf{R},t)\},$$

and with

$$N(\mathbf{R},t)=\det\{N_{\beta\gamma}(\mathbf{R},t)\}.$$

Equation (53) is a Gaussian distribution around the equilibrium position $\mathbf{R}$. For $t\neq0$ it has complex coefficients, the imaginary parts of which are of quantum origin.[32]

The correlation equation (52) between displacements is easily calculated using the functions $\omega_j(\mathbf{q})$, $\mathbf{e}_j(\mathbf{q})$ which express the frequency and unit vector of polarization of a plane-wave vibration (phonon) in terms of the wave vector $\mathbf{q}$ and the polarization index $j=1,\ 2,\ 3$. One finds

$$M_{\beta\gamma}(\mathbf{R},t)=\{\hbar v_0/(16\pi^3M)\}$$
$$\times\sum_j\int d\mathbf{q}\{e_j^\beta(\mathbf{q})e_j^\gamma(\mathbf{q})/\omega_j(\mathbf{q})\}\cdot\{1-\exp(-\hbar\beta\omega_j(\mathbf{q})\}^{-1}$$
$$\cdot\{\exp[-i(\mathbf{R}\cdot\mathbf{q}-t\omega_j(\mathbf{q}))]+\exp[-\hbar\beta\omega_j(\mathbf{q})]$$
$$\times\exp[i(\mathbf{R}\cdot\mathbf{q}-t\omega_j(\mathbf{q}))]\}, \tag{54}$$

where M is the atomic mass of the crystal, v_0 the volume of the cell, β^{-1} the quantity k_BT and where the integration is extended over a cell of the reciprocal lattice.[33] As functions of $\mathbf{q}$, ω_j, and $\mathbf{e}_j$ have the periodicity of the reciprocal lattice.

Equation (54) shows that $M_{\beta\gamma}(\mathbf{R},t)$ approaches zero when R or $|t|$ increase indefinitely. $N_{\beta\gamma}(\mathbf{R},t)$ approaches then the inverse $N_{\beta\gamma}^{(\infty)}$ of the real matrix $2M_{\beta\gamma}(0,0)$. Hence, asymptotically, for large $|t|$ or for large R but finite $|\mathbf{r}-\mathbf{R}|$,

$$G_R(\mathbf{r},t)\simeq G_R^{(\infty)}(\mathbf{r})=\{N^{(\infty)}/8\pi^3\}^{\frac{1}{2}}$$
$$\times\exp\{-\tfrac{1}{2}\sum_{\beta,\gamma}N_{\beta\gamma}^{(\infty)}(r_\beta-R_\beta)(r_\gamma-R_\gamma)\}.$$

[29] A fairly complete list of references is given in G. Placzek and L. Van Hove, Phys. Rev. 93, 1207 (1954). The unpublished work of R. J. Glauber (reference 10), which makes use of the correlations (52) below, must also be mentioned.

[30] When in subscript, R stands for the vector $\mathbf{R}$.

[31] This theorem is due to F. Bloch, Z. Physik 74, 295 (1932), especially footnote on p. 309.

[32] The above method for the calculation of scattering cross sections or pair distributions is applicable quite generally to systems with harmonic forces. Its main advantage is the very brief derivation of Eq. (51) based on Bloch's theorem. Alternative methods found in the literature are less general or more laborious: they have to rederive Bloch's theorem in disguised form.

[33] We define here the reciprocal lattice vectors as the vectors whose inner products with the vectors $\mathbf{R}$ of the crystal lattice are integral multiples of 2π.

This equation expresses the asymptotic vanishing of correlations between particles with widely separated equilibrium positions, and between neighboring particles considered at widely separated times.

For $t=\pm\infty$, the limiting values of the pair distributions Eq. (48) are thus

$$G(\mathbf{r},\infty)=\sum_R G_R^{(\infty)}(\mathbf{r}), \qquad (55)$$

$$G_s(\mathbf{r},\infty)=G_0^{(\infty)}(\mathbf{r}). \qquad (56)$$

The elastic part of coherent and incoherent neutron scattering follows immediately by insertion into Eqs. (28) and (29):

$$\left(\frac{d^2\sigma_{\text{coh}}}{d\Omega d\epsilon}\right)_{\text{el}}=\left[\langle a\rangle_{\text{Av}}^2\frac{(2\pi)^3N}{\hbar v_0}\right] \times\exp\{-\sum_{\beta,\gamma}M_{\beta\gamma}(0,0)\kappa_\beta\kappa_\gamma\}\delta(\omega)\sum_{\boldsymbol{\alpha}}\delta(\boldsymbol{\kappa}-\boldsymbol{\alpha}),$$

$$\left(\frac{d^2\sigma_{\text{incoh}}}{d\Omega d\epsilon}\right)_{\text{el}}=\left[(\langle a^2\rangle_{\text{Av}}-\langle a\rangle_{\text{Av}}^2)\frac{N}{\hbar}\right] \times\exp\{-\sum_{\beta,\gamma}M_{\beta\gamma}(0,0)\kappa_\beta\kappa_\gamma\}\delta(\omega).$$

It contains the familiar Debye-Waller factor and, in the coherent case, the interference condition $\boldsymbol{\kappa}=\boldsymbol{\alpha}$, where $\boldsymbol{\alpha}$ denotes the vectors of the reciprocal lattice.[33] The cross sections for inelastic scattering can be derived from the difference between G, G_s and their asymptotic values (55), (56); one obtains then immediately expressions previously derived by Glauber.[10]

It is of some interest to study the nature of the convergence of G and G_s toward their asymptotic limits. G is found to approach (55) both for $|t|\rightarrow\infty$, r fixed and for $r\rightarrow\infty$, t fixed, the convergence being in $|t|^{-3/2}$ in the former case, in r^{-1} in the latter. G_s approaches (56) for $|t|\rightarrow\infty$, with a convergence in $|t|^{-3/2}$. The convergence is very slow in all cases. As seen from Eqs. (28) and (29), this fact is closely related to the occurrence of singularities in the angular and energy distribution of neutrons scattered inelastically by a single crystal; these singularities have been studied in detail elsewhere.[34] The convergence of the pair distributions for large $|t|$ has also another important physical significance: it implies that the crystal, despite its over-all lack of ergodicity, exhibits locally a type of ergodic behavior, the return toward local equilibrium being in $|t|^{-3/2}$.[35]

We will here restrict ourselves to establishing the law of asymptotic convergence of pair distributions for $|t|\rightarrow\infty$. This law is entirely determined by certain special crystal vibrations, already met before in connection with the frequency distribution function of the crystal.[36] Applying the result thus obtained to G_s, we will then establish in an indirect way the existence, asserted before without proof,[34] of singularities in the energy distribution of incoherently scattered neutrons.

The convergence of G_R to $G_R^{(\infty)}$ is determined by the convergence of $M_{\beta\gamma}(\mathbf{R},t)$ to 0 for $|t|\rightarrow\infty$, which according to Eq. (54) is to be discussed by the method of stationary phases. For large $|t|$, the main contribution to the integral in (54) comes from the neighborhood of the points $\mathbf{q}_c$ where for some $j=j_c$,

$$\text{grad}\,\omega_j(\mathbf{q})=0. \qquad (57)$$

It has been shown that such points always exist for general values of the force constants of the crystal.[36] Their existence is implied by the periodicity of $\omega_j(\mathbf{q})$ in $\mathbf{q}$. In suitable local coordinates preserving the volume element $d\mathbf{q}$, the expansion of $\omega_{j_c}(\mathbf{q})$ near $\mathbf{q}_c$ can be written

$$\omega_{j_c}(\mathbf{q})=\omega_c+a_c\sum_{\beta=1,2,3}\epsilon_\beta{}^c\xi_\beta{}^2+\cdots,\quad \boldsymbol{\xi}=\mathbf{q}-\mathbf{q}_c,$$

with $\omega_c=\omega_{j_c}(\mathbf{q}_c)$, $\epsilon_\beta{}^c=\pm1$, $a_c>0$. Inserting in (54) and carrying out the integration over $\boldsymbol{\xi}$, one gets for $M_{\beta\gamma}(\mathbf{R},t)$ the asymptotic form:

$$M_{\beta\gamma}(\mathbf{R},t)\simeq\{\hbar v_0/(16\pi^{3/2}M|t|^{3/2})\}\sum_c\{e_{j_c}{}^\beta(\mathbf{q}_c)e_{j_c}{}^\gamma(\mathbf{q}_c)/(a_c{}^{3/2}\omega_c)\}\{1-\exp(-\hbar\beta\omega_c)\}^{-1}\{\exp(-i\mathbf{R}\cdot\mathbf{q}_c)\mathcal{E}_c(t)+\exp(-\hbar\beta\omega_c+i\mathbf{R}\cdot\mathbf{q}_c)\mathcal{E}_c{}^*(t)\}, \qquad (58)$$

with

$$\mathcal{E}_c(t)=\exp[it\omega_c+i(\pi/4)(t/|t|)\sum_\beta\epsilon_\beta{}^c].$$

$\mathcal{E}_c{}^*$ is the complex conjugate of $\mathcal{E}_c$. The sum $\sum_c$ extends over all solutions of Eq. (57). The decrease of $M_{\beta\gamma}$ for large $|t|$ is seen to be in $|t|^{-3/2}$. From (58) it is now an elementary matter to find the following asymptotic formula for G_R:

$$G_R(\mathbf{r},t)-G_R^{(\infty)}(\mathbf{r})\simeq G_R^{(\infty)}(\mathbf{r})|t|^{-3/2} \times\sum_c\{P_c(\mathbf{r})\mathcal{E}_c(t)+P_c{}'(\mathbf{r})\mathcal{E}_c{}^*(t)\}. \qquad (59)$$

P_c and $P_c{}'$ denote polynomials of second degree in the components of $\mathbf{r}$. Their explicit expression is not needed for our purpose. The asymptotic convergence of G_R, and thus of G and G_s, is again in $|t|^{-3/2}$.

Through the Fourier transform over t in Eq. (29), each term of the expression (59), taken for $\mathbf{R}=0$, contributes a singularity to the energy distribution of incoherently scattered neutrons. The analytic nature of the singularity is best obtained by Fourier transformation of simple functions of t with asymptotic behavior $|t|^{-3/2}\mathcal{E}_c(t)$ or $|t|^{-3/2}\mathcal{E}_c{}^*(t)$ for large $|t|$. We take for example the function,

$$f_c(t)=|t|^{-3/2}\mathcal{E}_c(t)(1\pm i\alpha/t)^{-3/2},$$

where $\alpha>0$ and the upper (lower) sign is taken when $\epsilon_c=\sum_\beta\epsilon_\beta{}^c=3$ or -1 (-3 or 1). It has the following

[34] See G. Placzek and L. Van Hove, reference 29.

[35] Properties of local ergodicity have been studied for a one-dimensional system of particles with harmonic interaction between nearest neighbors by G. Klein and I. Prigogine, Physica **19**, 1053 (1953).

[36] L. Van Hove, Phys. Rev. **89**, 1189 (1953).

Fourier transform:[37]

$$\bar{f}_c(\omega)=\int_{-\infty}^{\infty} e^{-i\omega t}f_c(t)dt=\begin{cases}\bar{f}(\omega-\omega_c) \text{ for } \epsilon_c=3\\ -\bar{f}(\omega_c-\omega) \text{ for } \epsilon_c=1\\ -\bar{f}(\omega-\omega_c) \text{ for } \epsilon_c=-1\\ \bar{f}(\omega_c-\omega) \text{ for } \epsilon_c=-3\end{cases},$$

with

$$\bar{f}(\omega)=\begin{cases}0 \text{ for } \omega<0\\ 4(\pi\omega)^{\frac{1}{2}}\exp(-\alpha\omega) \text{ for } \omega>0.\end{cases}$$

Hence, in the energy distribution of neutrons scattered in an arbitrary direction, the term in $\mathcal{E}_c(t)$ of (59) produces a singularity at $\omega=\omega_c$: near $\omega=\omega_c$, the energy distribution has the form $A\bar{f}_c(\omega)+F(\omega)$, where A is a constant and $F(\omega)$ a continuous function, the first derivative of which has at most a finite discontinuity at $\omega=\omega_c$. Both A and F depend on the scattering direction. One can easily show that the scattering processes responsible for this singularity involve excitation by the neutron of one phonon of wave vector $\mathbf{q}_c$ and polarization j_c.[38] Similarly, the term in $\mathcal{E}_c^*(t)$ produces a singularity at $\omega=-\omega_c$, with an energy distribution of form $A'\bar{f}_c(-\omega)+F'(\omega)$, where A' and F' have meanings similar to A and F. This singularity is due to annihilation by the neutron of one phonon again characterized by $\mathbf{q}_c$ and j_c.

VI. IDEAL QUANTUM GASES

To illustrate the effect of Bose-Einstein and Fermi-Dirac statistics on pair correlations we treat very briefly the case of ideal quantum gases. It is instructive to consider particles with nonvanishing spin and to study simultaneously the correlations imposed by the statistics on particle positions and on spin orientations. This is done by calculating the spin-dependent pair distribution function Γ defined in Eq. (24); a_j is an arbitrary function of the jth particle spin, the same function for each particle.

The expressions of Γ for the Fermi gas and for the Bose gas without condensed phase are very similar and their derivation, to be based on the analog of Eq. (8) for Γ, is quite straightforward. Only the final result will be given here:

$$\Gamma(r,t)=\rho\langle a^2\rangle_{\text{Av}}\{f(r,t)\pm(2s_0+1)^{-1}n_{\mp}(r,t)\}\cdot\{n_{\mp}(r,t)\}^*+\rho\langle a\rangle_{\text{Av}}^2. \quad (60)$$

The upper and lower signs refer to Bose and Fermi particles, respectively. The averages $\langle a^2\rangle_{\text{Av}}$ and $\langle a\rangle_{\text{Av}}^2$ have the same meaning as in Eq. (25). s_0 is the spin of the particles in units of $\hbar$. The functions f and $n_\pm$ are defined by

$$f(r,t)=(2\pi)^{-3}\rho^{-1}\int\exp\{-i(\mathbf{k}\cdot\mathbf{r}-\omega_k t)\}d\mathbf{k}$$
$$=-\frac{2}{\rho}\left(1-i\frac{|t|}{t}\right)\left(\frac{M}{4\pi\hbar|t|}\right)^{\frac{3}{2}}\exp\left(-\frac{iMr^2}{2\hbar t}\right),$$

$$n_{\mp}(r,t)=(2\pi)^{-3}\rho^{-1}\int\exp\{-i(\mathbf{k}\cdot\mathbf{r}-\omega_k t)\}\cdot\{B\exp(\hbar\beta\omega_k)\mp1\}^{-1}d\mathbf{k}. \quad (61)$$

M is the mass of the particles, β is $(k_BT)^{-1}$, and ω_k stands for $\hbar k^2/2M$. The constant $B\gtrless\frac{1}{2}(1\pm1)$ is determined by $n_{\mp}(0,0)=1$.

According to Eq. (60), the range of the pair correlations in space and time is determined by the convergence of $n_{\mp}$ to zero for r or $t\to\infty$. This convergence can be discussed in all cases from Eq. (61). We consider here only the case $B>1$, for which expansion in powers of B^{-1} gives

$$n_{\mp}(r,t)\simeq\rho^{-1}\left(\frac{M}{2\pi\hbar}\right)^{\frac{3}{2}}\sum_{l=1}^{\infty}\frac{(\pm1)^{l-1}}{B^l(lt_T-it)^{\frac{3}{2}}}\times\exp\left\{-\frac{Mr^2}{2\hbar(lt_T-it)}\right\}, \quad (62)$$

where $t_T=\hbar\beta=\hbar/(k_BT)$ is a measure of the relevant relaxation time. For B not too close to one, an estimate of the spatial range of the pair correlations is obtained from the first term of the series. It gives

$$r\sim(\hbar/M)^{\frac{1}{2}}(t_T^2+t^2)^{\frac{1}{4}},$$

and for $t\lesssim t_T$, reduces essentially to the mean de Broglie wavelength $(\hbar^2\beta/2M)^{\frac{1}{2}}=\lambda_B$. The expansion Eq. (62) becomes impractical when B is close to one, in particular for the Bose gas. For the latter and for $0<B-1\ll1$ a more convenient expression has been obtained by Placzek[39] for $n_-(r,0)$; it can be used for $n_-(r,t)$ by introducing it into the identity,

$$n_{\mp}(r,t)=\rho\int n_{\mp}(r',0)f(|\mathbf{r}-\mathbf{r}'|,t)d\mathbf{r}',$$

and shows that the correlation range becomes of order $(B-1)^{-1/2}\lambda_B$, thus increasing indefinitely as condensation is approached.

From Eq. (60) the difference between Γ and its asymptotic value $\rho\langle a\rangle_{\text{Av}}^2$ is seen to depend on the spin through $\langle a^2\rangle_{\text{Av}}$ only. This fact is obviously due to the absence of spatial correlation between particles in different spin states. Applied to neutron scattering by

[37] The various cases correspond to the possible signatures of the stationary point of $\omega_{j_c}(\mathbf{q})$ at $\mathbf{q}_c$: minimum, saddle point of one of two types, maximum, respectively.

[38] This is shown for cubic crystals in reference 34.

[39] G. Placzek, Proceedings of the Second Berkeley Symposium on Mathematical Statistics and Probability (University of California Press, Berkeley, 1951), pp. 581–588, especially Eq. (36).

nuclei with spin-dependent scattering length a, it illustrates how little sense is made by the conventional terminology of calling coherent (or incoherent) the part of the scattering containing $\langle a\rangle_{Av}{}^2$ (or $\langle a^2\rangle_{Av}-\langle a\rangle_{Av}{}^2$), as soon as some correlation exists between spins, resulting either from symmetry requirements of the wave function or from spin interactions. It is only for systems of Boltzmann particles with free nuclear spins that this terminology is physically reasonable.[40]

For a Bose gas in the condensation region, the pair distribution Γ has the following expression:

$$\Gamma(r,t)=\rho\langle a^2\rangle_{Av}[\{f(r,t)+(2s_0+1)^{-1}(n(r,t)+n_0)\}\cdot(n(r,t)+n_0)^*-(2s_0+1)^{-1}n_0{}^2]+\rho(\langle a^2\rangle_{Av}-\langle a\rangle_{Av}{}^2)\times(2s_0+2)^{-1}n_0{}^2+\rho\langle a\rangle_{Av}{}^2. \quad (63)$$

The function f is the same as above; n and n_0 are defined by

$$n(r,t)=(2\pi)^{-3}\rho^{-1}\int \exp\{-i(\mathbf{k}\cdot\mathbf{r}-\omega_k t)\}\cdot\{\exp(\hbar\beta\omega_k)-1\}^{-1}d\mathbf{k},$$

$$n_0=1-n(0,0)=1-(\rho_c/\rho),$$

where ρ_c is the condensation density at temperature T. The quantity $\rho-\rho_c=n_0\rho$, supposed to be positive, is the density of the condensed phase. The asymptotic behavior of n is easily shown to be in λ_T/r for $r\to\infty$ and in $(t_T/|t|)^{\frac{1}{2}}$ for $t\to\infty$.

In the derivation of Eq. (63), the only point which is not quite elementary is the calculation of the thermal average $\langle N_\alpha N_\beta\rangle$, where N_α, N_β denote the number of particles of momentum zero in spin states α, β ($\alpha,\beta=1,\cdots 2s_0+1$). With the help of generating functions for the distribution of values of the N_α's, one easily shows that

$$\langle N_\alpha N_\beta\rangle=\frac{2s_0+1}{2s_0+2}\langle N_\alpha\rangle^2-\frac{1}{2s_0+1}\langle N_\alpha\rangle, \quad (\alpha\neq\beta)$$

$$\langle N_\alpha{}^2\rangle=2\frac{2s_0+1}{2s_0+2}\langle N_\alpha\rangle^2+\frac{2s_0}{2s_0+2}\langle N_\alpha\rangle.$$

In the right-hand sides, the second terms can be neglected in comparison with the first ones in the limit of an infinite number of particles.

In the special case $t=0$, $a_j=1$, Eqs. (60) and (63) reduce to the instantaneous pair distributions derived for ideal quantum gases by London.[41]

VII. CONCLUDING REMARKS

Our aims have been to introduce the time-dependent generalization of the familiar pair distribution function, to indicate its interest from the standpoint of statistical mechanics, and to establish its role in scattering theory, showing at the same time how slow neutron scattering makes it experimentally accessible.

The use of scattering experiments for the study of the pair distribution in space and time seems to us to be of real interest for systems of nontrivial and poorly known dynamical properties, mainly liquids and dense gases. It is our hope that increasingly complete and accurate data on such systems will become available. The case of liquid helium, with its marked quantum properties and its complex-valued pair distribution, undoubtedly deserves special attention.[42]

From the theoretical standpoint, the determination of the $g(\mathbf{r})$ function in terms of the intermolecular forces is well known to be a difficult and challenging problem for liquids and dense gases. Both the difficulty and the theoretical interest of a determination of the time-dependent pair distribution are likely to be greater, in view of the fact that the relaxation properties of the system are involved. On a more modest scale, approximate discussions of the time dependence of G, based on suitable models, would probably be instructive and might provide considerable help in the analysis of scattering experiments, since for some time to come, complete angular and energy distributions will not be readily measurable.

The author wishes to express his gratitude to Dr. G. Placzek for many stimulating discussions and suggestions on the various aspects of the present work.

[40] This remark holds of course also for isotope disorder. Other terminologies, introduced by G. Ç. Wick, Physik. Z. 38, 689 (1937), and J. M. Cassels, Progr. Nuclear Phys. 1, 185 (1950), have the same limitation.

[41] F. London, J. Chem. Phys. 11, 203 (1943).

[42] Theoretical discussions of neutron scattering for various models of liquid helium have been given by A. Akhiezer and I. Pomeranchuk, J. Phys. (U.S.S.R.) 9, 461 (1945); Goldstein, Sweeney, and Goldstein, Phys. Rev. 77, 319 (1950); L. Goldstein and D. W. Sweeney, Phys. Rev. 80, 141 (1950).

PHYSICAL REVIEW VOLUME 95, NUMBER 6 SEPTEMBER 15, 1954

Time-Dependent Correlations between Spins and Neutron Scattering in Ferromagnetic Crystals*

LÉON VAN HOVE
Institute for Advanced Study, Princeton, New Jersey

(Received May 25, 1954)

The pair correlation between spins considered at different times in a ferromagnetic crystal is used to derive a general formula for the angular and energy distribution of magnetically scattered neutrons. The qualitative properties of the correlation are established for various temperature ranges and a number of characteristic features of the scattering and of its temperature variation are thus accounted for. From the study of the long-range part of the correlation an explicit expression is derived for the "critical magnetic scattering" produced in the neighborhood of the Curie point by the large spontaneous fluctuations of the magnetization.

I. INTRODUCTION

As was shown in an earlier paper,[1] the Born approximation scattering cross section can be simply expressed in terms of the four-dimensional Fourier transform of a pair distribution function depending on a space vector and a time variable. The formula thus obtained provides a new and physically very intuitive method of analyzing the properties of slow neutron scattering by systems of particles, in the most interesting energy region where energy transfers are of the order of the incident neutron energy or larger. The formula is the natural extension to neutron scattering of the classical Zernike-Prins formula[2] for scattering of x-rays. In full analogy with the latter, it is expected to be of most practical interest in the case of scattering systems of complicated dynamical and statistical structure, like liquids or dense gases, for which a theoretical calculation of the scattering is not possible.

This general method of describing slow-neutron scattering in terms of a time-dependent pair distribution function finds a very fruitful application in the case of magnetic inelastic scattering by ferromagnetic crystals. The total magnetic cross section of iron has been measured by Palevsky and Hughes for neutrons of wavelengths ranging from 5 to 13 A, from very low temperatures to well above the Curie point.[3] Similar measurements were made by Squires for iron and nickel.[4] As was briefly shown in an earlier paper,[5] striking features in the temperature variation of the total cross section are readily understood in terms of the general properties of the time-dependent pair distribution (or correlation) for spin orientations. The present paper is devoted to the detailed derivation and discussion of these properties as well as to a more complete account of the predictions which can be made on their basis for the magnetic inelastic scattering of slow neutrons. Despite the well-known impossibility to deal in any exact way with the dynamical properties of a ferromagnetic spin system, it turns out that all the most important qualitative properties of the correlation, and thus of the scattering, can be derived by means of general statistical arguments completed with macroscopic considerations. The success of this approach must be ascribed to the simple and direct physical meaning of the correlation as a function of space and time variables. It therefore illustrates in a striking way the practical usefulness of the concepts introduced and studied in II in more abstract terms.

The general formula expressing the magnetic scattering cross section in terms of the pair correlation between spins is derived and discussed in the next section. Section III deals with the correlation calculated by spin wave theory for temperatures very low compared to the Curie temperature. The qualitative properties of the correlation and of the magnetic inelastic scattering are discussed in Sec. IV for general temperatures, neither too small nor too close to the Curie point. The long range part of the correlation present at temperatures close to the Curie point and resulting from the occurrence of large spontaneous fluctuations in the magnetization is studied in the following section, where it is also used to derive the characteristic features of the "critical magnetic scattering" produced by those fluctuations. The experimental evidence confirming the existence of the critical magnetic scattering is mentioned. The final section is devoted to a few concluding remarks.

II. SCATTERING FORMULA

For the description of ferromagnetic crystals we adopt the atomic (Heisenberg) model of ferromagnetism which attributes to each atom a spin of fixed length s_0. Apart from assuming not too large overlap integrals, this model can be a fair approximation only when the magneton number ν_0 per atom is close to an integer. This is the case for iron ($\nu_0=2.2$), for which s_0 must be given the value 1. For nickel ($\nu_0=0.6$) the model does not hold.

Although there is no difficulty in writing down

* Part of this work was done at Brookhaven National Laboratory where it was supported by the U. S. Atomic Energy Commission.

[1] Léon Van Hove, Phys. Rev. **95**, 249 (1954). This paper will be referred to as II, and its equations denoted by Eq. (II $\cdots$).

[2] F. Zernike and J. A. Prins, Z. Physik **41**, 184 (1927).

[3] H. Palevsky and D. J. Hughes, Phys. Rev. **92**, 202 (1953).

[4] G. L. Squires (to be published).

[5] Léon Van Hove, Phys. Rev. **93**, 268 (1954), henceforth referred to as I.

formulas taking polarization effects into account,[6,7] we limit ourselves to scattering of unpolarized neutrons by a ferromagnetic crystal and leave the polarization of the scattered beam out of consideration. The differential cross section $d^2\sigma/d\Omega d\epsilon$ per unit solid angle and unit interval of outgoing neutron energy ϵ is then the sum of a term entirely due to the nuclear interaction of the neutron with the nuclei of the crystal, and a term $d^2\sigma_{\text{magn}}/d\Omega d\epsilon$ resulting from the magnetic interaction of the neutron with the magnetic electrons of the crystal.[8] Following Halpern and Johnson,[9] the magnetic cross section is

$$\frac{d^2\sigma_{\text{magn}}}{d\Omega d\epsilon}=\left(\frac{2ge^2}{m_0c^2}\right)^2\frac{1}{\hbar}\cdot\frac{k}{k_0}|F(\kappa)|^2 \times\sum_{\alpha,\beta}\left(\delta_{\alpha\beta}-\frac{\kappa_\alpha\kappa_\beta}{\kappa^2}\right)\mathcal{S}_{\alpha\beta}(\boldsymbol{\kappa},\omega), \quad (1)$$

$$\mathcal{S}_{\alpha\beta}(\boldsymbol{\kappa},\omega)=\sum_{n_0} p_{n_0}\sum_n\left[\sum_R S_R{}^\alpha\exp(-i\boldsymbol{\kappa}\cdot\mathbf{r}_R)\right]_n^{n_0} \times\left[\sum_{R'} S_{R'}{}^\beta\exp(i\boldsymbol{\kappa}\cdot\mathbf{r}_{R'})\right]_{n_0}^n \cdot\delta\left(\omega+\frac{E_{n_0}-E_n}{\hbar}\right), \quad (2)$$

where e and m_0 are the electron charge and mass, $g=1.91$ is the neutron magnetic moment in nuclear magnetons, c is the velocity of light, $\mathbf{k}_0$ and $\mathbf{k}=\mathbf{k}_0-\boldsymbol{\kappa}$ are the initial and final wave vectors of the neutron, whereas $\omega=\hbar(k_0{}^2-k^2)/2m$, m being the neutron mass. The indices α, $\beta=x$, y, z refer to rectangular coordinates in space. The function $F(\kappa)$ is the form factor of the magnetic electrons normalized to $F(0)=1$. The atoms in the crystal have their equilibrium positions $\mathbf{R}$ at the sites of a lattice which we assume to be of Bravais type (one particle per cell). We denote their actual position vectors by $\mathbf{r}_R=\mathbf{R}+\mathbf{u}_R$ and the resultant spin vector of their electron cloud by $\mathbf{S}_R$.[10] The initial and final quantum states of the crystal (including the spin system) are labeled by n_0, n; their energies are E_{n_0}, E_n; the bracket $[\cdots]_n{}^{n_0}$ denotes a matrix element and p_{n_0} is the Boltzmann factor,

$$p_{n_0}=Z^{-1}\exp(-E_{n_0}/k_BT), \quad \sum_{n_0} p_{n_0}=1,$$

containing the temperature T and Boltzmann's constant k_B.

[6] F. Bloch, Phys. Rev. **50**, 259 (1936).
[7] J. Schwinger, Phys. Rev. **51**, 544 (1937).
[8] The weak neutron-electron interaction of nonmagnetic nature is neglected.
[9] O. Halpern and M. H. Johnson, Phys. Rev. **55**, 898 (1939).
[10] R stands for $\mathbf{R}$ when in suffix. We make the assumption that the orbital motion of the electrons does not contribute to the magnetic moment of the atom.

By the method of II, Eq. (2) is transformed into

$$\mathcal{S}_{\alpha\beta}(\boldsymbol{\kappa},\omega)=(2\pi)^{-1}N\int\exp[i(\boldsymbol{\kappa}\cdot\mathbf{r}-\omega t)]\cdot\Gamma_{\alpha\beta}(\mathbf{r},t)d\mathbf{r}dt, \quad (3)$$

where N is the number of atoms in the crystal. The pair distribution $\Gamma_{\alpha\beta}$ is defined by

$$\Gamma_{\alpha\beta}(\mathbf{r},t)=N^{-1}\sum_{R'}\sum_R\left\langle\int d\mathbf{r}'\cdot S_{R'}{}^\alpha(0)\cdot\delta(\mathbf{r}+\mathbf{r}_{R'}(0)-\mathbf{r}') \times S_R{}^\beta(t)\cdot\delta(\mathbf{r}'-\mathbf{r}_R(t))\right\rangle_T, \quad (4)$$

where, for each operator A, one writes

$$A(t)=\exp(itH/\hbar)\cdot A\cdot\exp(-itH/\hbar) \quad (5)$$

in terms of the Hamiltonian H of the crystal (including spins), and also

$$\langle A\rangle_T=\sum_{n_0} p_{n_0}[A]_{n_0}^{n_0}.$$

All atoms being identical, the sum over $\mathbf{R}'$ in Eq. (4) may be restricted to $\mathbf{R}'=0$ and the factor N^{-1} dropped.

It is a good approximation to assume that there is no coupling between atomic positions $\mathbf{r}_R$ and atomic spins $\mathbf{S}_R$. The correlation (4) then becomes

$$\Gamma_{\alpha\beta}(\mathbf{r},t)=\sum_R\gamma_R{}^{\alpha\beta}(t)G_R(\mathbf{r},t). \quad (6)$$

$\gamma_R{}^{\alpha\beta}(t)$ is the time-dependent correlation between pairs of spins,

$$\gamma_R{}^{\alpha\beta}(t)=\langle S_0{}^\alpha(0)S_R{}^\beta(t)\rangle_T. \quad (7)$$

It is complex-valued and satisfies the hermiticity condition,

$$\gamma_R{}^{\alpha\beta}(t)=\{\gamma_{-R}{}^{\beta\alpha}(-t)\}^*.$$

The function G_R, already introduced and calculated in II, describes the pair distribution in space and time of two atoms with equilibrium positions separated by $\mathbf{R}$:

$$G_R(\mathbf{r},t)=\left\langle\int d\mathbf{r}'\delta(\mathbf{r}+\mathbf{r}_0(0)-\mathbf{r}')\delta(\mathbf{r}'-\mathbf{r}_R(t))\right\rangle_T. \quad (8)$$

The theoretical discussion of the magnetic scattering reduces thus to the study of the time-dependent correlation (7) between pairs of spins. It could be carried out in full detail if an actual calculation of this correlation were possible. Except for temperatures small compared to the Curie temperature, where spin wave theory is applicable,[11] such a calculation presents great difficulties, comparable to the difficulties involved in the theoretical determination of pair distribution functions in liquids (see II). As in the case of liquids one has to proceed by deriving, rigorously when possible and qualitatively

[11] The discussion of magnetic scattering of neutrons by spin wave theory has been given by R. G. Moorhouse, Proc. Phys. Soc. (London) **A64**, 1097 (1951).

otherwise, as many general properties of the correlation $\gamma_R^{\alpha\beta}(t)$ as can be found. On the basis of these one could further select approximate methods to obtain more quantitative results. Our present aim is to deal with the first problem and to derive from its solution the main qualitative properties of the magnetic scattering of slow neutrons.

By far the main part of the interaction between atomic spins is of the exchange type, so that the main term in the Hamiltonian H_0 of the spin system is of form

$$H_0=-\sum_{\mathbf{R}\neq\mathbf{R}'} J_{R-R'}\mathbf{S}_R\cdot\mathbf{S}_{R'}, \qquad (9)$$

where $-2J_R$ is the negative exchange energy of two atoms separated by a lattice vector $\mathbf{R}$, negligible for all but the shortest lattice vectors. Additional terms in the Hamiltonian, like the dipole-dipole interaction between spins, are very much smaller. If they are neglected, the cross-section formula (1) greatly simplifies for scattering by a polycrystal: averaging over crystal orientations gives

$$\frac{d^2\sigma_{\text{magn}}}{d\Omega d\epsilon}=\left(\frac{2ge^2}{m_0c^2}\right)^2\frac{2}{3\hbar}\cdot\frac{k}{k_0}\cdot|F(\kappa)|^2\cdot \mathcal{S}(\boldsymbol{\kappa},\omega), \qquad (10)$$

where $\mathcal{S}$, the trace of the 3×3 matrix $\mathcal{S}_{\alpha\beta}$, is the 4-dimensional Fourier transform of Γ, trace of $\Gamma_{\alpha\beta}$:

$$\mathcal{S}(\boldsymbol{\kappa},\omega)=(2\pi)^{-1}N\int \exp[i(\boldsymbol{\kappa}\cdot\mathbf{r}-\omega t)]\cdot\Gamma(\mathbf{r},t)d\mathbf{r}dt. \qquad (11)$$

Equations (6) and (7) reduce to

$$\Gamma(\mathbf{r},t)=\sum_R \gamma_R(t)G_R(\mathbf{r},t), \qquad (12)$$

$$\gamma_R(t)=\langle\mathbf{S}_0(0)\cdot\mathbf{S}_R(t)\rangle_T. \qquad (13)$$

As was discussed in II, the separation between elastic and inelastic scattering can be obtained by separating the pair distribution $\Gamma_{\alpha\beta}(\mathbf{r},t)$ into its asymptotic value for $t=\pm\infty$ and a term converging to zero when $|t|\to\infty$. It will be seen in Sec. IV that (for large N)

$$\gamma_R^{\alpha\beta}(t)=N^{-2}\langle S^\alpha\rangle_T\langle S^\beta\rangle_T+\gamma'_R{}^{\alpha\beta}(t),\quad \lim_{|t|\to\infty}\gamma'_R{}^{\alpha\beta}(t)=0, \qquad (14)$$

with $\mathbf{S}=\sum_R\mathbf{S}_R$ the total spin of the system.[12] Similarly

$$G_R(\mathbf{r},t)=G_R^{(\infty)}(\mathbf{r})+G_R'(\mathbf{r},t),\quad \lim_{|t|\to\infty}G_R'(\mathbf{r},t)=0, \qquad (15)$$

$G_R^{(\infty)}$ has been calculated in II. Insertion of (14) into (6) gives

$$\Gamma_{\alpha\beta}(\mathbf{r},t)=N^{-2}\langle S^\alpha\rangle_T\langle S^\beta\rangle_T G(\mathbf{r},t)+\sum_R\gamma'_R{}^{\alpha\beta}(t)G_R(\mathbf{r},t), \qquad (16)$$

where

$$G(\mathbf{r},t)=\sum_R G_R(\mathbf{r},t) \qquad (17)$$

is the pair distribution function of the crystal which determines the coherent nuclear scattering (see II).

The part $d^2\sigma_1/d\Omega d\epsilon$ of the magnetic scattering originating from the first term in the right-hand side of Eq. (16) will thus be very similar to the coherent nuclear scattering.[13] The main difference results from the magnetic form factor $F(\kappa)$ occurring in Eq. (1), which will strongly depress all scattering processes with κ^{-1} of the order of atomic dimensions or smaller, and from the factor $N^{-2}\langle S^\alpha\rangle_T\langle S^\beta\rangle_T$ in (16) obviously related to the magnetization of the system. This scattering is elastic as far as the spin system is concerned. As far as the crystal vibrations are concerned it subdivides into an elastic and an inelastic subpart, obtained respectively by replacing G by $\sum_R G_R^{(\infty)}$ and $\sum_R G_R'$. The former subpart, i.e., the truly elastic magnetic scattering, is readily calculated to be

$$\left(\frac{d\sigma_{\text{magn}}}{d\Omega}\right)_{\text{el}}=\frac{1}{N}\left(\frac{2ge^2}{m_0c^2}\right)^2|F(\kappa)|^2\langle(\mathbf{S}\cdot\mathbf{S})-\kappa^{-2}(\mathbf{S}\cdot\boldsymbol{\kappa})^2\rangle_T \times\sum_R\int\exp(i\boldsymbol{\kappa}\cdot\mathbf{r})G_R^{(\infty)}(\mathbf{r})d\mathbf{r}.$$

Inserting the explicit expression of $G_R^{(\infty)}$ found in II, one gets

$$\left(\frac{d\sigma_{\text{magn}}}{d\Omega}\right)_{\text{el}}=\frac{8\pi^3}{Nv_0}\left(\frac{2ge^2}{m_0c^2}\right)^2|F(\kappa)|^2\cdot\langle(\mathbf{S}\cdot\mathbf{S})-\kappa^{-2}(\mathbf{S}\cdot\boldsymbol{\kappa})^2\rangle_T \times\exp\{-\langle(\boldsymbol{\kappa}\cdot\mathbf{u})^2\rangle_T\}\sum_\tau\delta(\boldsymbol{\kappa}-\boldsymbol{\tau}), \qquad (18)$$

where v_0 is the volume of the crystal cell, $\mathbf{u}$ is the displacement vector of any atom, and the $\boldsymbol{\tau}$'s are the reciprocal lattice vectors.[14] The exponential is the familiar Debye-Waller factor.

Whereas the total spin, i.e., the total magnetization, is the only magnetic property affecting the part $d^2\sigma_1/d\Omega d\epsilon$ of the cross section, the rest of the magnetic scattering, the cross section of which will be denoted by $d^2\sigma_2/d\Omega d\epsilon$, involves the last term in Eq. (16) and depends through $\gamma'_R{}^{\alpha\beta}(t)$ on the full space and time variation of the correlation (7). Only this part, which is inelastic in the spin system and will hereafter be called magnetic inelastic scattering, requires therefore a further analysis. We are at present interested in its main qualitative properties and for this purpose we can neglect the atomic displacements, thus replacing $G_R(\mathbf{r},t)$ by $\delta(\mathbf{r}-\mathbf{R})$. One

[12] In the ferromagnetic case, where $\langle\mathbf{S}\rangle_T\neq 0$, our considerations apply to scattering by one ferromagnetic domain. Except for very small angle effects (angles of the order of a few minutes), the scattering of various domains adds up incoherently.

[13] For a discussion of nuclear scattering by crystals and for a list of earlier papers devoted to it, see G. Placzek and L. Van Hove, Phys. Rev. 93, 1207 (1954).

[14] We define them as the vectors $\boldsymbol{\tau}$ for which $(2\pi)^{-1}(\boldsymbol{\tau}\cdot\mathbf{R})$ is an integer for each lattice vector $\mathbf{R}$. In suffix τ stands for $\boldsymbol{\tau}$.

gets

$$\frac{d^2\sigma_2}{d\Omega d\epsilon}=\left(\frac{2ge^2}{m_0c^2}\right)^2\frac{N}{2\pi\hbar}\cdot\frac{k}{k_0}\cdot|F(\kappa)|^2\cdot\sum_{\alpha,\beta}\left(\delta_{\alpha\beta}-\frac{\kappa_\alpha\kappa_\beta}{\kappa^2}\right)\times\sum_R\int dt\,\exp[i(\boldsymbol{\kappa}\cdot\mathbf{R}-\omega t)]\gamma'_R{}^{\alpha\beta}(t),\quad(19)$$

and, for a polycrystal,

$$\frac{d^2\sigma_2}{d\Omega d\epsilon}=\left(\frac{2ge^2}{m_0c^2}\right)^2\frac{N}{3\pi\hbar}\cdot\frac{k}{k_0}\cdot|F(\kappa)|^2\times\sum_R\int dt\,\exp[i(\boldsymbol{\kappa}\cdot\mathbf{R}-\omega t)]\gamma_R'(t),\quad(20)$$

with

$$\gamma_R'(t)=\gamma_R(t)-N^{-2}|\langle\mathbf{S}\rangle_T|^2.\quad(21)$$

At first sight it would seem that the atomic displacements could be approximately taken into account by simple insertion of the Debye-Waller factor $\exp\{-\langle(\boldsymbol{\kappa}\cdot\mathbf{u})^2\rangle_T\}$ into Eqs. (19) and (20). This would amount to the replacement of $G_R(\mathbf{r},t)$ by its asymptotic value $G_R^{(\infty)}(\mathbf{r})$ in the last term of Eq. (16). The improvement obtained in this way is however in general illusory, since the differences,

$$G_R'=G_R-G_R^{(\infty)},\quad G_R^{(\infty)}-\delta(\mathbf{r}-\mathbf{R}),$$

are of the same order of magnitude. It is only with the exact expression of $G_R(\mathbf{r},t)$, Eq. (II 53), that the effect of atomic vibrations can be calculated properly. Such a calculation is completely unwarranted at present in view of our poor knowledge of the magnetic correlation function $\gamma_R{}^{\alpha\beta}(t)$, with the exception of the low-temperature region where spin wave theory applies[11] and of the critical magnetic scattering occurring near the Curie point (Sec. V).

We now begin the discussion of the spin correlation function and of the effect of its properties on magnetic scattering. Only for temperatures small compared to the Curie temperature T_c is a complete calculation possible. It is briefly outlined in the next section. A general, qualitative discussion is then given for higher temperatures, comparable to T_c but not too close to it. The special long-range effects occurring near the Curie point are studied separately.

III. SPIN WAVE THEORY OF CORRELATION FUNCTION

For temperatures T small compared to T_c, in a ferromagnetic domain magnetized in the z direction, the spin operators $\mathbf{S}_R$ can be approximately represented by[15]

[15] T. Holstein and H. Primakoff, Phys. Rev. **58**, 1098 (1940).

$$\left.\begin{aligned}S_R{}^x&=(s_0/2N)^{\frac12}\textstyle\sum_q\exp(i\mathbf{q}\cdot\mathbf{R})(a_q{}^*+a_{-q})\\ S_R{}^y&=(s_0/2N)^{\frac12}i\textstyle\sum_q\exp(i\mathbf{q}\cdot\mathbf{R})\cdot(a_q{}^*-a_{-q})\\ S_R{}^z&=s_0-N^{-1}[\textstyle\sum_q\exp(i\mathbf{q}\cdot\mathbf{R})a_q{}^*]\\ &\qquad\times[\textstyle\sum_q\exp(-i\mathbf{q}\cdot\mathbf{R})a_q]\end{aligned}\right\}\quad(22)$$

We assume the domain to have $N^{\frac13}$ cells along each of the three lattice axes. The vector $\mathbf{q}$[16] runs then over the values

$$\mathbf{q}=N^{-\frac13}(n_1\boldsymbol{\tau}_1+n_2\boldsymbol{\tau}_2+n_3\boldsymbol{\tau}_3),$$

where $\boldsymbol{\tau}_1$, $\boldsymbol{\tau}_2$, $\boldsymbol{\tau}_3$ are basic vectors of the reciprocal lattice, and n_1, n_2, n_3 take all integral values in the interval $-\frac12N^{\frac13}<n_i\leqslant\frac12N^{\frac13}$. The only nonvanishing commutators of the operators a_q, $a_q{}^*$ are

$$a_qa_q{}^*-a_q{}^*a_q=1.$$

Equations (22) are valid apart from terms of third and higher order in the a_q and $a_q{}^*$. In the same approximation the Hamiltonian (9) of the spin system reduces to

$$H_0=-Ns_0{}^2(\textstyle\sum_R J_R)+\hbar\sum_q\omega_qa_q{}^*a_q,\quad(23)$$

with

$$\hbar\omega_q=2s_0\textstyle\sum_R J_R[1-\cos(\mathbf{q}\cdot\mathbf{R})].\quad(24)$$

The operators $a_q{}^*$ and a_q respectively create and annihilate an excitation of wave vector $\mathbf{q}$ and frequency ω_q. Following Bloch[17] such excitations are called spin waves. In the present approximation there is no interaction between spin waves.

On the basis of Eqs. (22) and (23) the calculation of the time-dependent correlation (7) is straightforward. It leads to the following result, valid in the limit of large N:

$$\gamma_R{}^{xx}(t)=\gamma_R{}^{yy}(t)=\frac{v_0s_0}{16\pi^3}\int d\mathbf{q}\cdot\{1-\exp(-\hbar\beta\omega_q)\}^{-1}\times\{\exp[-i(\mathbf{R}\cdot\mathbf{q}-t\omega_q)]+\exp(-\hbar\beta\omega_q)\cdot\exp[i(\mathbf{R}\cdot\mathbf{q}-t\omega_q)]\},$$

$$\gamma_R{}^{xy}(t)=-\gamma_R{}^{yx}(t)=\frac{v_0s_0i}{16\pi^3}\int d\mathbf{q}\cdot\{1-\exp(-\hbar\beta\omega_q)\}^{-1}\times\{\exp[-i(\mathbf{R}\cdot\mathbf{q}-t\omega_q)]-\exp(-\hbar\beta\omega_q)\cdot\exp[i(\mathbf{R}\cdot\mathbf{q}-t\omega_q)]\},$$

$$\gamma_R{}^{zz}(t)=N^{-2}\langle S_z\rangle^2{}_T=N^{-2}|\langle\mathbf{S}\rangle_T|^2=s_0{}^2-\frac{v_0s_0}{4\pi^3}\int d\mathbf{q}\frac{\exp(-\hbar\beta\omega_q)}{1-\exp(-\hbar\beta\omega_q)},$$

$$\gamma_R{}^{xz}(t)=\gamma_R{}^{yz}(t)=0.$$

β is the reciprocal of k_BT and the integration extends over one cell of the reciprocal lattice. The vector $\mathbf{S}$ is the total spin $\sum_R\mathbf{S}_R$.

[16] q stands for $\mathbf{q}$ when in suffix.

[17] F. Bloch, Z. Physik **61**, 206 (1930).

TABLE I. Magnetic inelastic cross section from spin wave theory.

T in °K	0	100	200	300	400	500	600
σ_2/λ_0 in mb per A	0	0.4	1.7	3.5	5.5	8	10

From these formulas a closed expression of the magnetic scattering cross section $d^2\sigma_2/d\Omega d\epsilon$ at low temperature is obtained by insertion into (19). The result is of course equivalent with what follows from a direct spin wave treatment of the scattering problem, as given by Moorhouse.[11] We refer to this author for a detailed discussion. It will be enough to mention here, for comparison with the transmission measurements of Palevsky and Hughes[3] and of Squires,[4] the numerical values of the total cross section,

$$\sigma_2=\int (d^2\sigma_2/d\Omega d\epsilon)d\Omega d\epsilon,$$

in the long wavelength region ($\lambda_0=2\pi/k_0\gg 2A$) where it is proportional to the incident wavelength λ_0. They have been calculated for iron, with the value $s_0=1$ for the atomic spin and the value $J=205$°K for the exchange interaction between nearest neighbors.[18] Table I gives the values of σ_2/λ_0 in millibarns per angstrom for various temperatures T. A comparison with the observations of Palevsky and Hughes is shown in the figure of I.[5] It gives a crude idea of the domain of validity of spin wave theory for the magnetic cross section σ_2. It is certainly limited to the low-temperature region ($T\lesssim 300°$) where σ_2 is quite small compared to the nuclear scattering cross section, and where the magnetic scattering could thus better be separated by its peculiar angular and energy distribution, as discussed by Moorhouse.[11]

As far as our present aims are concerned, the main interest of spin wave theory is to provide us with an explicit expression for the correlation $\gamma_R^{\alpha\beta}(t)$ for at least one temperature region, however restricted it may be. One can, for example, discuss the convergence of the correlation toward its asymptotic value $N^{-2}\langle S^\alpha\rangle_T\langle S^\beta\rangle_T$ when R or $|t|\rightarrow\infty$. It is determined by the convergence to zero of $\gamma_R^{xx}(t)$ and $\gamma_R^{xy}(t)$ as expressed in the formulas above. At any nonvanishing temperature and for $R\rightarrow\infty$, the convergence is in R^{-1}, as a consequence of the singularity of $\{1-\exp(-\hbar\beta\omega_q)\}^{-1}$ at $\mathbf{q}=0$,

$$\{1-\exp(-\hbar\beta\omega_q)\}^{-1}\simeq(\hbar\beta\omega_q)^{-1}\propto q^{-2}.$$

For $|t|\rightarrow\infty$ the convergence is in $|t|^{-\frac{3}{2}}$; this last result is best obtained by the method of stationary phases already used in the section of II devoted to crystals. The slow convergence, especially in R, is characteristic of the low-temperature region. As the temperature goes up, the number of spin waves excited increases rapidly and their interactions start playing a predominant role. The main effect of these interactions on the correlation is to make it converge much more rapidly toward its asymptotic value. The energy distribution of magnetically scattered neutrons, highly singular at low temperature, becomes correspondingly smoother.

Another interesting point concerns the time-dependent correlation at absolute zero. It has the following expression:

$$\gamma_R^{xx}(t)=\gamma_R^{yy}(t)=-i\gamma_R^{xy}(t)=i\gamma_R^{yx}(t)$$
$$=\frac{v_0s_0}{16\pi^3}\int\exp[-i(\mathbf{R}\cdot\mathbf{q}-t\omega_q)]d\mathbf{q}, \quad (25)$$
$$\gamma_R^{zz}(t)=s_0^2,\quad \gamma_R^{xz}(t)=\gamma_R^{yz}(t)=0.$$

Although the convergence of the first four components toward zero is again in $|t|^{-\frac{3}{2}}$ for large times, the convergence in R for finite t is quite different from what it is at positive temperatures: from the expression (24) of the spin wave frequency one can show it to be exponential with a range of order of a few interatomic distances for all times not very large compared to $\hbar/J$, where J is the exchange interaction for nearest neighbors. In this case, however, despite the rapid convergence of the correlation for $R\rightarrow\infty$, the angular and energy distribution of scattered neutrons is still highly singular. This is possible only in view of the very special functional form of the right-hand side in Eq. (25).

IV. THE CORRELATION FUNCTION AT GENERAL TEMPERATURES

At temperatures too high for the application of spin wave theory, no explicit calculation is possible for either the inelastic scattering cross section $d^2\sigma_2/d\Omega d\epsilon$ or the time-dependent correlation $\gamma_R^{\alpha\beta}(t)$. It is in such a situation that the description of the scattering in terms of the correlation is actually useful, since the properties of the correlation, with their more direct significance in space and time, are easier to discuss on an approximate basis than those of the scattering. We limit ourselves in the present paper to the most qualitative features of the correlation and to their consequences for the temperature dependence of the magnetic inelastic scattering.

The first point to discuss is the limiting value of

$$\gamma_R^{\alpha\beta}(t)=\langle S_0^\alpha(0)S_R^\beta(t)\rangle_T \quad (26)$$

for R or $|t|\rightarrow\infty$. Under the assumption that the spin system is large (N large), as is usually the case in statistical mechanics, the two factors in the right-hand side of Eq. (26) will be statistically independent as soon as they refer to locations sufficiently distant in space or instants sufficiently distant in time. We thus have, for large R or $|t|$,

$$\gamma_R^{\alpha\beta}(t)\simeq\langle S_0^\alpha(0)\rangle_T\langle S_R^\beta(t)\rangle_T,$$

[18] This value is determined from the low-temperature variation of the magnetization. See C. Kittel, Revs. Modern Phys. 21, 541 (1949), especially Eq. (2.1.17).

and, since $\langle S_R^\beta(t)\rangle_T$ is independent of $\mathbf{R}$ and t,

$$\gamma_R^{\alpha\beta}(t)\simeq N^{-2}\langle S^\alpha\rangle_T\langle S^\beta\rangle_T = s_T^\alpha s_T^\beta, \quad (27)$$

where $\mathbf{S}=\sum_R \mathbf{S}_R$ is the total spin and $\mathbf{s}_T=N^{-1}\langle\mathbf{S}\rangle_T$ is the average spin vector per atom. Above the Curie point $\mathbf{s}_T=0$. Below the Curie point, the foregoing argument and equations apply to a single ferromagnetic domain, in which the magnetization has a definite orientation, so that $\mathbf{s}_T\neq 0$.

Equation (27) requires a further comment. It is possible to derive an apparently different asymptotic formula for the correlation, namely,

$$\gamma_R^{\alpha\beta}(t)\simeq N^{-2}\langle S^\alpha(0)S^\beta(t)\rangle_T. \quad (28)$$

For t finite and $R\rightarrow\infty$, it follows from the fact that if $\gamma_R^{\alpha\beta}(t)$ has a limit, the latter can be written for large N in the form $N^{-1}\sum_R \gamma_R^{\alpha\beta}(t)$, leading readily to (28). For R fixed and $|t|\rightarrow\infty$, Eq. (28) is also found to hold if one makes the assumption that the Hamiltonian is invariant for simultaneous rotations of all spins, as in Eq. (9). Actually, of course, Eqs. (27) and (28) are equivalent in the limit of large systems, $N\rightarrow\infty$. The total spin, although of order N, has then a mean square fluctuation of the same order, so that the average of the product in Eq. (28) can be replaced by the product of the averages, the error in the equation being of order N^{-1} and thus negligible.

The consequences of the asymptotic formula (27) for scattering have been discussed in Sec. II. The asymptotic value of the correlation was shown to determine the part $d^2\sigma_1/d\Omega d\epsilon$ of the scattering which is elastic in the spin system.

We consider next the *range* r_0 and *relaxation time* t_0 of the correlation (26), i.e., the distance and time interval such that Eq. (27) holds for $R\gg r_0$, t arbitrary and for $|t|\gg t_0$, R arbitrary. They have meaning only when the convergence of the correlation toward the asymptotic value (27) is rapid, a condition which is expected to be always verified except at very low temperature (see foregoing section) and near the Curie point, where long-range and slowly varying spontaneous fluctuations of the magnetization affect the correlation (see Sec. V).[19]

Unless one solves first the difficult theoretical problem of finding reliable approximate methods for the calculation of the time-dependent correlation, it is not possible, outside the exceptional temperature regions mentioned above, to determine the actual dependence of $\gamma_R^{\alpha\beta}(t)$ or $\mathbf{R}$ and t, nor even to give an accurate theoretical definition of the range r_0 and the relaxation time t_0. All that can be done is to predict their orders of magnitude. Whereas r_0 must be of order of a few interatomic distances, t_0 is presumably of order of a somewhat larger multiple of the period $\hbar/J$ associated with the interaction J between spins. These estimates, which are known to be correct for liquids (J being replaced by the intermolecular interaction) and can be sharpened on the basis of the experimental data (see below), must hold for temperatures both below and above the Curie point. One would also expect that r_0 and t_0 do not vary too rapidly with the temperature T as long as it does not approach absolute zero or the Curie temperature T_c. It is clear however that, quantitatively, there must be a definite variation with T and a definite difference between the regions $T<T_c$ and $T>T_c$.

Beyond asymptotic value, range and relaxation time, another very important aspect of the time-dependent correlation about which one would like to have at least some qualitative information is its decomposition into real and imaginary parts. In the low-temperature region where spin wave theory applies, the situation is quite simple. As seen immediately from the expressions given in Sec. III, only the real part of the correlation varies with temperature, the imaginary part retaining always the value it has at absolute zero. Although so simple a behavior cannot rigorously prevail at higher temperatures, it is probably always true that the imaginary part $\mathrm{Im}\gamma_R^{\alpha\beta}(t)$, which is due to the noncommutativity of $S_0^\alpha(0)$ and $S_R^\beta(t)$, has a much weaker temperature dependence than the real part. Definite support for this prediction is obtained by considering the asymptotic value of $\mathrm{Im}\gamma_R^{\alpha\beta}(t)$ for R or $|t|\rightarrow\infty$ and the range over which it converges toward this value for $R\rightarrow\infty$. As follows from Eq. (27), the asymptotic value is zero for all temperatures. From what was said in Sec. III on the correlation at absolute zero and from the discussion of r_0 in the present section, one concludes that the range of $\mathrm{Im}\gamma_R^{\alpha\beta}(t)$ for $R\rightarrow\infty$ is of microscopic magnitude at low as well as at general temperatures. This remains true even in the neighborhood of the Curie point since the long-range part which is then present in the correlation originates from macroscopic fluctuations and is therefore real (see Sec. V). Both the asymptotic value of $\mathrm{Im}\gamma_R^{\alpha\beta}(t)$ and the order of magnitude of its convergence range are thus independent of temperature.

Returning now to magnetic scattering of neutrons, we want to extract from the admittedly very crude and incomplete considerations just developed some equally

[19] Even away from these exceptional temperatures, the convergence of the correlation for $|t|\rightarrow\infty$ is not strictly short ranged. The actual situation is very likely to be the following. For sufficiently small $|t|$, the $\mathbf{R}$ dependence of $\gamma_R^{\alpha\beta}(t)$ extends only over R values of microscopic dimension of which r_0 gives a measure and which do not exceed a few interatomic distances. This microscopic $\mathbf{R}$ dependence of the correlation is completely damped after a certain time interval, namely for $|t|\gg t_0$, thus giving a slightly more precise definition of the relaxation time t_0. For $|t|\gg t_0$, $\gamma_R^{\alpha\beta}(t)$ reduces to a small macroscopic function, practically constant over microscopic distances, decreasing with time as $|t|^{-\frac{3}{2}}$ and having a macroscopic range in space which increases as $|t|^{\frac{1}{2}}$. This macroscopic part of the correlation, which is entirely due to macroscopic fluctuations, plays no appreciable role in neutron scattering. Although it was not mentioned in II, a similar long-range part should exist for the pair distribution function $G(r,t)$ in liquids and dense gases. Although again unimportant for neutrons in the presently available wavelength range, it affects light scattering, the properties of which were deduced directly from macroscopic fluctuation theory by L. Landau and G. Placzek, Physik Z. Sowjetunion, 5, 172 (1934). A detailed exposition and discussion of the above remarks will be left to another publication.

crude consequences concerning the temperature dependence of the magnetic inelastic scattering (total cross section σ_2 in the notation of Sec. II). We restrict ourselves to polycrystals. We have thus to consider only the scalar correlation $\gamma_R(t)$ defined in Eq. (13), and the difference $\gamma_R'(t)$ defined in Eq. (21). As far as these functions are concerned, the results of our discussion can be summarized as follows:

(i) For R or $|t|\rightarrow\infty$, $\gamma_R(t)$ converges to s_T^2 and $\gamma_R'(t)$ converges to zero.

(ii) $\gamma_0(0)=s_0(s_0+1)$ and $\gamma_0'(0)=s_0+s_0^2-s_T^2$.

(iii) The convergence in (i) takes place over distances and time intervals which do not change rapidly with temperature, the low-temperature region and the neighborhood of the Curie point T_c being excepted.

(iv) The common imaginary part of $\gamma_R(t)$ and $\gamma_R'(t)$ depends much less on temperature than the real parts of these functions.

These qualitative facts indicate that, if the temperature is increased from the upper limit of validity of spin wave theory (around 200°K or 300°K at most for iron) up to a temperature close to the Curie point T_c (some 100°K below $T_c=1043$°K for iron), the main variation in the function $\gamma_R'(t)$ affects its real part, and, without radical change in its range of convergence toward zero, its value $\gamma_0'(0)$ at $R=t=0$ increases from a number very close to s_0 to a number close to $s_0+s_0^2$. Such a rapid variation of magnitude is on the contrary absent in the temperature range starting somewhat above T_c (around T_c+100°K for iron). As a consequence, in view of Eq. (20), one expects a marked increase of the magnetic inelastic scattering (cross section σ_2) when the temperature varies from low values up to the neighborhood of the Curie point, whereas the temperature variation should be less pronounced beyond the neighborhood of the Curie point. The rapid increase of the cross section σ_2 with temperature below T_c must be particularly striking when the incident neutrons are very slow, so that practically no magnetic scattering takes place at low temperature. One expects then an increase roughly proportional to

$$\gamma_0'(0)-[\gamma_0'(0)]_{T=0}=s_0^2-s_T^2, \qquad (29)$$

i.e., proportional to $1-(I_T/I_0)^2$, where I_T is the intensity of magnetization of the magnetic domains at temperature T and I_0 the same quantity at absolute zero. Qualitatively, as shown in I, this expectation is in agreement with the temperature variations of σ_2 for iron, measured by Palevsky and Hughes[3] for neutrons of wavelength ranging from 5 to 13 A, and by Squires[4] for neutrons of 7 A.

No quantitative agreement can of course be hoped for since the actual shape of $\gamma_R(t)$ must unavoidably change to a certain extent with temperature. A measurement of the angular and energy distribution of scattered neutrons would indeed reveal a much more complicated temperature dependence than the simple proportionality factor (29). All we can say at present about this distribution concerns a rough order of magnitude for average momentum and energy transfers in magnetic scattering. From the Fourier transformations in Eqs. (19) and (20) the transfers have to be of order $\hbar/r_0$ and $\hbar/t_0$, respectively, for all incident neutron wavelengths λ_0 for which the collective properties of the spin system appreciably affect the scattering ($\lambda_0 \gtrsim 1$ A).

As already mentioned, in order to go beyond the quite crude considerations of this section, in particular to obtain more theoretical information on the angular and energy distribution of scattered neutrons, one has to develop proper approximate methods for the quantitative determination of the correlation. Although this problem falls outside the scope of the present paper, we would like to stress its importance and its interest from the standpoint of general statistical mechanics. Regarding the absolute magnitude of the total cross section, although its accurate calculation would also require a complete determination of the correlation, it is possible to check the consistency of the observed values with the expected orders of magnitude of correlation range r_0 and relaxation time t_0 by choosing some reasonable analytical form for the $\mathbf{R}$ and t dependence of $\gamma_R(t)$. This has been done by C. E. Porter for the case of iron, using the experimental data of Palevsky and Hughes[3] and of Squires.[4] Consistency is obtained for $r_0 \simeq 2.3v_0^{\frac{1}{3}}$ (v_0 volume per particle) and $t_0 \simeq 23\hbar/J$, and the requirement that reasonable values be obtained for both r_0 and t_0 turns out to determine the two quantities within surprisingly narrow limits, especially t_0 (within some 50 percent). The fact that the microscopic relaxation time t_0 can be determined with fair accuracy from a total scattering cross section measurement is noteworthy and illustrates strikingly the close relationship between inelastic scattering and time-dependence of the correlation between spin orientations.

To the main qualitative feature encountered for the temperature dependence of the magnetic inelastic scattering, namely, a rapid increase with temperature below the Curie point, roughly governed by the decrease of the magnetization, and a less pronounced temperature variation above T_c, one has, of course, to superimpose the very sudden and sharp increase in scattering when the Curie point is approached from below and from above. This additional scattering, the study of which is the object of the next section, is responsible for the sharp peaks observed at the Curie point by Palevsky and Hughes as well as by Squires in the σ_2 *versus* temperature curve for iron.

V. THE NEIGHBORHOOD OF THE CURIE POINT

From the fact that the susceptibility of a ferromagnet increases without limit as the Curie point is approached, there results an unbounded increase in magnitude for the spontaneous fluctuations of the magnetization. These fluctuations in turn scatter neutrons with increasing intensity. Since the fluctuations extend over distances large compared to interatomic distances and decay over times long compared to the microscopic relaxation time t_0 considered above, they produce magnetic scattering with an angular and energy distribution radically different from what is expected at general temperatures. At the same time, from the theoretical standpoint, the applicability of macroscopic methods makes a more complete discussion possible, at least for temperatures above T_c.

Basically the phenomenon under study is very similar to the abnormally abundant scattering occurring in a liquid or a dense gas near critical conditions. In this case, as the critical point is approached, the spontaneous density fluctuations at constant pressure increase indefinitely in magnitude and produce an increasing amount of scattering both for electromagnetic waves (x-rays or light; for light the phenomenon is known as critical opalescence) and for neutrons. In the case of electromagnetic waves it is a very good approximation to neglect the energy transferred by scattering in comparison to the incident energy. The scattering depends then only on the average instantaneous shape of the density distribution as seen from a particle. This shape, expressed by the familiar pair distribution $g(r)$, has been calculated near critical conditions, for T above the critical temperature and r macroscopic, by Ornstein and Zernike, who thus were able to derive the properties of critical scattering in the electromagnetic case.[20] The extension of this theory to neutrons, for which the ratio of energy transfers to incident energy is much larger, requires a knowledge of the time variation of the average density distribution as seen from a point where a particle passed at some initial time. The proper description is given by the time-dependent pair distribution $G(r,t)$ introduced in II, and its calculation near critical conditions, for macroscopic distances and arbitrary times, is carried out in Sec. IV of that paper on the basis of the phenomenological equation for heat conduction.

An entirely analogous procedure can be followed to deal with the present problem of what we might call *critical magnetic scattering*, at temperatures above the Curie point and close to it. One has to calculate the correlation $\gamma_R^{\alpha\beta}(t)$ for R large compared to interatomic distances by determining first, from statistical considerations analogous to those of Ornstein and Zernike, the instantaneous correlation $\gamma_R^{\alpha\beta}(0)$, and by then deriving the time dependence from the phenomenological theory of macroscopic irreversible processes. These two steps will now be carried out under the simplifying assumption that the properties of the spin system are invariant with respect to simultaneous relations of all spins. The correlation $\gamma_R^{\alpha\beta}(t)$ is then of the form $\frac{1}{3}\delta_{\alpha\beta}\gamma_R(t)$, at least in the absence of external magnetic field, and the calculation can be restricted to the scalar correlation $\gamma_R(t)$.

Following the Ornstein-Zernike method in the improved form given to it by Klein and Tisza,[21] we imagine the crystal to be divided into a cubic array of identical cells, of macroscopic size but small compared to the total dimensions of the crystal. We denote by $\mathbf{M}_j$ the magnetic moment of the jth cell. Since the temperature T is assumed larger than T_c, $\mathbf{M}_j$ fluctuates around a vanishing mean value. In view of the macroscopic size of the cells the joined probability distribution of the vectors $\mathbf{M}_j$ is Gaussian:

$$\text{prob}=A\exp\{-\tfrac{1}{2}a_0\textstyle\sum \mathbf{M}_j\cdot\mathbf{M}_j+a_1\sum \mathbf{M}_j\cdot\mathbf{M}_{j'}\},$$

where the first sum extends over all cells and the second over all pairs of adjacent cells. a_0 and a_1 are positive constants depending on the temperature. A is a normalization constant. Consider now the correlation $\langle\mathbf{M}_j\cdot\mathbf{M}_l\rangle_T$ between the magnetic moments of two cells. It depends only on the relative position of the cells j and l and verifies the equation,

$$a_0\langle\mathbf{M}_j\cdot\mathbf{M}_l\rangle_T-a_1\sum_{j'}\langle\mathbf{M}_{j'}\cdot\mathbf{M}_l\rangle_T=3\delta_{jl}, \tag{30}$$

with the sum extending over the cells adjacent to j. This equation results from the Gaussian character of the probability distribution. It gives immediately for the fluctuation of the total magnetic moment $\mathbf{M}=\sum_j\mathbf{M}_j$,

$$\langle\mathbf{M}\cdot\mathbf{M}\rangle_T=3n(a_0-za_1)^{-1},$$

where n and z are the number of cells in the crystal and the number of cells adjacent to a given cell. The same fluctuation is obtained independently from thermodynamical fluctuation theory,

$$\langle\mathbf{M}\cdot\mathbf{M}\rangle_T=3Vk_BT\psi,$$

V being the volume of the crystal and χ the magnetic susceptibility. From the two last equations,

$$(a_0-za_1)^{-1}=vk_BT\chi, \tag{31}$$

with v the cell volume.

As the Curie point is approached χ increases indefinitely; a_0-za_1 is thus seen to approach zero, so that the correlation occurring in Eq. (30) must have a longer and longer range for the equation to be satisfied. When this range is long compared to the cell dimension $v^{\frac{1}{3}}$, the correlation between cells separated by a distance $R\gg v^{\frac{1}{3}}$ can be identified with the instantaneous correlation $\gamma_R(0)$ according to the equation

$$\langle\mathbf{M}_j\cdot\mathbf{M}_l\rangle_T\simeq(2\beta v/v_0)^2\gamma_R(0),$$

where $\beta=\hbar e/2m_0c$ is the Bohr magneton. In this case the long-range part of $\gamma_R(0)$ can thus be obtained from the solution of Eq. (30), itself easily derived by Fourier

[20] L. S. Ornstein and F. Zernike, Proc. Am. Acad. Arts. Sci. **17**, 793 (1914).

[21] M. J. Klein and L. Tisza, Phys. Rev. **76**, 1861 (1949).

analysis.[22] Taking the asymptotic expression of the solution for small values of $v^{\frac{1}{3}}/R$ and of a_0-za_1 (T near T_c), and using further Eq. (31), one finds

$$\gamma_R(0)\simeq(4\pi r_1^2R)^{-1}v_0s_0(s_0+1)\cdot\exp(-\kappa_1R) \qquad (32)$$

in terms of two lengths r_1 and κ_1^{-1}, related by the formula

$$(\kappa_1r_1)^2=\chi_1/\chi, \qquad (33)$$

where χ_1 is the value which the susceptibility would have at temperature T if there were no exchange interaction between the spins (paramagnetic susceptibility),

$$\chi_1=4\beta^2s_0(s_0+1)/(3k_BTv_0).$$

In contrast with the product κ_1r_1 the length r_1 is unavoidably obtained in terms of the cell size and of the constant a_1,

$$r_1^2=\tfrac{1}{6}k_BT\chi_1za_1v^{5/3}, \qquad (34)$$

although its occurrence in Eqs. (32) and (33) clearly establishes its independence of the cell system. Equation (34) shows that r_1 does not vary rapidly with temperature even in the neighborhood of the Curie point. Its order of magnitude is easily obtained from the following remark. For T rising to values substantially larger than T_c, the ratio χ/χ_1 decreases rapidly to values of order one, and, from Eq. (33), the range κ_1^{-1} decreases toward values of order r_1. We know, on the other hand, that the range has to decrease to microscopic size, so that r_1 must certainly be of microscopic dimension, probably of the same order as the correlation range r_0 for temperatures outside the neighborhood of the Curie point (Sec. IV). Whereas r_1 is thus seen to be a microscopic length changing little with temperature, κ_1^{-1} behaves, of course, quite differently. Indeed, for T decreasing toward T_c, the right-hand side of (33) approaches zero and the range κ_1^{-1} of $\gamma_R(0)$ grows beyond any limit until the Curie point is reached and the correlation becomes

$$\gamma_R(0)\simeq(4\pi r_1^2R)^{-1}v_0s_0(s_0+1).$$

Our derivation of Eq. (32) holds only when R and the range κ_1^{-1} are large compared to the cell size. Since the cell size can be chosen at will with the only restriction that it be macroscopic, the essential limits of validity of Eq. (32) are

$$R\gg v_0^{\frac{1}{3}}, \quad \kappa_1v_0^{\frac{1}{3}}=(v_0^{\frac{1}{3}}/r_1)(\chi_1/\chi)^{\frac{1}{2}}\ll 1,$$

or, more quantitatively,

$$R\gtrsim 10v_0^{\frac{1}{3}}, \quad \kappa_1v_0^{\frac{1}{3}}\lesssim 0.1. \qquad (35)$$

The last condition defines the upper limit T_1 of the temperature interval $T_c\leqslant T\lesssim T_1$ to which the considerations of the present section apply. Its actual determination is, however, difficult, even with full knowledge of the susceptibility χ, because of the uncertainty concerning the actual magnitude of r_1. The best procedure at present would probably be to consider r_1 as a parameter and to determine its value from neutron scattering data.

Before turning to the time variation of the correlation we want still to draw attention to the complete similarity between Eqs. (32), (33) and the analogous Eqs. (II 36), (II 37) derived in II for the long-range pair distribution function in gases near critical conditions. In particular, the part played there by the isothermal compressibility χ_T is taken here by the magnetic susceptibility χ and the isothermal compressibility in absence of forces $(\rho k_BT)^{-1}$ (ideal gas) is here replaced by the paramagnetic susceptibility χ_1.

The time dependence of the correlation $\gamma_R(t)$ must now be derived for macroscopic R. For the reasons explained in II in the case of gases near critical conditions, the time dependence is given by the average decay in time of fluctuations of the magnetization, itself described by the phenomenological equations for irreversible processes in the spin system. A formal derivation of the latter from the conservation equations and the equation for entropy production can be obtained by the methods of the thermodynamics of irreversible processes in a way entirely similar to the derivation of the Navier-Stokes equations.[23] The situation is here particularly simple above the Curie point if, with a good approximation, the system is invariant for simultaneous rotations of all spins. For reasons of invariance the phenomenological equations contain then no coupling between the magnetization and any other macroscopic variable. The equation for the density of magnetization $\mathfrak{M}(\mathbf{r},t)$ is of the diffusion type

$$\partial\mathfrak{M}/\partial t=(\lambda/\chi)\Delta\mathfrak{M}, \qquad (36)$$

where Δ is the Laplacian in $\mathbf{r}$ and λ a phenomenological constant related by

$$\tau(S)=\frac{\lambda}{T\chi^2}\sum_{\alpha,\beta}\left(\frac{\partial\mathfrak{M}_\alpha}{\partial x_\beta}\right)^2 \qquad (37)$$

to the amount $\tau(S)$ of entropy produced per unit volume and unit time by the dissipative processes occurring when the system returns to equilibrium from a state characterized by an inhomogeneous distribution of magnetization of small magnitude. The constant λ in Eqs. (36) and (37) is so chosen that the entropy production $\tau(S)$ does no longer contain the susceptibility χ when (37) is expressed in terms of the intensive variable conjugate to $\mathfrak{M}$ in the sense of thermodynamics. This variable (the magnetic field which would produce the

[22] For this solution see Klein and Tisza (reference 21), also F. Zernike, Physica 7, 565 (1940) where a similar equation is studied in connection with the order-disorder problem.

[23] For the phenomenological theory of irreversible processes, see I. Prigogine, *Etude Thermodynamique des Phénomènes Irréversibles* (Editions Desoer, Liège, 1947), and S. R. de Groot, *Thermodynamics of Irreversible Processes* (North-Holland Publishing Company, Amsterdam and Interscience Publishers, New York, 1951).

magnetization) retains spontaneous fluctuations of normal size even when T approaches T_c, so that λ remains finite in the neighborhood of the Curie point.[24] It would clearly be desirable to get some insight into the actual mechanism of the dissipative processes here involved and to obtain in this way for Eq. (36) and for the finiteness of λ a more reliable justification than the highly formal derivation sketched above. One would then get also a theoretical estimate of the order of magnitude of λ. No attempt will be made to answer these questions here.

Accepting the validity of Eq. (36) we conclude immediately that the decay in time of a plane wave fluctuation of the magnetization is given by the factor $\exp(-\Lambda_1 k^2 t)$ for $t>0$, with $\mathbf{k}$ the wave vector and $\Lambda_1=\lambda/\chi$.[25] Proceeding as in II, one obtains

$$\gamma_R(t)\simeq(4\pi r_1^2)^{-1}v_0 s_0(s_0+1)(4\pi\Lambda_1|t|)^{-\frac{3}{2}}\times\int\exp\left\{-\frac{|\mathbf{R}-\mathbf{R}'|^2}{4\Lambda_1|t|}-\kappa_1 R'\right\}\cdot\frac{d\mathbf{R}'}{R'},\quad(38)$$

or

$$\gamma_R(t)\simeq(4\pi r_1^2 R)^{-1}v_0 s_0(s_0+1)\Psi[\kappa_1(4\Lambda_1|t|)^{\frac{1}{2}},R(4\Lambda_1|t|)^{-\frac{1}{2}}],$$

in terms of the function Ψ defined in II, Eq. (II 43). These equations hold in the R and T ranges defined by Eqs. (35), for all macroscopic times.

The cross section for critical magnetic scattering can now be obtained by replacing $\gamma_R'^{\alpha\beta}(t)$ in Eq. (19) by $\frac{1}{3}\delta_{\alpha\beta}\gamma_R(t)$ as given by Eq. (38). The calculation is straightforward and gives for a single crystal

$$\left(\frac{d^2\sigma}{d\Omega d\epsilon}\right)_{\text{crit}}=\left(\frac{2ge^2}{m_0c^2}\right)^2\frac{2N}{3\pi\hbar}s_0(s_0+1)\frac{k}{k_0}|F(\kappa)|^2\times\sum_\tau\frac{1}{r_1^2\{|\boldsymbol{\kappa}-\boldsymbol{\tau}|^2+\kappa_1^2\}}\cdot\frac{\Lambda|\boldsymbol{\kappa}-\boldsymbol{\tau}|^2}{\Lambda_1^2|\boldsymbol{\kappa}-\boldsymbol{\tau}|^4+\omega^2}.\quad(39)$$

This formula, which is applicable only in the temperature interval $T_c\lesssim T\lesssim T_1$ here defined by the condition $\kappa_1 v_0^{\frac{1}{3}}\lesssim 0.1$, must be understood as describing a special type of scattering which appears in addition to the general scattering described in the last section when the Curie point is approached. Since both Λ_1 and κ_1 tend to zero when $T\to T_c$, this scattering is characterized by small energy transfers and by momentum transfers $\hbar\boldsymbol{\kappa}$ with $\boldsymbol{\kappa}$ close to some reciprocal lattice vector $\boldsymbol{\tau}$

$$|\boldsymbol{\kappa}-\boldsymbol{\tau}|\ll v_0^{-\frac{1}{3}},\quad \hbar\omega\ll J,\quad(40)$$

where J gives the order of magnitude of energy transfers in noncritical scattering. The conditions (40) give at the same time the limits of applicability of Eq. (39). It is seen in particular that in the sum over reciprocal lattice vectors only one term can be significant for each scattering, namely, the term belonging to the vector $\boldsymbol{\tau}$ for which the first condition (40) holds.

Equation (19), and thus Eq. (39), neglect the atomic vibrations. In the case of the critical scattering, in view of the slow variation of the long-range correlation (38) with $\mathbf{R}$ and t, it is consistent to take the atomic vibrations partly into account by replacing $\delta(\mathbf{r}-\mathbf{R})$ by $G_R^{(\infty)}(\mathbf{r})$ in the derivation of Eq. (19). The improvement thus obtained in Eq. (39) is the multiplication of the cross section by the Debye-Waller factor $\exp\{-\langle(\boldsymbol{\kappa}\cdot\mathbf{u})^2\rangle_T\}$. It does not affect the very special distribution of momentum and energy transfers described by the conditions (40). In view of the first of these, the cross section can be written[26]

$$\left(\frac{d^2\sigma}{d\Omega d\epsilon}\right)_{\text{crit}}=\left(\frac{2ge^2}{m_0c^2}\right)^2\frac{2N}{3\pi\hbar}s_0(s_0+1)\frac{k}{k_0}|F(\kappa)|^2\times\sum_\tau\frac{\exp\{-\langle(\boldsymbol{\tau}\cdot\mathbf{u})^2\rangle_T\}}{r_1^2\{|\boldsymbol{\kappa}-\boldsymbol{\tau}|^2+\kappa_1^2\}}\cdot\frac{\Lambda_1|\boldsymbol{\kappa}-\boldsymbol{\tau}|^2}{\Lambda_1^2|\boldsymbol{\kappa}-\boldsymbol{\tau}|^4+\omega^2}.\quad(41)$$

The experimental conditions under which critical magnetic scattering is observable are immediately determined by its distribution (40) of momentum and energy transfers. To the term with $\boldsymbol{\tau}=0$ in the cross section corresponds scattering with $\kappa\ll v_0^{-\frac{1}{3}}$, i.e., small angle scattering whenever the incident wavelength is not too large compared to the interatomic spacing $v_0^{\frac{1}{3}}$. In our approximations this scattering is independent of crystal orientation. It occurs in single crystals or polycrystals alike. Critical scattering corresponding to a term with $\boldsymbol{\tau}\neq0$ can only be observed if the form factor $F(\kappa)$ is not too small at $\kappa=\tau$ and if it is possible to satisfy simultaneously both conditions (40). The latter requirement can only be fulfilled for incident wavelengths close to or shorter than the Bragg cut-off wavelength, and, for a single crystal, near Bragg position. In the case of a polycrystal the critical scattering for $\boldsymbol{\tau}\neq0$ is greatly weakened by the averaging process over orientations and its observation is further hampered by its proximity to the intense Deybe-Scherrer rings.

Whereas we had noticed, as far as correlations are concerned, an almost perfect analogy between the considerations of the present section and the discussion of gases near the critical point presented in II, we have met with an important difference regarding the scattering, namely the occurrence in the cross section (41) of the terms with $\boldsymbol{\tau}\neq0$, evidently absent in the gas case. These terms reflect, of course, the fact that, despite the

[24] The situation is here analogous to the case of a gas or liquid near the critical point, where the coefficient of heat conduction remains finite.

[25] Λ_1 corresponds to one-fourth of the constant Λ_0 defined in II, Eq. (II 40).

[26] To take the effect of atomic vibrations completely into account one would still have to add to Eq. (41) a small amount of critical scattering coming formally from the difference between $G_R(\mathbf{r},t)$ and $G_R^{(\infty)}(\mathbf{r})$. This scattering, in contrast with the scattering described by (41), is inelastic in the lattice vibrations and, apart from being much smaller, it has an entirely different distribution of momentum and energy transfers. It is of more restricted experimental interest.

intense disorderly fluctuations of the magnetization, the spin system retains the regular arrangement of positions in space imposed by the lattice structure of the underlying crystal. Their occurrence is of considerable practical interest by permitting the observation of critical scattering in absence of any elastic peak for a single crystal rotated slightly from Bragg position.

Our theoretical discussion has dealt with a ferromagnetic spin system at temperatures higher than the Curie point. The situation for $T<T_c$ is complicated by the presence of permanent magnetization and would therefore require a special discussion. It is, however, to be expected that the properties of the critical magnetic scattering derived above hold true without essential modifications for $T<T_c$, T being again in the vicinity of T_c, since the magnetization has there also abnormally large fluctuations.

Both in transmission (total cross section) and in differential measurements there is clear evidence that the critical magnetic scattering has been experimentally observed. The peak at the Curie point obtained by Palevsky and Hughes[3] as well as by Squires[4] in the transmission *versus* temperature curve for iron is undoubtedly to be ascribed to critical scattering. It comes from the contribution of the term $\boldsymbol{\tau}=0$ of (41) to the total cross section. As the Curie point is approached, this contribution, unlike that of the other terms, would increase indefinitely in the ideal case of a perfect geometry. The greater height and sharpness of the peak obtained by Squires is a consequence of a better temperature control than in the experiment of Palevsky and Hughes.

The occurrence of abundant small angle scattering of 0.9-A neutrons in polycrystalline iron for temperatures in the vicinity of T_c has been observed by Wilkinson and Shull,[27] with a pronounced maximum in the amount of scattering at the Curie point itself. McReynolds and Riste,[28] investigating the magnetic structure of a single crystal of Fe_3O_4 with 1.3-A neutrons, have established the existence, around the Bragg directions, of diffuse magnetic peaks of rapidly increasing intensity as the Curie point is approached from either side. The results of both experiments are in good agreement with the theoretical predictions presented above. They tend to indicate that, at least for Fe and Fe_3O_4, critical scattering takes place over a rather wide neighborhood of the Curie point, extending roughly to some 100° below and above T_c.

[27] M. K. Wilkinson and C. G. Shull, Phys. Rev. **95**, 1439 (1954), and private communication.
[28] A. W. McReynolds and T. Riste (to be published).

VI. CONCLUDING REMARKS

Our discussion of the time-dependent correlation between spins and of magnetic neutron scattering in ferromagnetic crystals has dealt only with the points of greatest importance for the qualitative understanding of the phenomena. Several questions have been raised without any attempt being made at their solution. Some of them, although difficult, are of considerable interest from the standpoint of general statistical mechanics, and further experimentation is likely to make their study desirable also from a more practical standpoint.

The present paper is entirely based on the atomic (Heisenberg) model of ferromagnetism, ascribing a spin of fixed length to each atom. The general method, however, consisting in the use of time-dependent correlations between pairs of spins and founded on Eqs. (1), (3), and (4), is, of course, applicable to magnetic scattering by the spins of an arbitrary system of electrons. The spin vectors in Eq. (4) have only to be taken as belonging to the individual electrons.[29] One could thus attempt to carry out our whole discussion for the collective (electron band) theory of ferromagnetism. No deep alteration of our main qualitative conclusions is probably to be expected. Some support for this view is given by the case of nickel which, having an average of 0.6 electron spin per atom, clearly requires a collective treatment. The results of transmission experiments of Squires[4] with 7-A neutrons seem to be in rough agreement with the main qualitative predictions one would obtain from our methods: the transmission *versus* temperature curve has a peak at the Curie point, and the magnitude of the magnetic cross section, although very uncertain as a consequence of its small size, is compatible with what would be obtained from the observed magnitude in iron by correcting for the smaller average atomic spin.

Another problem deserving attention concerns the case of antiferromagnetic crystals. The dynamics of such systems is certainly less well understood than is the case for ferromagnets, and instructive information would undoubtedly be revealed by inelastic neutron scattering experiments. The extension of our theoretical discussion to antiferromagnets raises also a number of questions which might be worth investigating.

We would finally like to express our appreciation to D. J. Hughes, H. Palevsky, G. L. Squires, C. G. Shull, and A. W. McReynolds for making their experimental results available before publication and for many stimulating discussions, to G. Placzek for various useful comments, and to C. E. Porter for communicating the results of unpublished calculations.

[29] The vectorial indices R, R' must be replaced by numerical indices labeling the electrons.

ENERGY CORRECTIONS AND PERSISTENT PERTURBATION EFFECTS IN CONTINUOUS SPECTRA

by LÉON VAN HOVE

Instituut voor theoretische Natuurkunde der Rijksuniversiteit, Utrecht, Nederland

Synopsis

The quantum-mechanical perturbation theory of continuous energy spectra is investigated for a special class of perturbations possessing some of the formal properties of the familiar interaction energies of field theory. These formal properties entail the inapplicability of the familiar perturbation theory of continuous spectra. The latter, which implies that the perturbation causes transitions between unperturbed stationary states, with conservation of the unperturbed energy, is valid for scattering and reaction processes. The perturbations here considered are found to produce transitions between "asymptotically stationary states" differing from the unperturbed stationary states both by the admixture of other states and by correction of the energy value. This is in agreement with the situation intuitively expected but not explicitly verified in field theory (due to divergence and computational difficulties), according to which the interaction between fields causes, besides scattering, creation or annihilation processes, the persistent occurrence around each real particle of a cloud of virtual particles (photon cloud around an electron, meson cloud around a nucleon, etc.), with an accompanying self-energy effect.

1. *Introduction.* The quantum-mechanical perturbation theory of systems with a continuous energy spectrum has been studied by many authors for the situations encountered in scattering and reaction processes. Typically the perturbation term of the hamiltonian would for example be the interaction potential between two particles and would then produce scattering. It may also be the interaction energy between particles, one or both of which are composite (like a nucleus, an atom or a molecule), and it produces then reaction processes whereby the identity of the particles can be changed. For all such cases the theory has been worked out to arbitrary order in the perturbation, leading to the following conclusions [1]). For general (non-monoenergetic) wave packets the motion reduces asymptotically, in the distant past and in the distant future, to the unperturbed motion, and the essential effect of the perturbation consists in causing transitions between the unperturbed stationary states. These transitions conserve the unperturbed energy and are described by a unitary matrix, the well-known S-matrix.

There are however two important classes of quantum systems with continuous spectra to which this general theory does not apply, despite the fact that one term in their hamiltonian obviously plays the role of a perturbation and is regarded as such in all the (essentially incomplete and often unsatisfactory) treatments proposed so far for these systems. The two classes are best characterized by considering typical examples.

Characteristic of the first class is a non-conducting crystal, where the potential energy is the sum of a main term quadratic in the displacements of the atoms and a small anharmonic term containing third and higher powers of the displacements. The latter term is the perturbation. Under its neglection, and for the physically most important limiting case of a crystal with a very large number of particles, the system is harmonic and its stationary states are characterized by the presence of non interacting plane wave vibrations (phonons). Each phonon has a wave vector and an energy. In the limit of an infinite crystal, the former can take any of a continuum of possible values, whereas the latter is a continuous function of the former. The unperturbed energy spectrum can therefore indeed be regarded as continuous. Still, the effects of the perturbation consisting of the anharmonic terms are by no means of the sort occurring in scattering and reaction processes. The most striking difference is the presence of dissipative effects of which heat conduction is the most familiar manifestation: such effects take place for a wave packet irrespective of the relative phases of its plane wave components and consequently a S-matrix formalism is unable to describe them. Other examples of perturbations with similar effects of dissipative type are the interaction between spin waves in an (infinitely large) ferromagnetic crystal, the interaction between an electron and lattice vibrations in an (infinitely large) conducting crystal, etc.

The perturbations of the second class referred to above, — this class will form the main object of the present paper —, are encountered most commonly in quantum field theory as the interactions between quantized fields. Consider the electromagnetic interaction between the electron-positron field and the photon field, or any of the familiar interactions between a nucleon field and a meson field. Taking e.g. the latter case, we assume, because Lorentz invariance is of no concern for our present discussion and we do not want to deal with divergence difficulties, that a form factor has been introduced smearing out the nucleons in space. The unperturbed system is composed of the non-interacting nucleon and meson fields. The interaction between these fields is a perturbation, the effects of which are certainly not describable by an S-matrix theory of the standard type. Although it is true that the perturbation produces transitions between certain states stationary for large times, just like in scattering and reaction processes, these states are not the stationary states of the unperturbed hamiltonian, composed of free nucleons and mesons. They are rather states where each nucleon is surrounded by a meson cloud, each meson by a cloud of nucleon pairs, etc., and where these clouds contribute non vanishing corrections to the total energy. These cloud effects affect the motion at all times, whereas scattering, creation and annihilation processes are, for general wave packets, of transient nature. The cloud effects are responsible for the necessity to renormalize the primitive constants of the fields, — renormalization is necessary even in a convergent theory —, but it is clear that renormalization alone is not able to describe them completely: full knowledge of the meson cloud around a nucleon clearly requires an infinite number of parameters.

The two classes of perturbations just considered, characterized by the occurrence of dissipative effects and cloud effects respectively, have important features in common. The perturbations act upon systems of very large (in the limit, infinitely large) spatial extension, with, as a consequence, a continuous unperturbed energy spectrum *). The perturbations themselves extend over the whole system: the anharmonic term in the potential energy of a crystal is a lattice sum over the whole crystal; similarly the interaction between a nucleon field and a meson field is an integral over all space. This large spatial extension of the perturbations is the decisive property by which they differ from the simpler types of perturbation encountered in scattering and reaction processes. It is responsible for the inapplicability of the familiar methods as well as for the occurrence of novel physical effects, dissipation or cloud effects. It manifests itself mathematically as follows. Take for the eigenstates of the unperturbed system the most natural set of quantum numbers, i.e. the number, wave vectors and polarizations of the free quanta (phonons, nucleons and mesons, etc.). Denote this set by α, and by $|\alpha\rangle$ the unperturbed eigenstate of quantum numbers α. Some of the quantum numbers are continuous, some are discrete; we denote by $\delta(\alpha - \alpha')$ the product of δ-functions for all continuous quantum numbers and Kronecker symbols for all discrete ones and adopt the normalization

$$\langle \alpha \mid \alpha' \rangle = \delta(\alpha - \alpha').$$

Consider an operator

$$VA_1 VA_2 V \dots A_n V \tag{1.1}$$

where V is the perturbation and $A_1, \dots A_n$ are arbitrary operators diagonal in the $|\alpha\rangle$-representation

$$\langle \alpha | A_j | \alpha' \rangle = A_j(\alpha)\, \delta(\alpha - \alpha').$$

The large (in the limit, infinite) spatial extension of the perturbation energy V implies that for many choices of $n, A_1, \dots A_n$ the matrix element $\langle \alpha | VA_1 V \dots A_n V | \alpha' \rangle$ has a $\delta(\alpha - \alpha')$-singularity, i.e. that the operator (1.1) has a non-vanishing part diagonal in the $|\alpha\rangle$-representation, although the same does not hold for V itself.

*) In most cases the number of degrees of freedom of the system is also very large. This is however not necessary, as shown by the simplified model of meson theory recently proposed by Lee [2]).

The diagonal parts of the type just described, which never occur in the familiar cases of perturbations producing scattering or reaction processes only, are mathematically responsible for the novel features, dissipation or cloud effects, described above. How to decide whether a given perturbation produces dissipative or cloud effects is the first aim of the present paper. The answer is given in Section 4 and is based on rather extensive mathematical preparations to be found in Sections 2 and 3. The rest of the paper is devoted to the case of cloud effects, of interest for field theory, and studies it to general order in the perturbation. The asymptotic motion of wave packets for large times is investigated in Section 5 and is shown to be expressible as a superposition of asymptotically stationary states differing from the unperturbed stationary states by the admixture of other states as well as by a correction to the unperturbed energy. Section 6 deals with the motion of wave packets for finite times, i.e. with the transient effects of the perturbation. It establishes that this motion consists of transitions between the asymptotically stationary states, with conservation of the corrected energy. The results obtained are thus in agreement with the situation intuitively expected from the field theoretical examples.

The case of dissipative effects is not handled here. It has been considered in a previous paper where it was treated in the lowest non vanishing order [3]. Its study to general order has not yet been carried out.

2. *Diagonal parts of operators.* The hamiltonian $H + \lambda V$ to be studied contains a time-independent unperturbed part H and a time-independent perturbation term λV. We assume H to have a continuous spectrum, with eigenstates $|\, \alpha \rangle$ characterized by a number of parameters (quantum numbers) which we denote by the single symbol α, and eigenvalues $\varepsilon(\alpha)$:

$$H \,|\, \alpha \rangle = \varepsilon(\alpha) \,|\, \alpha \rangle. \tag{2.1}$$

It is essential that at least some of the parameters α are continuous variables and that $\varepsilon(\alpha)$ is a continuous function of them; other parameters may be discrete. Our notation will be adapted to continuous parameters but could of course easily be completed in order to take explicit account of some discrete ones. We write the normalization as in (1.1)

$$\langle \alpha \,|\, \alpha' \rangle = \delta(\alpha - \alpha') \tag{2.2}$$

The coefficient λ in front of the perturbation is a dimensionless quantity characterizing its size. The perturbation operator V is assumed to have a matrix element $\langle \alpha \,|V|\, \alpha' \rangle$ without $\delta[\varepsilon(\alpha) - \varepsilon(\alpha')]$-singularity; any such singularity could be incorporated into the unperturbed hamiltonian and thus eliminated. On the contrary δ-singularities are allowed in the matrix elements of product operators $VA_1VA_2 \ldots VA_nV$, where the A_j are diagonal in the $|\alpha\rangle$-representation

$$A_j \,|\alpha\rangle = A_j(\alpha) \,|\alpha\rangle. \tag{2.3}$$

These matrix elements are assumed to have the form

$$\langle \alpha | VA_1V \ldots A_nV | \alpha' \rangle = \delta(\alpha - \alpha')F_1(\alpha) + F_2(\alpha, \alpha'), \tag{2.4}$$

$F_2(\alpha, \alpha')$ possessing no $\delta[\varepsilon(\alpha) - \varepsilon(\alpha')]$-singularity. The function $F_1(\alpha)$ may of course vanish for certain values of n or certain choices of the A_j *). We are however interested in the cases where $F_1(\alpha)$ is not always zero, and it is precisely our object to investigate the influence of $\delta(\alpha - \alpha')$-singularities as appear in (2.4) on the motion of the system.

The situation where the singular term in (2.4) never occurs is also much more familiar and has been throroughly investigated in the general theory of scattering and reaction processes [1]). It is worth mentioning again, for later comparison, the main result of this theory. Any solution $\varphi(t)$ of the Schrödinger equation (we put $\hbar = 1$)

$$i\partial\varphi/\partial t = (H + \lambda V)\varphi \tag{2.5}$$

approacnes asymptotically for $t \to \pm \infty$ solutions of the unperturbed equation

$$i\partial\varphi_0/\partial t = H\,\varphi_0; \tag{2.6}$$

in formulae:

$$\varphi(t) \simeq \int |\alpha\rangle \exp[- it\varepsilon(\alpha)]c(\alpha)\mathrm{d}\alpha \quad \text{for } t \to -\infty, \tag{2.7}$$

$$\varphi(t) \simeq \int |\alpha\rangle \exp[- it\varepsilon(\alpha)]\tilde{c}(\alpha)\mathrm{d}\alpha \quad \text{for } t \to +\infty. \tag{2.8}$$

The connection between the initial and final amplitudes $c(\alpha)$ and $\tilde{c}(\alpha)$ has furthermore the following type

$$\tilde{c}(\alpha) = \int \langle \alpha |S| \alpha' \rangle c(\alpha')\mathrm{d}\alpha' \tag{2.9}$$

S is a unitary matrix, the so-called S-matrix. Its matrix element $\langle \alpha |S| \alpha' \rangle$ contains a factor $\delta[\varepsilon(\alpha) - \varepsilon(\alpha')]$ ensuring conservation of the unperturbed energy. The asymptotic validity of (2.7) and (2.8) shows that for each wave packet the action of the perturbation is concentrated within a finite time interval and produces transitions between unperturbed stationary states; the perturbation has thus exclusively a *transient* action. The results of this paper will show that perturbations for which the δ-singularity of (2.4) does occur produce, besides transient effects described by a S-matrix, also very important *persistent* effects affecting the asymptotic behaviour of $\varphi(t)$ for $t \to \pm \infty$.

The actual systems for which our discussion will be of interest are quantized fields. The energy H belongs then to the free fields and their interaction plays the role of perturbation. That the singular term of (2.4) is not identically zero in the case of interacting fields, and what its value is, can be found out by the usual method of quantizing the free fields in a cubic box of large volume Ω, with periodic boundary conditions. The states

*) In the conventional field theories, it always vanishes for even n.

$|\alpha\rangle$, characterized by the presence of a number of free field quanta in plane wave states, are then still discrete. They become continuous as $\Omega \to \infty$. In the matrix element (2.4) certain types of transitions, impossible when $\alpha \neq \alpha'$, may become possible when $\alpha = \alpha'$. They are the so-called self-energy transitions where virtual particles are first created with arbitrary values of their momentum and then reabsorbed. Their contribution to the matrix element is larger than the contribution of other transitions by a factor Ω. It gives rise in the limit $\Omega \to \infty$ to the term $\delta(\alpha - \alpha')F_1(\alpha)$ of (2.4). One can thus say that the perturbations of interest to us are essentially those which produce self-energy effects in the continuous spectrum. The fact that in relativistically invariant field theories the self-energies are found to diverge will be of no concern to us: we restrict ourselves from the outset to cases where all integrations over intermediate states are convergent. We will even assume the function $\varepsilon(\alpha)$ to be bounded.

The preceding remarks make it immediately clear that the perturbations to be studied will produce persistent effects: a self-energy effect is indeed in essence of persistent nature. We will find however that the energy corrections are necessarily accompanied by other persistent effects of the perturbation, resulting in the fact that the validity of the asymptotic formulae (2.7) and (2.8) is not restored even after introducing the corrected energies in the exponentials. These further effects correspond in field theory, in electrodynamics for example, to the presence of a photon cloud persistently attached to the electron even when no other charge is interacting with it. That field theory must imply such cloud effects has long been intuitively clear. Little progress has however been made toward their precise theoretical description as separated from all transient effects of the interaction. Our analysis will provide this description. We should mention at this point an attempt by Pirenne [4]) to construct a perturbation theory of continuous spectra including self-energy effects. This attempt must be regarded as incomplete. As shown by his equation (5), Pirenne has left out of consideration the cloud effects just discussed, overlooking that they are inseparably related to the self-energy effects.

We give now a closer analysis of the singular terms in the matrix elements (2.4). We call *diagonal part* of the matrix $VA_1V\ldots A_nV$ and denote by $\{VA_1V\ldots A_nV\}_d$ the diagonal *) operator with matrix elements

$$\langle\alpha|\,\{VA_1V\ldots A_nV\}_d\,|\alpha'\rangle = \delta(\alpha-\alpha')F_1(\alpha) \tag{2.10}$$

where $F_1(\alpha)$ is the same function as in (2.4). Considering the explicit value of the matrix element (2.4)

$$\langle\alpha\,|VA_1V\ldots A_nV\,|\alpha'\rangle = \int\langle\alpha\,|V|\,\alpha_1\rangle\,A_1(\alpha_1)\,\langle\alpha_1\,|V|\,\alpha_2\rangle\ldots$$
$$\ldots\,A_n(\alpha_n)\,\langle\alpha_n\,|V|\,\alpha'\,\rangle\,d\alpha_1\,\ldots\,d\alpha_n, \tag{2.11}$$

*) By diagonal we always mean diagonal in the $|\alpha>$ -representation.

we notice that some of the partial products $VA_jV\ldots A_kV$, $(1 \leqslant j \leqslant k \leqslant n;$ $k - j < n - 1)$ may have themselves a $\delta(\alpha_{j-1} - \alpha_{k+1})$-singularity in their matrix element $\langle\alpha_{j-1}|VA_jV\ldots A_kV|\alpha_{k+1}\rangle$, producing a contraction between the integration variables α_{j-1} and α_{k+1} in (2.11) *). Assume now such contributions to be excluded in (2.11) by the convention that each of the variables $\alpha_1, \ldots \alpha_n$ is kept outside some infinitesimal neighbourhood of each other as well as of α and α'. Consider again, in the result thus obtained for the integral (2.11) regarded as function of α and α', the separation

$$\delta(\alpha - \alpha')\tilde{F}_1(\alpha) + \tilde{F}_2(\alpha, \alpha')$$

similar to (2.4). We call *irreducible diagonal part* of $VA_1V\ldots A_nV$ and denote by $\{VA_1V\ldots A_nV\}_{id}$ the diagonal operator defined by

$$\langle\alpha|\,\{VA_1V\ldots A_nV\}_{id}\,|\alpha'\rangle = \delta(\alpha - \alpha')\tilde{F}_1(\alpha).$$

It is that portion of the diagonal part $\{VA_1V\ldots A_nV\}_d$ which is obtained when the intermediate states $|\alpha_1\rangle, \ldots |\alpha_n\rangle$ are kept different from each other and from the initial and final states $|\alpha'\rangle$, $|\alpha\rangle$.

The definitions of diagonal and irreducible diagonal parts are immediately extended to operators of the form $A_0VA_1\ldots A_nVA_{n+1}$, with $A_0, A_1, \ldots A_{n+1}$ diagonal, by the formulae

$$\{A_0VA_1V \ldots A_nVA_{n+1}\}_d = A_0\{VA_1V \ldots A_nV\}_d A_{n+1},$$
$$\{A_0VA_1V \ldots A_nVA_{n+1}\}_{id} = A_0\{VA_1V \ldots A_nV\}_{id} A_{n+1}.$$

We extend them also by mere additivity to sums of such operators.

We make now the assumption, always verified in the practical situations, that in calculating the non-irreducible part of (2.10), when one has two contractions between the intermediate states of (2.11), let say one between α_{j-1} and α_{k+1} and one between $\alpha_{j'-1}$ and $\alpha_{k'+1}$, one has never $j < j' < k < k'$ nor $j' < j < k' < k$. As a consequence of the assumption just made one can systematically determine the d.p. (diagonal part) of any product $P = VA_1V \ldots A_nV$ by a succession of operations consisting each of taking the i.d.p. (irreducible diagonal part) of a number of similar products. Each operation, to be called a *diagonalization process*, proceeds as follows:

i) One selects in P one or more subproducts

$$VA_{j_1}VA_{j_1+1}V\ldots A_{j_1'-1}V,\ VA_{j_2}V\ldots A_{j_2'-1}V,\ \ldots,\ VA_{j_\varrho}VA_{j_\varrho+1}V\ldots A_{j_\varrho'-1}V,$$
$$(1 \leqslant j_1 < j_1' < j_2 < j_2' < \ldots j_\varrho < j_\varrho' \leqslant n+1),$$

and one replaces each of them by its i.d.p.

ii) These i.d.p. are considered as diagonal operators. Remembering that a product of diagonal operators is a diagonal operator, one finds for P

*) If $j = 1$, replace α_{j-1} by α; if $k = n$, replace α_{k+1} by α'.

after step i) either a diagonal operator, in which case the operation is ended, or a product $A'_0VA'_1V \dots A'_{n'}VA'_{n'+1}$ with $A'_0, A'_1, \dots A'_{n'+1}$ diagonal and $n' < n$.

iii) In the latter case, step i) is applied to $VA'_1V \dots A'_{n'}V$ selecting this time only subproducts which were not already present in the same form before the previous application of step i). This process is continued, until after a total number ν of applications of step i) the operation ends through obtention of a diagonal operator.

The number ν is called the *order* of the d. pr. (diagonalization process) and the diagonal operator obtained at its end is called its *contribution*. It is clear that for given P many different d.pr. can be carried out, since each application of step i) requires a choice of subproducts: two d.pr. are different as soon as they do not make identical choices of subproducts in all applications of step i). The important point is now that the d.p. of $P = VA_1V \dots A_nV$ is the sum of the contributions of all different d.pr. which can be carried out on P.

A diagonalization process Δ for a sum

$$\Sigma_j A_0^{(j)}VA_1^{(j)}V \dots A_{n_j}^{(j)}VA_{n_j+1}^{(j)}$$

is by definition a combination of d.pr. Δ_j of the type defined above, one for each product

$$VA_1^{(j)}V \dots A_{n_j}^{(j)}V.$$

Let B_j be the contribution and ν_j the order of Δ_j; the contribution and order of the d.pr. Δ are respectively defined by

$$B = \Sigma_j A_0^{(j)} B_j A_{n_j+1}^{(j)}, \quad \nu = \max \nu_j.$$

3. *Separation of diagonal parts in the resolvent.* We are now prepared to investigate the diagonal part of an operator which will play an important role in the sequel, the so-called resolvent operator, defined by

$$R_l = (H + \lambda V - l)^{-1} \tag{3.1}$$

for each complex number l with non vanishing imaginary part. The connection of the resolvent with the unitary operator of the motion is well known and will be used later on. The resolvent can be expanded in powers of the perturbation

$$R_l = D_l^{(0)} - \lambda D_l^{(0)}VD_l^{(0)} + \lambda^2 D_l^{(0)}VD_l^{(0)}VD_l^{(0)} - \dots$$

with $D_l^{(0)} = (H - l)^{-1}$, and this expansion, about which the assumption of convergence is made once and for all, will enable us to calculate the d.p.

$$\{R_l\}_d = D_l^{(0)} + \lambda^2 D_l^{(0)}\{VD_l^{(0)}V - \lambda VD_l^{(0)}VD_l^{(0)}V + \dots\}_d D_l^{(0)}. \tag{3.2}$$

We shall consider successively the contributions of d.pr. of increasing orders.

Define first the diagonal operator

$$\mathcal{G}_l^{(1)} = \{VD_l^{(0)}V - \lambda VD_l^{(0)}VD_l^{(0)}V + \ldots\}_{id}. \tag{3.3}$$

As can be easily established, the sum $\Sigma_l^{(1)}$ of the contributions to

$$\{VD_l^{(0)}V - \lambda VD_l^{(0)}VD_l^{(0)}V + \ldots\}_d \tag{3.4}$$

of all d.pr. of order 1 has the value

$$\Sigma_l^{(1)} = \mathcal{G}_l^{(1)} + \lambda^2\mathcal{G}_l^{(1)}D_l^{(0)}\mathcal{G}_l^{(1)} + \lambda^4\mathcal{G}_l^{(1)}D_l^{(0)}\mathcal{G}_l^{(1)}D_l^{(0)}\mathcal{G}_l^{(1)} + \ldots$$

It can be summed explicitly, with the result

$$\Sigma_l^{(1)} = \mathcal{G}_l^{(1)}[1 - \lambda^2\mathcal{G}_l^{(1)}D_l^{(0)}]^{-1} = \mathcal{G}_l^{(1)}D_l^{(1)}/D_l^{(0)} \tag{3.5}$$

where the diagonal operator $D_l^{(1)}$ is defined by

$$D_l^{(1)} = [(D_l^{(0)})^{-1} - \lambda^2\mathcal{G}_l^{(1)}]^{-1} = [H - l - \lambda^2\mathcal{G}_l^{(1)}]^{-1}. \tag{3.6}$$

The total contribution $\Sigma_l^{(2)}$ to (3.4) of all d.pr. of orders 1 and 2 is calculated next and found to be

$$\Sigma_l^{(2)} = \mathcal{G}_l^{(2)} + \lambda^2\mathcal{G}_l^{(2)}D_l^{(0)}\mathcal{G}_l^{(2)} + \lambda^4\mathcal{G}_l^{(2)}D_l^{(0)}\mathcal{G}_l^{(2)}D_l^{(0)}\mathcal{G}_l^{(2)} + \ldots \tag{3.7}$$

where $\mathcal{G}_l^{(2)}$ is defined by

$$\mathcal{G}_l^{(2)} = \{V(D_l^{(0)} + \lambda^2 D_l^{(0)}\,\Sigma_l^{(1)}\,D_l^{(0)})\,V -$$
$$- \lambda V(D_l^{(0)} + \lambda^2 D_l^{(0)}\,\Sigma_l^{(1)}\,D_l^{(0)})V(D_l^{(0)} + \lambda^2 D_l^{(0)}\,\Sigma_l^{(1)}\,D_l^{(0)})V + \ldots\}_{id}.$$

We notice that, from (3.5) and (3.6),

$$D_l^{(0)} + \lambda^2 D_l^{(0)}\,\Sigma_l^{(1)}\,D_l^{(0)} = D_l^{(0)}(1 + \lambda^2 D_l^{(1)}\mathcal{G}_l^{(1)}) = D_l^{(1)}.$$

Thus

$$\mathcal{G}_l^{(2)} = \{VD_l^{(1)}\,V - \lambda VD_l^{(1)}VD_l^{(1)}V + \ldots\}_{id}$$

and we obtain for $\Sigma_l^{(2)}$, by summation of (3.7),

$$\Sigma_l^{(2)} = \mathcal{G}_l^{(2)}[1 - \lambda^2\mathcal{G}_l^{(2)}D_l^{(0)}]^{-1} = \mathcal{G}_l^{(2)}D_l^{(2)}/D_l^{(0)}$$

where

$$D_l^{(2)} = [H - l - \lambda^2\mathcal{G}_l^{(2)}]^{-1}.$$

This procedure can be continued indefinitely, with the result that the total contribution $\Sigma_l^{(\nu)}$ to (3.4) of all d.pr. of orders 1, 2, ... ν is given by

$$\Sigma_l^{(\nu)} = \mathcal{G}_l^{(\nu)}D_l^{(\nu)}/D_l^{(0)}, \tag{3.8}$$

where the diagonal operators $\mathcal{G}_l^{(\nu)}$ and $D_l^{(\nu)}$ are defined by the recurrence relations

$$\mathcal{G}_l^{(\nu)} = \{VD_l^{(\nu-1)}V - \lambda VD_l^{(\nu-1)}VD_l^{(\nu-1)}V + \ldots\}_{id}, \tag{3.9}$$

$$D^{(\nu)} = [H - l - \lambda^2\mathcal{G}_l^{(\nu)}]^{-1}. \tag{3.10}$$

Assuming convergence, we go to the limit $\nu \to \infty$ and define the diagonal operators

$$\mathcal{G}_l = \lim_{\nu\to\infty} \mathcal{G}_l^{(\nu)},\ D_l = \lim_{\nu\to\infty} D_l^{(\nu)}. \tag{3.11}$$

Equation (3.10) becomes in the limit

$$D_l = [H - l - \lambda^2 \mathcal{G}_l]^{-1}, \tag{3.12}$$

whereas (3.9) gives the identity

$$\mathcal{G}_l = \{VD_lV - \lambda VD_lVD_lV + \ldots\}_{id}, \tag{3.13}$$

.e. essentially an implicit equation verified by $\mathcal{G}_l$. One will observe that the operators $\mathcal{G}_l^{(1)}$, $\mathcal{G}_l^{(2)}$, ... $\mathcal{G}_l^{(\nu)}$, ... are simply obtained by solving (3.13) by successive approximations starting from $\mathcal{G}_l^{(0)} = 0$. Going to the limit in (3.8) one finds

$$\{VD_l^{(0)}V - \lambda VD_l^{(0)}VD_l^{(0)}V + \ldots\}_d = \mathcal{G}_l D_l/D_l^{(0)}$$

and, with the help of (3.2),

$$\{R_l\}_d = D_l. \tag{3.14}$$

With this result one can also rewrite the resolvent itself as

$$R_l = D_l - \lambda D_lVD_l + \lambda^2 D_l\{VD_lV - \lambda VD_lVD_lV + \ldots\}_{nd}D_l, \tag{3.15}$$

where the notation $\{\ldots\}_{nd}$, meaning *non-diagonal part*, is defined for a product $VA_1V \ldots A_nV$, ($A_1, \ldots A_n$ diagonal) by restricting in (2.11) *all* states $|\alpha\rangle$, $|\alpha_1\rangle$, ... $|\alpha_n\rangle$ and $|\alpha'\rangle$ to be outside infinitesimal neighbourhoods of each other *), and is extended by additivity to a sum of such products.

We will describe now some properties of the diagonal operators $\mathcal{G}_l$ and D_l which may be expected to hold barring exceptional analytic complications. Denote by $Im(l)$ the imaginary part of l. From the hermiticity of $H + \lambda V$ it follows, as is well known, that the resolvent R_l is holomorphic in l for $Im(l) \neq 0$. From (3.14) and the definition of the diagonal part we may conclude that D_l is also holomorphic in l for $Im(l) \neq 0$. Equation (3.12) implies then the same property for $\mathcal{G}_l$. Similarly, denoting by the star the complex conjugate of a number and the hermitian conjugate of an operator, we have

$$R_{l^*} = R_l^*$$

and thus

$$D_{l^*} = D_l^*,\ \mathcal{G}_{l^*} = \mathcal{G}_l^* \tag{3.16}$$

From (3.14) and (3.13), and from the fact that the spectrum of H is bounded, we can conclude further

$$\lim_{|l|\to\infty} D_l = 0,\ \lim_{|l|\to\infty} \mathcal{G}_l = 0.$$

*) The value of $<\alpha|\{VA_1V\ldots A_nV\}_{nd}|\alpha>$ is then to be taken as the limit of $<\alpha|\{VA_1V\ldots A_nV\}_{nd}|\alpha'>$ for $\alpha' \to \alpha$ with $\alpha' \neq \alpha$.

The definition (3.1) of R_l implies on the other hand

$$R_{l'} - R_l = (l' - l)R_{l'}R_l \tag{3.17}$$

and thus $D_{l'} - D_l = (l' - l)\{R_{l'}R_l\}_d$.

Using (3.12) and (3.15) one transforms this relation into

$$\mathcal{G}_{l'} - \mathcal{G}_l = (l' - l)\{\{V - \lambda V D_{l'} V + \ldots\}_{nd} D_{l'} D_l \{V - \lambda V D_l V + \ldots\}_{nd}\}_d \tag{3.18}$$

where $\{V\}_{nd}$ must of course be understood as equal to V. Put now $l' = l^*$. Since $D_{l^*} = D_l^*$, the diagonal part in the right hand side becomes non negative and we conclude that $i(\mathcal{G}_{l^*} - \mathcal{G}_l)$ is semi-definite positive when $Im(l) > 0$, or

$$Im[\mathcal{G}_l(\alpha)] \geqslant 0 \text{ for } Im(l) > 0, \tag{3.19}$$

where $\mathcal{G}_l(\alpha)$ is the eigenvalue of $\mathcal{G}_l$ for the state $|\alpha\rangle$. The inequality can be improved a little by noting that for given α

$$Im[\mathcal{G}_l(\alpha)] > 0 \text{ for } Im(l) > 0,$$

unless $\mathcal{G}_l(\alpha) = 0$ for all l, because the function $Im[\mathcal{G}_l(\alpha)]$ is harmonic in the upper half of the l-plane and can thus only attain its minimum on the boundary. Finally, from (3.19) and from the form taken by (3.13) when the right hand side is written in terms of the matrix elements $\langle\alpha|V|\alpha'\rangle$, with integrals over intermediate states, one may conclude, always barring exceptional complications, that $\mathcal{G}_l$ converges to a finite limit for $l = E + i\eta$, E real, $\eta > 0$, $\eta \to 0$. We write for this limit

$$\lim \mathcal{G}_{E+i\eta} = K_E + iJ_E \tag{3.20}$$

where K_E and J_E are diagonal operators, with real eigenvalues $K_E(\alpha)$, $J_E(\alpha)$. Furthermore, from (3.16),

$$\lim_{0<\eta\to 0} \mathcal{G}_{E-i\eta} = K_E - iJ_E \tag{3.21}$$

and from (3.19), for all $|\alpha\rangle$,

$$J_E(\alpha) \geqslant 0. \tag{3.22}$$

4. *The case of vanishing line width.* A fundamental distinction must now be introduced according to whether the operator D_l remains bounded or becomes unbounded when l approaches the real axis from either side. It will correspond physically to the distinction between the two classes of perturbations described in the introduction, producing dissipative effects and cloud effects respectively. For each state $|\alpha\rangle$, consider the equation (E real)

$$\varepsilon(\alpha) - E - \lambda^2 K_E(\alpha) = 0. \tag{4.1}$$

Under our assumptions it has at least one root $E = E(\alpha)$, and we shall suppose that it has only one.

If one has for each α the inequality

$$J_E(\alpha) \neq 0 \text{ when } E = E(\alpha) \quad (4.2)$$

the operator D_l remains bounded in the neighbourhood of the real axis and has a finite discontinuity when passing accross it. Under these circumstances one must expect that the perturbation produces for the system a motion of dissipative type, like in absorption or diffusion processes. This is indeed the type of motion found in a previous paper [3]) where the effects of the perturbation were studied in lowest order in λ under the assumption (4.2), also taken in lowest order *). The quantity $J_E(\alpha)$ for $E = E(\alpha)$ was there found to play the role of a line width, its inverse being essentially the decay time or relaxation time of the state $|\alpha\rangle$ in the dissipative process.

We want to study here the complementary case where $J_E(\alpha)$ vanishes when E verifies (4.1). We assume a little more, namely that *for each state* $|\alpha\rangle$ *the function* $\mathcal{G}_l(\alpha)$ *is holomorphic in the point* $l = E(\alpha)$ *of the real axis*. It then follows of course that $J_E(\alpha)$ vanishes for E real around $E(\alpha)$, so that $D_l(\alpha)$ becomes singular when l approaches the real value $E(\alpha)$.

The assumption just made has far reaching consequences. Clearly, the identity (3.13) requires that if $\mathcal{G}_l(\alpha)$ is holomorphic in l on a given portion of the real axis for some $|\alpha\rangle$, the function $D_l(\alpha_1)$ must also be holomorphic on the same portion of the real axis for all the states $|\alpha_1\rangle$ which intervene as intermediate states when the products of operators in (3.13) are written out as integrals in terms of the matrix elements of V. Indeed, quite remarkable cancellations of singularities in the right hand side of (3.13) would otherwise be needed, and we may safely exclude such a situation as highly exceptional.

Let us formulate the above statement more precisely. We need therefore an important definition. Consider the matrix element

$$\langle\alpha|VD_lV - \lambda VD_lVD_lV + \ldots|\alpha'\rangle = \int\langle\alpha|V|\alpha_1\rangle D_l(\alpha_1)\langle\alpha_1|V|\alpha'\rangle d\alpha_1$$
$$-\lambda\int\langle\alpha|V|\alpha_1\rangle D_l(\alpha_1)\langle\alpha_1|V|\alpha_2\rangle D_l(\alpha_2)\langle\alpha_2|V|\alpha'\rangle d\alpha_1 d\alpha_2 + \ldots \quad (4.3)$$

According to (3.13) we can obtain from this expression the value of $\mathcal{G}_l(\alpha)$ by keeping in the right hand side $\alpha_1 \neq \alpha_2, \ldots$ in the terms of order 1, 2, ... in λ and separating the part of the expression obtained which has a $\delta(\alpha-\alpha')$-singularity. The coefficient of this singularity is $\mathcal{G}_l(\alpha)$. Call x_α the smallest family of states $|\alpha''\rangle$ such that the correct value of $\mathcal{G}_l(\alpha)$ would be obtained if at the start of the above operations on (4.3) the integrations over $|\alpha_1\rangle$, $|\alpha_2\rangle$ ... were restricted to x_α. This family is well defined if we require it to be continuous in those parameters α which are continuously varying. We can now reformulate our statement in the form of a lemma: *If for some* $|\alpha\rangle$ *the function* $\mathcal{G}_l(\alpha)$ *is holomorphic in* l *for* l *on a portion* δ *of the real axis, the*

*) The inequality (4.2) taken in lowest order reduces to the condition $W(E\alpha' ; E\alpha) \neq 0$ of Reference [3]).

function $D_l(\alpha_1)$ *and therefore the function* $\mathcal{G}_l(\alpha_1)$ *have the same property for all states* $|\alpha_1\rangle$ *belonging to* x_α.

The family of states x_α will play an important role in the sequel. Let us comment a little more on its properties. In general x_α will change with α, and would also have to be replaced by another domain of integration in order to calculate (4.3) for $\alpha \neq \alpha'$. Barring again exceptional cancellations, one may however admit that, given the perturbation V, x_α is completely determined by $|\alpha\rangle$ and does not depend for example on the special value of l in (4.3). More generally, x_α would be the same if it had been defined for operators $VA_1V + VA_2VA_3V + \ldots$, $(A_1, A_2, \ldots$ arbitrary diagonal operators), instead of the special operator in (4.3). As an example let us consider quantum electrodynamics. If $|\alpha\rangle$ is a state characterized by the presence of one electron of momentum $\mathbf{q}$, x_α contains all states with one electron and one photon, one electron and two photons, ..., for which the total m. (momentum) is $\mathbf{q}$. If $|\alpha\rangle$ is the state with one electron of m. $\mathbf{q}$ and one photon of m. $-\mathbf{q}$, x_α contains e.g. states with one electron of m. $\mathbf{q} - \mathbf{q}'$ and two photons of m. $-\mathbf{q}$ and $\mathbf{q}'$ but does not contain states with one electron of m. $\mathbf{q}' \neq \mathbf{q}$ and one photon of m. $-\mathbf{q}'$, neither states with one electron of m. $-\mathbf{q}_1 - \mathbf{q}_2$ and two photons of m. $\mathbf{q}_1 \neq -\mathbf{q}$ and $\mathbf{q}_2 \neq -\mathbf{q}$. If $|\alpha\rangle$ is the state with two electrons of m. $\mathbf{q}$ and $-\mathbf{q}$, x_α contains no other states with two electrons only, and involves only those states with one photon and two electrons in which one electron has m. $\mathbf{q}$ or $-\mathbf{q}$.

We notice now that our lemma can be easily extended to a family of states larger than x_α. For each α, call $x_\alpha^{(1)}$ the family of states $|\alpha'\rangle$ such that either $|\alpha'\rangle$ is in x_α or $|\alpha'\rangle$ is in the family $x_{\alpha''}$ for some $|\alpha''\rangle$ in x_α, call (for $n = 2, 3, \ldots$) $x_\alpha^{(n)}$ the family of states $|\alpha'\rangle$ such that either $|\alpha'\rangle$ is in $x_\alpha^{(n-1)}$ or it is in the family $x_{\alpha''}$ for some $|\alpha''\rangle$ in $x_\alpha^{(n-1)}$, and call finally y_α the family of states $|\alpha'\rangle$ such that $|\alpha'\rangle$ is in $x_\alpha^{(n)}$ for some n. From this definition, the family y_α contains the family $y_{\alpha'}$ corresponding to each of its elements $|\alpha'\rangle$.

By induction we conclude now from the lemma: if for some state $|\alpha\rangle$ the function $\mathcal{G}_l(\alpha)$ is holomorphic in l for l on a portion δ of the real axis, the functions $D_l(\alpha_1)$ and $\mathcal{G}_l(\alpha_1)$ have the same property for all states $|\alpha_1\rangle$ belonging to y_α. From the form of $D_l(\alpha_1)$ this implies that

$$J_E(\alpha_1) = 0,\ \varepsilon(\alpha_1) - E - \lambda^2 K_E(\alpha_1) \neq 0 \tag{4.4}$$

for E on δ and $|\alpha_1\rangle$ in y_α. We have assumed above $\mathcal{G}_l(\alpha)$ to be holomorphic for l around $E(\alpha)$. We may thus conclude that *for each state* $|\alpha\rangle$ *there is an energy interval* δ_α *around* $E(\alpha)$ *such that* (4.4) *holds whenever* E *is on* δ_α *and* $|\alpha_1\rangle$ *in* y_α. In particular $|\alpha\rangle$ is not contained in y_α. These conclusions will play a central role in the following.

A remark must still be included on the significance of the family of states y_α. For given $|\alpha\rangle$ the family x_α is the collection of states which intervene as intermediate states when one calculates the eigenvalue for $|\alpha\rangle$ of operators of the form $\{VA_1V + VA_2VA_3V + \ldots\}_{id}$ with arbitrary diagonal A_1, A_2, ... Similarly the family y_α is the collection of states intervening in addition to $|\alpha\rangle$ as intermediate states when the eigenvalue for $|\alpha\rangle$ is calculated for operators $\{VA_1V + VA_2VA_3V + \ldots\}_d$ with diagonal $A_1, A_2, \ldots$. Remembering how y_α was defined in terms of x_α one verifies this property immediately by means of the fact that any diagonal part can be obtained by successive calculation of a number of irreducible diagonal parts. For each $|\alpha\rangle$ let us now define the diagonal projection operator Y_α by

$$Y_\alpha |\alpha_1\rangle = \begin{cases} |\alpha_1\rangle & \text{for } |\alpha_1\rangle \text{ in } y_\alpha, \\ 0 & \text{otherwise.} \end{cases} \tag{4.5}$$

The above property of y_α can then be expressed by the identity

$$\begin{aligned} \{VA_1VA_2V \ldots A_nV\}_d |\alpha\rangle = &\{VA_1V \ldots A_{j-1}V(Y_\alpha A_j)V \ldots A_nV\}_d |\alpha\rangle \\ &+ \{VA_1V \ldots A_{j-1}V\}_d A_j \{VA_{j+1}V \ldots A_nV\}_d |\alpha\rangle \end{aligned} \tag{4.6}$$

for arbitrary diagonal $A_1, A_2, \ldots A_n$, $(1 \leqslant j \leqslant n)$. Use is made of this identity in the next section where the physical significance of the family of states y_α will be established: y_α contains the states persistently attached to the state $|\alpha\rangle$ when it moves under the influence of the perturbation, i.e. the states present in the "cloud" surrounding $|\alpha\rangle$.

5. *The asymptotic motion of wave packets.* The mathematical properties of the hamiltonian $H + \lambda V$ and its resolvent R_l have now been sufficiently investigated to permit a discussion of the motion of the system. We study in the present section the asymptotic motion of a general wave packet, i.e. the time variation for $t \to \pm \infty$ of a general non-monochromatic solution $\varphi(t)$ of the Schrödinger equation

$$i\partial\varphi/\partial t = (H + \lambda V)\varphi \tag{5.1}$$

This asymptotic motion has been described in Section 2, Equations (2.7) and (2.8), for the case of a "normal" perturbation producing no diagonal parts, i.e., no δ-term in the matrix elements of type (2.4). In this case the asymptotic motion is unaffected by the perturbation, being a superposition of unperturbed stationary states $|\alpha\rangle$ with time-dependent phase factors $\exp[-it\varepsilon(\alpha)]$, corresponding to the unperturbed energy value $\varepsilon(\alpha)$. We can thus say that in the presence of a normal perturbation the states $|\alpha\rangle$, although not stationary, are *asymptotically stationary* with energy $\varepsilon(\alpha)$.

Our first concern will be to show that for the perturbations here studied the states $|\alpha\rangle$ are no longer asymptotically stationary, not even with an energy value different from $\varepsilon(\alpha)$. Let us assume them to be asymptotically stationary with energy values $\varepsilon'(\alpha)$. Putting for each t_0

$$\psi(t_0) = \int |\alpha\rangle \exp[-it_0\varepsilon'(\alpha)]c(\alpha)d\alpha \tag{5.2}$$

and assuming the coefficients $c(\alpha)$ to be smooth functions of α, we would then have for finite t, in the limit $t_0 \to \pm\infty$,

$$\exp[-it(H+\lambda V)]\psi(t_0) \simeq \psi(t_0+t),$$

and therefore

$$\lim_{t_0\to\pm\infty} \langle\psi(t_0+t)\,|\exp[-it(H+\lambda V)]|\,\psi(t_0)\rangle = \int |c(\alpha)|^2 d\alpha \tag{5.3}$$

Introduce the resolvent by means of

$$\exp[-it(H+\lambda V)] = (2\pi)^{-1} i \int_\gamma \exp(-ilt) R_l \, dl. \tag{5.4}$$

γ is a contour in the complex plane encircling a sufficiently large portion of the real axis and is to be described counterclockwise. From the definition of the diagonal part of an operator one gets

$$\lim_{t_0\to\pm\infty} \langle\psi(t_0+t)\,|R_l|\,\psi(t_0)\rangle = \langle\psi(t_0+t)\,|\{R_l\}_d|\,\psi(t_0)\rangle$$

$$= \int \exp[it\varepsilon'(\alpha)] \,.\, D_l(\alpha) \,.\, |c(\alpha)|^2 \,.\, d\alpha \tag{5.5}$$

We are thus led to calculate the expression

$$(2\pi)^{-1} i \int_\gamma \exp(-ilt) D_l(\alpha) dl = r_t(\alpha) \,.\, \exp[-itE(\alpha)]. \tag{5.6}$$

From the results of Sections 3 and 4 one finds

$$r_t(\alpha) = N(\alpha) + \pi^{-1}\lambda^2 \int_{-\infty}^{\infty} \frac{\exp[it(E(\alpha)-E)] \,.\, J_E(\alpha) \,.\, dE}{[\varepsilon(\alpha) - E - \lambda^2 K_E(\alpha)]^2 + \lambda^4 [J_E(\alpha)]^2} \tag{5.7}$$

with

$$[N(\alpha)]^{-1} = 1 + \lambda^2 [\partial \mathcal{G}_l(\alpha)/\partial l]_{l=E(\alpha)}. \tag{5.8}$$

In (5.7) the integration is restricted to the values of E for which $J_E(\alpha) \neq 0$; the denominator does not vanish for these values. Notice that $r_t(\alpha)$ reduces to 1 for $t = 0$,

$$r_0(\alpha) = (2\pi)^{-1} i \int_\gamma D_l(\alpha) dl = 1,$$

because

$$(2\pi)^{-1} i \int_\gamma D_l \, dl = (2\pi)^{-1} i \int_\gamma \{R_l\}_d \, dl = \{(2\pi)^{-1} i \int_\gamma R_l \, dl\}_d = \{1\}_d = 1.$$

Therefrom two inequalities follow, the second for $t \neq 0$,

$$0 < N(\alpha) < 1 \tag{5.9}$$

$$|r_t(\alpha)| < 1 \tag{5.10}$$

unless the function $J_E(\alpha)$ is identically zero for all E, a circumstance which under our assumptions would imply

$$\mathcal{G}_l(\alpha) = 0, \; D_l(\alpha) = [\varepsilon(\alpha) - l]^{-1} \tag{5.11}$$

for all l, just as for a normal perturbation. Using (5.4), (5.5) and (5.6) we now determine the left-hand side of (5.3). It is

$$\int \exp[it(\varepsilon'(\alpha) - E(\alpha))] . r_t(\alpha) . |c(\alpha)|^2 . d\alpha.$$

From (5.10) it is seen to be less than the right hand side of (5.3) except in the "normal case" where (5.11) holds for all l and α.

The question is now whether the replacement in Equation (5.2) of the states $|\alpha\rangle$ by others would restore the asymptotic validity of the formula. This will be shown to be the case if the new states are chosen to be

$$|\alpha\rangle_{as} = [N(\alpha)]^{\frac{1}{2}} \cdot \left[1 + \Sigma_{n=1}^{\infty} \left\{ \left(\frac{\lambda Y_\alpha}{E(\alpha) + \lambda^2 K_{E(\alpha)} - H} V \right)^n \right\}_{nd} \right] |\alpha\rangle, \quad (5.12)$$

and the corresponding energy values $E(\alpha)$. The numbers $E(\alpha)$ and $N(\alpha)$, the symbol $\{\ldots\}_{nd}$ and the diagonal operators Y_α, K_E have all been defined before. $K_{E(\alpha)}$ is the operator K_E for $E = E(\alpha)$. Notice that in (5.12) the denominator never vanishes: because of the presence of Y_α its eigenvalues occur only for states $|\alpha_1\rangle$ belonging to the family y_α, so that (4.4) can be applied for $E = E(\alpha)$. As a further consequence of (4.4) we can use in (5.12) the equality

$$\frac{Y_\alpha}{E(\alpha) + \lambda^2 K_{E(\alpha)} - H} = \lim_{l' \to E(\alpha)} (- Y_\alpha D_{l'}) \quad (5.13)$$

The property we have to establish is the following. Put for smoothly varying $c(\alpha)$

$$\varphi(t_0) = \int |\alpha\rangle_{as} \exp[- it_0 E(\alpha)] c(\alpha) d\alpha. \quad (5.14)$$

Then one has, for finite t and in the limit $t_0 \to \pm \infty$,

$$\exp[- it(H + \lambda V)] \varphi(t_0) \simeq \varphi(t + t_0).$$

Since the operator on the left-hand side is unitary, it is sufficient to prove in the limit $t_0 \to \pm \infty$

$$\langle \varphi(t + t_0) \mid \exp[- it(H + \lambda V)] \mid \varphi(t_0) \rangle \simeq$$
$$\langle \varphi(t_0) \mid \varphi(t_0) \rangle \simeq \langle \varphi(t + t_0) \mid \varphi(t + t_0) \rangle. \quad (5.15)$$

Calculate first

$$\langle \varphi(t_0) \mid \varphi(t_0) \rangle = \int [N(\alpha)\, N(\alpha')]^{\frac{1}{2}} \, . \, \exp[it_0(E(\alpha) - E(\alpha'))].$$

$$\langle \alpha | \left[1 + \Sigma_{n=1}^{\infty} \left\{ \left(\lambda V \frac{Y_\alpha}{E(\alpha) + \lambda^2 K_{E(\alpha)} - H} \right)^n \right\}_{nd} \right] .$$

$$\cdot \left[1 + \Sigma_{n'=1}^{\infty} \left\{ \left(\frac{\lambda Y_{\alpha'}}{E(\alpha') + \lambda^2 K_{E(\alpha')} - H} V \right)^{n'} \right\}_{nd} \right] |\alpha'\rangle$$

$$c^*(\alpha)\, c(\alpha') d\alpha d\alpha' \quad (5.16)$$

In the limit $t_0 \to \pm \infty$ only the diagonal part of the operator under the integral sign gives a non vanishing contribution, so that

$$\lim_{t_0 \to \pm\infty} \langle \varphi(t_0) \mid \varphi(t_0) \rangle = \int N(\alpha) \, . \, B(\alpha) \, . \, |c(\alpha)|^2 \, . \, d\alpha \quad (5.17)$$

if $B(\alpha)$ is the eigenvalue of this diagonal part for the state $|\alpha\rangle$. Using (5.13) we can write

$$B(\alpha)\,|\alpha\rangle = \lim_{l'\to E(\alpha)} \{[1 + \Sigma_{n=1}^{\infty} \{(-\lambda V D_{l'} Y_{\alpha})^{n}\}_{nd}] . \\ [1 + \Sigma_{n'=1}^{\infty} \{(-\lambda Y_{\alpha} D_{l'} V)^{n'}\}_{nd}]\}_{d}\,|\alpha\rangle. \quad (5.18)$$

By application of (4.6) we may drop in the right hand side all factors Y_{α} and notice then from (3.15) that we may also write

$$B(\alpha)\,|\alpha\rangle = \lim_{l'\to E(\alpha)} [D_{l'}]^{-1} \{R_{l'} R_{l'}\}_{d} [D_{l'}]^{-1} |\alpha\rangle. \quad (5.19)$$

This is further simplified by means of the identity

$$R_{l'} R_{l'} = \partial R_{l'}/\partial l',$$

a limiting case of (3.17). One gets

$$\{R_{l'} R_{l'}\}_{d} = \partial\{R_{l'}\}_{d}/\partial l' = \partial D_{l'}/\partial l' = [D_{l'}]^{2}.[1 + \lambda^{2}\partial \mathcal{G}_{l'}/\partial l'].$$

The expression for $B(\alpha)$ reduces then finally to

$$B(\alpha)\,|\alpha\rangle = \lim_{l'\to E(\alpha)} [1 + \lambda^{2}\partial \mathcal{G}_{l'}/\partial l']\,|\alpha\rangle = [N(\alpha)]^{-1}\,|\alpha\rangle,$$

where the definition (5.8) of $N(\alpha)$ has been used. Insertion into (5.17) gives

$$\lim_{t_0\to\pm\infty} \langle\varphi(t_0)\,|\varphi(t_0)\rangle = \int |c(\alpha)|^{2}\,d\alpha. \quad (5.20)$$

It is obvious that the same limit would be obtained for $\langle\varphi(t+t_0)|\varphi(t+t_0)\rangle$.

The left hand side of (5.15) must now be calculated and its value must be found equal to (5.20). We determine first the limit of the expression $\langle\varphi(t+t_0)\,|R_l|\,\varphi(t_0)\rangle$ for $t_0 \to \pm\infty$. Proceeding in the same manner as for (5.17) and (5.18) we find

$$\lim_{t_0\to\pm\infty} \langle\varphi(t+t_0)\,|R_l|\,\varphi(t_0)\rangle = \int N(\alpha).\exp[itE(\alpha)].B'(\alpha).\,|c(\alpha)|^{2}.d\alpha \quad (5.21)$$

with $B'(\alpha)$ defined by

$$B'(\alpha)\,|\alpha\rangle = \lim_{l'\to E(\alpha)} \{[1+\Sigma_{n=1}^{\infty}\{(-\lambda V D_{l'} Y_{\alpha})^{n}\}_{nd}] R_l [1+\Sigma_{n'=1}^{\infty}\{(-\lambda Y_{\alpha} D_{l'} V)^{n'}\}_{nd}]\}_{d}|\alpha\rangle \\ = \lim_{l'\to E(\alpha)} [D_{l'}]^{-1} \{R_{l'} R_l R_{l'}\}_{d} [D_{l'}]^{-1} |\alpha\rangle. \quad (5.22)$$

Further $R_{l'} R_l R_{l'} = (l' - l)^{-1} (R_{l'} - R_l) R_{l'}$

$$= (l' - l)^{-1} (\partial R_{l'}/\partial l') + (l' - l)^{-2} (R_l - R_{l'})$$

and $\{R_{l'} R_l R_{l'}\}_{d} = (l' - l)^{-1} . [D_{l'}]^{2} . [1 + \lambda^{2}\partial \mathcal{G}_{l'}/\partial l'] + (l' - l)^{-2} (D_l - D_{l'})$.

Consequently, remembering that

$$\lim_{l'\to E(\alpha)} [D_{l'}]^{-1}\,|\alpha\rangle = 0,$$

one gets for $B'(\alpha)$ the simple expression

$$B'(\alpha) = [E(\alpha) - l]^{-1} \quad . [N(\alpha)]^{-1}. \quad (5.23)$$

Insertion into (5.21) and application of (5.4) give the desired result

$$\lim_{t_0\to\pm\infty} \langle\varphi(t+t_0)\,|\exp[-it(H+\lambda V)]|\,\varphi(t_0)\rangle = \int |c(\alpha)|^{2} . d\alpha.$$

This completes our proof: (5.14) describes correctly the asymptotic motion of wave packets. From (5.12) it follows that (barring exceptional complications) the states $|\alpha\rangle_{as}$ are linearly independent and every state is expressible as linear combination of them. Consequently we can conclude that the $|\alpha\rangle_{as}$ form a *complete set of asymptotically stationary states*, with the $E(\alpha)$ as corresponding energy values.

Some comments are in order on the significance to be attached to the asymptotically stationary states $|\alpha\rangle_{as}$. It is a priori obvious that the concept of asymptotically stationary state, in contrast to that of stationary state in the ordinary sense of the word, is not unambiguously defined. All kinds of terms could be added to the states (5.12) without affecting the validity of the formula (5.14) for the asymptotic motion of wave packets; one could for example take for (5.12) the true stationary states of the system. The concept of asymptotically stationary state must rather be considered with respect to the a priori given separation of the hamiltonian in an unperturbed term H and a perturbation λV. The situation is quite simple in the case of what we have called before a "normal" perturbation: the eigenstates of H, although no longer truly stationary in presence of the perturbation, retain at least the property of asymptotic stationarity and are thus observable as monochromatic components of wave packets which no longer (or not yet) undergo scattering and reaction processes.

For the perturbations here studied, as a consequence of the diagonal effects incorporated in the operator $\mathcal{G}_l$, the unperturbed eigenstates $|\alpha\rangle$ are deprived not only of their stationarity but even of their asymptotic stationarity, and the state $|\alpha\rangle_{as}$ given by (5.12) may now be regarded as obtained from $|\alpha\rangle$ by a minimal amount of admixture of other unperturbed states sufficient to restore the property of asymptotic stationarity. Although we have not proved rigorously that the admixing contained in (5.12) is strictly minimal, we consider this statement to be justified by the following consideration. The expression (5.12) of $|\alpha\rangle_{as}$ differs in two respects from the expression obtained for a perturbed stationary state in the usual perturbation calculus of discrete spectra: the corrections to the energy levels are incorporated in the denominators $E(\alpha) + \lambda^2 K_{E(\alpha)} - H$, and the states admixed to $|\alpha\rangle$ are restricted by the presence of the operators Y_α to the family y_α, i.e. to the smallest family of states giving their true value to the diagonal parts of operators appearing in (5.22) and needed for establishing the asymptotic stationarity. It is the presence of Y_α which makes the admixing minimal.

This question of giving a strictly unambiguous definition for the asymptotically stationary states is clearly a very delicate one and will not be studied further in the present paper. We shall content ourselves with having in (5.12) a self contained and tractable expression for a complete set of asymptotically stationary states, i.e. essentially a formal description for the "cloud" effects so often talked about in qualitative terms in field theory. To appreciate the utility of (5.12) one must realize how very much simpler and more tractable this expression is than the complete expression for the true stationary states of the system (here not written down). This relative simplicity is possible because the states $|\alpha\rangle_{as}$ incorporate only the persistent effects caused by the perturbation. They have however the merit of incorporating all the persistent effects and will enable us to write down, in the following section, a S-matrix formula for the other effects of the perturbation, which are of transient nature and consist of transitions between asymptotically stationary states.

One should remark that the states $|\alpha\rangle_{as}$ do not form an orthonormal set, because the scalar product ${}_{as}\langle\alpha|\alpha'\rangle_{as}$ (where ${}_{as}\langle\alpha|$ is the conjugate of $|\alpha\rangle_{as}$) differs from $\delta(\alpha - \alpha')$ by some smooth function of α and α'. This is to be expected from the field-theoretical examples: if one considers a state $|\alpha\rangle$ composed of two electrons with momenta $\mathbf{q}$ and $-\mathbf{q}$, and a state $|\alpha'\rangle$ composed of two electrons with momenta $\mathbf{q}' \neq \pm\,\mathbf{q}$ and $-\mathbf{q}'$, the clouds around $|\alpha\rangle$ and $|\alpha'\rangle$ have in common, among others, states with two electrons and one photon, and are therefore non-orthogonal; this non-orthogonality is essential because it is responsible for the interaction between the two electrons. In the asymptotic limit of large times, however, the states $|\alpha\rangle_{as}$ may be treated as orthonormal. Consider indeed the waves (5.14) and

$$\varphi'(t_0) = \int |\alpha\rangle_{as} \,.\, \exp[-\,it_0E(\alpha)] \,.\, c'(\alpha)d\alpha'.$$

A derivation identical to that of (5.20) gives

$$\lim_{t_0\to\pm\infty} \langle\varphi(t_0) \mid \varphi'(t_0)\rangle = \int c^*(\alpha)c'(\alpha)d\alpha.$$

We may thus say that the states $|\alpha\rangle_{as}$ are *asymptotically orthonormal.*

6. *The S-matrix.* The problem to be treated now concerns the connection between the asymptotic motion of a wave packet before and after all transient effects take place. More precisely, let us consider a general solution $\varphi(t)$ of the Schrödinger equation

$$-\,i\partial\varphi/\partial t = (H + \lambda V)\varphi. \tag{6.1}$$

From the results of the foregoing section it follows that $\varphi(t)$ has in the limits of $t \to \pm\,\infty$ the two asymptotic forms

$$\varphi(t) \simeq \int |\alpha\rangle_{as} \exp[-\,itE(\alpha)].c(\alpha)d\alpha \text{ for } t \to -\,\infty, \tag{6.2}$$

$$\varphi(\tilde{t}) \simeq \int |\alpha\rangle_{as} \exp[-\,i\tilde{t}E(\alpha)].\tilde{c}(\alpha)d\alpha \text{ for } \tilde{t} \to +\,\infty. \tag{6.3}$$

The problem is to find the relation between the coefficients $c(\alpha)$ and $\tilde{c}(\alpha)$. As will be established hereunder this relation is given by

$$\tilde{c}(\alpha) = \int \langle\alpha\,|S|\,\alpha'\rangle\, c(\alpha')d\alpha' \tag{6.4}$$

with the following expression for the S-matrix

$$\langle \alpha |S| \alpha' \rangle = \delta(\alpha - \alpha') - 2\pi i \lambda \delta[E(\alpha) - E(\alpha')] .$$
$$[N(\alpha)N(\alpha')]^{\frac{1}{2}} \, . \, \langle \alpha | \, V - \lambda \{ V R_{E(\alpha)+i0} V \}_{nd} \, |\alpha' \rangle . \tag{6.5}$$

The symbol R_{E+i0}, here to be taken for $E = E(\alpha)$, is defined by

$$R_{E+i0} = \lim R_l \text{ for } l = E + i\eta, \ \eta > 0, \ \eta \to 0, \tag{6.6}$$

and the notation $\{VR_lV\}_{nd}$ means $\{VD_lV - \lambda VD_lVD_lV + \ldots\}_{nd}$.

To prove the assertion it is sufficient to show that for all smooth functions $c(\alpha)$ and $c_1(\alpha)$

$$\lim_{t\to -\infty, \, \bar{t} \to +\infty} \langle \varphi_1(\bar{t}) \mid \exp[- i(\bar{t} - t) \, (H + \lambda V)] \, |\varphi(t)\rangle$$
$$= \int c_1^*(\alpha) \, \langle \alpha |S| \alpha' \rangle \, c(\alpha') \mathrm{d}\alpha \mathrm{d}\alpha', \tag{6.7}$$

where $\varphi(t)$ is defined by (5.14) in terms of $c(\alpha)$ and similarly

$$\varphi_1(\bar{t}) = \int |\alpha\rangle_{as} \, . \, \exp[- i\bar{t}E(\alpha)] c_1(\alpha) \mathrm{d}\alpha .$$

Firstly, since $\bar{t} - t > 0$, we may write

$$\exp[- i(\bar{t} - t) \, (H + \lambda V)] = (2\pi)^{-1} \quad i \int_\gamma \exp[- i(\bar{t} - t)l] R_l \mathrm{d}l$$
$$= (2\pi i)^{-1} \int_{-\infty}^{\infty} \exp[- i(\bar{t} - t)E] R_{E+i0} \, \mathrm{d}E .$$

Consequently

$$\left.\begin{aligned} &\langle \varphi_1(\bar{t}) \, |\exp[- i(\bar{t} - t) \, (H + \lambda V)]|\varphi(t)\rangle = (2\pi i)^{-1} \int c_1^*(\alpha) [N(\alpha)]^{\frac{1}{2}} \mathrm{d}\alpha \\ &\int c(\alpha') \, [N(\alpha')]^{\frac{1}{2}} \mathrm{d}\alpha' \int_{-\infty}^{\infty} \exp[i\bar{t}(E(\alpha') - E) - it(E(\alpha) - E)] \mathrm{d}E \\ &\langle \alpha | \left[1 + \Sigma_{n=1}^{\infty} \left\{ \left(\lambda V \frac{Y_\alpha}{E(\alpha) + \lambda^2 K_{E(\alpha)} - H} \right)^n \right\}_{nd} \right] . \\ &\quad . \, R_{E+i0} \left[1 + \Sigma_{n'=1}^{\infty} \left\{ \left(\frac{\lambda Y_{\alpha'}}{E(\alpha') + \lambda^2 K_{E(\alpha')} - H} \, V \right)^{n'} \right\}_{nd} \right] |\alpha'\rangle \end{aligned}\right\} \tag{6.8}$$

We need the asymptotic value of this expression for $t \to -\infty$, $\bar{t} \to +\infty$. It originates from the terms which are singular for $E(\alpha') = E$ and $E(\alpha) = E$, all other terms giving zero contribution in the limit. These singular terms in the matrix element in (6.8) are obtained in two ways:

i) by considering the diagonal part of the whole operator in the matrix element;
ii) by putting one of the intermediate states intervening in R_{E+i0}, let us call it $|\alpha_1\rangle$, identical to $|\alpha\rangle$, and another intermediate state $|\alpha_1'\rangle$ intervening in R_{E+i0} (more to the right than $|\alpha_1\rangle$) identical to $|\alpha'\rangle$. The operator products comprised between $|\alpha\rangle$ and $|\alpha_1\rangle$ must be replaced by their diagonal part, as well as those between $|\alpha_1'\rangle$ and $|\alpha'\rangle$.

Case i) requires the calculation of the eigenvalue for $|\alpha\rangle$ of the operator

$$\left\{\left[1+\Sigma_{n=1}^{\infty}\left\{\left(\lambda V\frac{Y_\alpha}{E(\alpha)+\lambda^2K_{E(\alpha)}-H}\right)^n\right\}_{nd}\right].\right.$$

$$\left.\cdot R_{E+i0}\left[1+\Sigma_{n'=1}^{\infty}\left\{\left(\frac{\lambda Y_\alpha}{E(\alpha)+\lambda^2K_{E(\alpha)}-H}\right)^{n'}\right\}_{nd}\right]\right\}_d . \quad (6.9)$$

This eigenvalue can be immediately gotten from the quantity $B'(\alpha)$ introduced in the preceding section, Equation (5.22), and there calculated, Equation (5.23). It is

$$[N(\alpha)]^{-1}\lim_{0<\eta\to 0}[E(\alpha)-E-i\eta]^{-1}=[N(\alpha)]^{-1}\,.\,[E(\alpha)-E-i0]^{-1}.$$

The contribution of the diagonal part (6.9) to (6.8) is thus simply found to be

$$(2\pi i)^{-1}\int c_1^*(\alpha)c(\alpha)\mathrm{d}\alpha\int_{-\infty}^{\infty}\exp[i(\bar{t}-t)\,(E(\alpha)-E)]\,\mathrm{d}E/(E(\alpha)-E-i0)$$

and reduces to the integral

$$\int c_1^*(\alpha)c(\alpha)\mathrm{d}\alpha \quad (6.10)$$

originating when the $\delta(\alpha-\alpha')$-term of $\langle\alpha\,|S|\,\alpha'\rangle$ is considered alone in the right hand side of (6.7).

When case ii) is taken for all possible choices of the intermediate states $|\alpha_1\rangle$ and $|\alpha_1'\rangle$ among the intermediate states intervening in the explicit expression of R_{E+i0} one sees easily that the total expression obtained for the matrix element in (6.8) is the following

$$-\lambda\langle\alpha|\left\{\left[1+\Sigma_{n=1}^{\infty}\left\{\left(\lambda V\frac{Y_\alpha}{E(\alpha)+\lambda^2K_{E(\alpha)}-H}\right)^n\right\}_{nd}\right]R_{E+i0}\right\}_d.[V-\lambda\{VR_{E+i0}V\}_{nd}]\times$$

$$\times\left\{R_{E+i0}\cdot\left[1+\Sigma_{n'=1}^{\infty}\left\{\left(\frac{\lambda Y_{\alpha'}}{E(\alpha')+\lambda^2K_{E(\alpha')}-H}V\right)^{n'}\right\}_{nd}\right]\right\}_d|\alpha'\rangle. \quad (6.11)$$

The two diagonal parts appearing in (6.11) are again handled by the method used in Section 5, and one finds for their eigenvalues

$[E(\alpha)-E-i0]^{-1}$ and $[E(\alpha')-E-i0]^{-1}$, so that the matrix element (6.11) reduces to

$$-\lambda[E(\alpha)-E-i0]^{-1}\,.\,[E(\alpha')-E-i0]^{-1}\,.\,\langle\alpha|\,V-\lambda\{VR_{E+i0}V\}_{nd}\,|\alpha'\rangle.$$

We now remark that

$$\lim_{t\to-\infty}\frac{\exp[-it(E(\alpha)-E)]}{E(\alpha)-E-i0}=2\pi i\delta[E(\alpha)-E]$$

and similarly

$$\lim_{\bar{t}\to+\infty}\frac{\exp[i\bar{t}(E(\alpha')-E)]}{E(\alpha')-E-i0}=2\pi i\delta[E(\alpha')-E].$$

Consequently the contribution of case ii) to the right hand side of (6.8) is, in the limit $t \to -\infty, \tilde{t} \to +\infty$, equal to

$$- 2\pi i\lambda \int c_1^*(\alpha) [N(\alpha)]^{\frac{1}{2}} d\alpha \int c(\alpha') [N(\alpha')]^{\frac{1}{2}} d\alpha'$$
$$\int_{-\infty}^{\infty} \delta[E(\alpha) - E] . \delta[E(\alpha') - E] dE . \langle\alpha | V - \lambda\{VR_{E+i0}V\}_{nd} |\alpha'\rangle.$$

Carrying out the integration over E, and adding the contribution (6.10) of case i), one finds exactly the right hand side of (6.7). This completes the proof of the S-matrix formulae (6.4), (6.5).

One notices how conservation of energy in transient processes is ensured by the occurrence of the $\delta[E(\alpha) - E(\alpha')]$-factor in the S-matrix (6.5). As is indeed required for the consistency of the theory, the energies conserved are the true energies $E(\alpha)$ of the asymptotically stationary states, and not the original uncorrected energies $\varepsilon(\alpha)$. Another point which deserves verification is the unitarity of the S-matrix. In view of the asymptotic orthonormality of the states $|\alpha\rangle_{as}$, the unitary character of S is simply expressed by the identity

$$\int \langle\alpha |S^*| \alpha_1\rangle d\alpha_1 \langle\alpha_1 |S| \alpha'\rangle = \delta(\alpha - \alpha') \tag{6.12}$$

The verification of (6.12), although rather lengthy, involves no essential difficulty. We restrict ourselves here to mentioning three formulae which have successively to be relied upon in the course of the derivation. They are ($\eta > 0$)

$$R_{E+i0} - R_{E-i0} = \lim_{\eta\to 0} (R_{E-i\eta} - R_{E-i\eta}) = 2i \lim_{\eta\to 0} \eta R_{E-i\eta} R_{E+i\eta},$$
$$\lim_{\eta\to 0} \eta\, R_{E-i\eta} R_{E+i\eta} = \pi R_{E-i0}\, \delta(H - E - \lambda^2 K_E) R_{E+i0}, \tag{6.13}$$
$$\delta(H - E - \lambda^2 K_E) |\alpha\rangle = \delta[E(\alpha) - E] . N(\alpha) . |\alpha\rangle.$$

Only equation (6.13) is not immediate; the central point in its proof is the relation

$$\lim_{\eta\to 0} \eta\, D_{E-i\eta} A D_{E+i\eta} |\alpha\rangle = N(\alpha) \delta(H - E - \lambda^2 K_E) A |\alpha\rangle$$

valid for A diagonal, whereas the limit would be zero if the operator A has no diagonal part, i.e. has no $\delta(\alpha - \alpha')$-singularity in its matrix element $\langle\alpha |A| \alpha'\rangle$.

7. *Remarks*. Many questions can still be raised in connection with the above contribution to the perturbation theory of continuous spectra, and the present paper does not claim to have touched upon all points deserving clarification. Our object has been to define and study, within the framework of standard quantum mechanics, a class of perturbations characterized by certain formal properties which are exhibited in particular by the conventional field-theoretical interactions, and to derive in detail how these formal properties imply the physical effects (self-energy and cloud effects) which, from our field-theoretical experience, we intuitively expect them to

produce. Two additional remarks will still be made in order to delimit more clearly the scope of our results.

Firstly, our whole discussion and the results arrived at have meaning only with respect to a given separation of the hamiltonian in an unperturbed part H and a perturbation λV, and with respect to a given representation $|\alpha\rangle$. Neither the separation $H + \lambda V$ of the hamiltonian nor the special representation of basic states $|\alpha\rangle$ can be given in general an absolute physical significance, although this may very well turn out to be possible for the special systems encountered in field theory. However this may be, the standpoint adopted here was to consider both the separation $H + \lambda V$ and the basic set $|\alpha\rangle$ as given *a priori* without enquiring into their origin. Still one might observe that, once the separation $H + \lambda V$ of the hamiltonian is known, the states $|\alpha\rangle$ may be uniquely defined as the simultaneous eigenvectors of H and of the operators D_l for all l. The operator D_l itself can be defined in terms of H alone by noticing that its matrix element in any representation $|\beta\rangle$ diagonalizing H is the part of the matrix element $\langle\beta\, |R_l|\, \beta'\rangle$ of the resolvent R_l which has a $\delta[\varepsilon'(\beta) - \varepsilon'(\beta')]$-singularity, $\varepsilon'(\beta)$ being the eigenvalue of H for $|\beta\rangle$.

Our second remark concerns the relation existing between the separation of diagonal parts of operators systematically used in the present paper and the well known renormalization technique of quantum field theory, as developed by Feynman and Dyson [5]) in the perturbation expansion by means of graphs. The separation of diagonal parts of operators would essentially correspond in the field-theoretical cases with what Dyson calls the elimination of the self-energy parts of graphs. The only difference is that we consider here states of the system as a whole whereas Dyson deals with particle states. Consequently our procedure would lead in field theory to the determination of the complete propagation functions. It does not lead to the complete vertex functions. It would thus permit, in electrodynamics for example, to renormalize the mass of the electron but not its charge.

Received 17-9-55.

REFERENCES

1) For a short presentation of the general quantum-mechanical theory of scattering and reaction processes, see Pauli, W., Meson Theory of Nuclear Forces, Interscience, New York (1946), chapter IV (except the considerations on radiation damping). Another standard exposition is contained in Lippmann, B. A. and Schwinger, J., Phys. Rev. **79** (1950) 469.

2) Lee, T. D., Phys. Rev. **95** (1954) 1329.

3) Van Hove, L., Physica **21** (1955) 517.

4) Pirenne, J., Helv. phys. Acta **21** (1948) 226. See also Gell-Mann, M. and Goldberger, M. L., Phys. Rev. **91** (1953) 398.

5) Feynman, R. P., Phys. Rev. **74** (1948) 939 and 1430; Dyson, F. J., Phys. Rev. **75** (1949) 486 and 1736.

ENERGY CORRECTIONS AND PERSISTENT PERTURBATION EFFECTS IN CONTINUOUS SPECTRA

II. THE PERTURBED STATIONARY STATES

by LÉON VAN HOVE

Instituut voor theoretische natuurkunde der Rijksuniversiteit, Utrecht, Nederland

Synopsis

The paper continues the systematic investigation undertaken earlier [1]) of a class of perturbations of continuous energy spectra producing, in addition to scattering and reaction processes, self-energy and cloud effects which affect at all times the motion of wave packets and which are of the type occurring in the quantum theory of interacting fields. The main result presented here is the explicit determination of the perturbed stationary states. The formula obtained is used to express the motion of wave packets and to connect it with its asymptotic properties for large times as established earlier. A special example is treated as illustration of the general method and a crude preliminary discussion is given of the aspect under which the renormalization program will present itself in the present formalism

1. *Introduction.* In a previous paper [1]), to be referred to hereafter as I, we have introduced and analyzed a class of quantum-mechanical perturbations of continuous energy spectra characterized by the most important formal properties through which the interaction energies encountered in the quantum theory of fields differ from the interactions studied in conventional collision theory (theory of scattering and reaction processes, S-matrix theory). We have established in I that the perturbations there considered give rise, in line with the physical situation expected to occur for interacting fields and in contrast with the case of ordinary collisions, not only to scattering and reaction processes but also to permanent effects modifying the motion of arbitrary wave packets at all times. These effects consist of energy corrections in the continuous spectrum (self-energy effects in the terminology of field theory) and of what may be called cloud effects, i.e. the persistent admixture to each unperturbed stationary state of a "cloud" of other unperturbed stationary states, even in the asymptotic motion of wave packets long before or after all scattering and reaction processes have taken place. These self-energy and cloud effects have been derived to general order in the perturbation by a method more suitable for this purpose than the usual methods of field theory. They are contained in the perturbed energy $E(\alpha)$ and the "asymptotically stationary" state $|\alpha\rangle_{as}$ associated in I to each unperturbed

stationary state $|\alpha\rangle$. Their defining equations are (I.4.1.)*) for $E(\alpha)$, $-E=E(\alpha)$ is the root of this equation —, and (I.5.12) for the state $|\alpha\rangle_{as}$. A further result derived in I is the S-matrix formulae (I.6.4), (I.6.5.) expressing the connection between the asymptotic motions of wave packets before and after all transient (i.e. scattering and reaction) processes have taken place.

The main object of the present paper is to derive for the perturbations considered in I an explicit expression to general order for the perturbed stationary states. This is achieved in the next section. As an application of this result we then consider the exact expression for the time evolution of a wave packet under the perturbation and derive from it the asymptotic motion for large times, thus obtaining in another way the results established in I without knowledge of the explicit solution of the Schrödinger equation. Such is the contents of Section 3. Two more or less complementary examples of the general formalism are then considered. The first one (Section 4), only mentioned very briefly, is the case of perturbations producing transient effects only, no self-energy or cloud effects; the general equations then reduce to the well known results of collision theory. The second example (Section 5), dealt with in more detail, is a type of perturbation producing non-vanishing self-energy and cloud effects, but sufficiently simple to be calculated in closed form, and thus particularly well suited as illustration of the developments forming the main contribution of I and of the present paper. Finally, in the last section, some indications without aim at completeness are given on the aspect taken in the present formalism by the well known renormalization program of quantum field theory, and a few comparative remarks are made on a very recent paper by De Witt [2]) devoted to a subject closely related to ours.

The definitions, notations and results of I will be used throughout. In this paper as in I we adopt a notation adapted to the assumption that all quantum numbers defining the unperturbed states $|\alpha\rangle$ are continuous. This excludes the consideration of polarization indices, spin indices, etc. The extension of the formalism to include such discrete quantum numbers would present no essential difficulty. The main difference with the case considered here and in I would be that the diagonal part of a product $VA_1V \ldots A_nV$ (V is the perturbation and $A_1, \ldots A_n$ are operators diagonal in the $|\alpha\rangle$-representation) should be defined by (I.2.4) with the δ-function referring to the continuous quantum numbers alone, F_1 being consequently a finite matrix in the polarization indices. Similarly the quantities $\mathcal{G}_l(\alpha)$ and $D_l(\alpha)$ are finite matrices which can be diagonalized for each l, a step necessary for the definition of the perturbed energies $E(\alpha)$ and of the asymptotically stationary states $|\alpha\rangle_{as}$ as well as for the definition of the true stationary states by the method of the next section. Except for this short remark we

*) By Equation (I.4.1) we mean Equation (4.1) of paper I.

leave out of consideration as we did in I the complications connected with polarization indices. Another point which is assumed here as it was in I is the convergence of all expansions in powers of the perturbation which are used in the course of our derivations. This assumption excludes for example the possibility of bound states.

2. *The perturbed stationary states.* The resolvent operator R_l extensively used in I is also a convenient tool for determining the stationary states of the perturbed hamiltonian $H + \lambda V$. From its definition (I.3.1) one obtains for the spectral resolution of $H + \lambda V$ the equation

$$H + \lambda V = \int_{-\infty}^{+\infty} E\, P_E \,\mathrm{d}E,$$

where

$$P_E = (2\pi i)^{-1} \lim_{\eta\to 0} (R_{E+i\eta} - R_{E-i\eta}),\ \eta > 0. \tag{2.1}$$

The identity (I.3.17) gives on the other hand

$$R_{E+i\eta} - R_{E-i\eta} = 2\eta i\, R_{E\pm i\eta}\, R_{E\mp i\eta} \tag{2.2}$$

Here and in subsequent equations upper (lower) signs must be taken together. The limiting value of the right hand side of (2.2) for $\eta \to 0$ is determined by means of the following identities, which are quite easy to establish. If the matrix element $\langle\alpha|B|\alpha'\rangle$ considered as function of α and α' has no $\delta(\alpha - \alpha')$ — singularity, one has

$$\lim_{\eta\to 0} \eta\, D_{E\pm i\eta}\, B\, D_{E\mp i\eta} = 0. \tag{2.3}$$

If on the contrary B is diagonal in the $|\alpha\rangle$-representation this equation is replaced by *)

$$\lim_{\eta\to 0} \eta D_{E\pm i\eta}\, B D_{E\mp i\eta} = \pi\, NB\, \delta(H - E - \lambda^2 K_E),\ \eta > 0, \tag{2.4}$$

where N is the diagonal operator defined in terms of (I.5.8) by

$$N\,|\alpha\rangle = N(\alpha)\,|\alpha\rangle.$$

By separating in (2.2) the diagonal parts occurring in the product of two resolvents and by taking (2.3) and (2.4) into account one obtains

$$\lim \eta\, R_{E\pm i\eta}\, R_{E\mp i\eta} = \pi \lim R_{E\pm i\eta}\, D^{-1}_{E\pm i\eta}\, \delta(H - E - \lambda^2 K_E)\, D^{-1}_{E\mp i\eta}\, R_{E\mp i\eta}, \tag{2.5}$$

or, with the familiar notation $A_{E\pm i0} = \lim_{\eta\to 0} A_{E\pm i\eta}$ for $\eta > 0$,

$$P_E = [1 + \Sigma_{n=1}^{\infty} \{(-\lambda\, D_{E\pm i0} V)^n\}_{nd}]\cdot$$
$$\delta(H - E - \lambda^2 K_E).[1 + \Sigma_{n'=1}^{\infty} \{(-\lambda V D_{E\mp i0})^{n'}\}_{nd}]. \tag{2.6}$$

*) The last equation of I and equation (I.6.13) contain misprints whose correction is found hereunder in (2.4) and (2.5).

We now define

$$|\alpha\rangle_{\pm} = [N(\alpha)]^{\frac{1}{2}}.[1 + \Sigma_{n=1}^{\infty} \{(-\lambda D_{E(\alpha)\pm i0}\, V)^n\}_{nd}]\, |\alpha\rangle \tag{2.7}$$

and denote by $_{\pm}\langle\alpha|$ the hermitian conjugate state vector of $|\alpha\rangle_{\pm}$.

An easy transformation of (2.6) gives

$$P_E = \int |\alpha\rangle_{\pm}\, \delta[E - E(\alpha)]\, d\alpha\ _{\pm}\langle\alpha| \tag{2.8}$$

and consequently for the spectral resolution

$$H + \lambda V = \int |\alpha\rangle_{\pm}\, E(\alpha)\, d\alpha\ _{\pm}\langle\alpha| \tag{2.9}$$

As will now be established, these relations readily imply that the states $|\alpha\rangle_{+}$ (the states $|\alpha\rangle_{-}$) form a complete orthonormal set of eigenstates of the hamiltonian $H + \lambda V$; in formulae

$$(H + \lambda V)\, |\alpha\rangle_{\pm} = E(\alpha)\, |\alpha\rangle_{\pm},\quad _{\pm}\langle\alpha \mid \alpha'\rangle_{\pm} = \delta(\alpha - \alpha') \tag{2.10}$$

where as always upper (lower) signs have to be taken together. The proof runs as follows. A well known property of spectral resolutions is expressed by the identity

$$P_E . P_{E'} = \delta(E - E')\, P_E.$$

Multiplying this equation on the left by the operator

$$N^{-\frac{1}{2}}\, [1 + \Sigma_1^{\infty} \{(-\lambda D_{E\pm i0} V)^n\}_{nd}]^{-1}$$

and on the right by

$$[1 + \Sigma_1^{\infty} \{(-\lambda V D_{E'\mp i0})^{n'}\}_{nd}]^{-1}\, N^{-\frac{1}{2}}$$

one obtains by means of (2.8)

$$\int |\alpha\rangle\, \delta[E - E(\alpha)]\, \mathrm{d}\alpha\ _{\pm}\langle\alpha \mid \alpha'\rangle_{\pm}\, \mathrm{d}\alpha'\, \delta[E' - E(\alpha')]\, \langle\alpha'| =$$
$$= \delta(E - E') \int |\alpha\rangle\, \delta[E - E(\alpha)]\, \mathrm{d}\alpha\, \langle\alpha|.$$

This is further reduced through multiplication on the left by $\langle\alpha_1|$ and on the right by $|\alpha_1'\rangle$:

$$\delta[E - E(\alpha_1)]\ \delta[E' - E(\alpha_1')]\ _{\pm}\langle\alpha_1\, |\alpha_1'\rangle_{\pm} = \delta(E - E')\ \delta[E - E(\alpha_1)]\ \delta(\alpha_1 - \alpha_1').$$

Integration over all values of E and E' for fixed α_1 and α_1' and application of (2.9) gives then (2.10).

3. *The asymptotic motion of wave packets.* The two complete sets of eigenstates obtained in the foregoing section provide us with two representations

$$\varphi(t) = \int |\alpha\rangle_{\pm}\, \exp\,[-\,it\, E(\alpha)]\, c_{\pm}(\alpha)\, \mathrm{d}\alpha \tag{3.1}$$

for an arbitrary solution of the time-dependent Schrödinger equation

$$i\, \partial\varphi/\partial t = (H + \lambda V)\varphi.$$

We have put $\hbar = 1$. The present section gives the connection between these representations and the results of I (Sections 5 and 6) on the asymptotic motion of wave packets. The following equations will be established

$$\left.\begin{aligned} &\lim_{t\to\mp\infty} [\varphi(t) - \int |\alpha\rangle_{as} \exp[-it\,E(\alpha)]\, c_\pm(\alpha)\, d\alpha] = 0 \\ &\lim_{t\to+\infty} [\varphi(t) - \int |\alpha\rangle_{as} \exp[-it\,E(\alpha)]\, d\alpha\, \langle\alpha|S|\alpha'\rangle\, c_+(\alpha')\, d\alpha'] = 0 \\ &\lim_{t\to-\infty} [\varphi(t) - \int |\alpha\rangle_{as} \exp[-it\,E(\alpha)]\, d\alpha\, \langle\alpha|S^*|\alpha'\rangle\, c_-(\alpha')\, d\alpha'] = 0 \end{aligned}\right\} \tag{3.2}$$

The limits are taken with the meaning that a state vector approaches zero when its norm (length) does. We note from (3.2) that $|\alpha\rangle_+$ corresponds to the situation where all scattering and reaction events produced by V contribute only to the outgoing wave components of the stationary state, while in $|\alpha\rangle_-$ they contribute to the incoming waves alone.

If two vectors $\varphi(t)$, $\psi(t)$ have norms approaching one for $t \to \pm\infty$, the equation

$$\lim_{t\to\pm\infty} [\varphi(t) - \psi(t)] = 0$$

is equivalent to

$$\lim_{t\to\pm\infty} \langle\psi(t) \mid \varphi(t)\rangle = 1.$$

To establish (3.2) we are thus led to calculate for $t \to \pm\infty$ the limiting value of a scalar product $\langle\psi(t) \mid \varphi(t)\rangle$ with $\varphi(t)$ of the form (3.1) and $\psi(t)$ of the form

$$\psi(t) = \int |\alpha\rangle_{as} \exp[-it\,E(\alpha)]\, \gamma(\alpha)\, d\alpha \tag{3.3}$$

We carry out this calculation considering the upper sign in (3.1). The case of the lower sign is completely analogous. According to the respective definitions (I.5.12) and (2.7) of $|\alpha\rangle_{as}$ and $|\alpha\rangle_+$ we have

$$\begin{aligned} \langle\psi(t) \mid \varphi(t)\rangle &= \int [N(\alpha)\, N(\alpha')]^{\frac{1}{2}} \exp[it\,(E(\alpha) - E(\alpha'))] \\ \langle\alpha| \, [1 + \Sigma_{n=1}^{\infty} &\{(-\lambda V Y_a D_{E(a)\pm i0})^n\}_{nd}] \cdot \\ &\cdot [1 + \Sigma_{n'=1}^{\infty} \{(-\lambda D_{E(\alpha')+i0} V)^{n'}\}_{nd}]\, |\alpha'\rangle\, \gamma^*(\alpha)\, c_+(\alpha')\, d\alpha\, d\alpha'. \end{aligned} \tag{3.4}$$

In the product $Y_a D_{E(a)\pm i0}$ the choice of sign is irrelevant (I, Section 4). The limiting value of (3.4) for $t \to \pm\infty$ originates from the terms in the integrand which are singular at $E(\alpha) = E(\alpha')$. They are of two types. Firstly the diagonal part of the whole operator comprised in the matrix element gives

$$\langle\alpha|\, \{\ldots\}_d\, |\alpha'\rangle = [N(\alpha)]^{-1}\, \delta(\alpha - \alpha') \tag{3.5}$$

as was established in I, Equations (I.5.18) and following. Its contribution to (3.4) is time-independent. Secondly there are the further diagonal parts to be separated in the matrix element. Since $Y_a D_{E(a)\pm i0}$ is non singular, the only singularities which can occur originate from terms where

$$[1 + \Sigma_{n=1}^{\infty} \{(-\lambda V Y_a D_{E(a)\pm i0})^n\}_{nd}]$$

appears as a whole within the diagonal part. One obtains by summing over all separations satisfying this condition the expression

$$\langle\alpha| \{[1 + \Sigma_{n=1}^{\infty} \{(-\lambda V Y_a D_{E(\alpha)\pm i0})^n\}_{nd}].$$

$$[1 + \Sigma_{n'=1}^{\infty} \{(-\lambda D_{E(\alpha')+i0} V)^{n'}\}_{nd}]\}_d D_{E(\alpha')+i0}$$

$$[-\lambda V + \lambda^2 \{V R_{E(\alpha')+i0} V\}_{nd}] |\alpha'\rangle =$$

$$= -\lambda [N(\alpha)]^{-1} D_{E(\alpha')+i0}(\alpha) \langle\alpha| V - \lambda \{V R_{E(\alpha')+i0} V\}_{nd} |\alpha'\rangle. \quad (3.6)$$

The singular factor is

$$D_{E(\alpha')+i0}(\alpha) = [\varepsilon(\alpha) - E(\alpha') - i0 - \lambda^2 \mathcal{G}_{E(\alpha')+i0}(\alpha)]^{-1} =$$

$$= [E(\alpha) - E(\alpha') - i0]^{-1} N(\alpha) + \text{regular terms}, \quad (3.7)$$

where $N(\alpha)$ occurs through (I.5.8.). Its contribution for large times follows from

$$\lim \frac{\exp [it (E(\alpha) - E(\alpha'))]}{E(\alpha) - E(\alpha') - i0} = \begin{cases} 2\pi i \, \delta[E(\alpha) - E(\alpha')] \text{ for } t \to +\infty, \\ 0 \text{ for } t \to -\infty. \end{cases} \quad (3.8)$$

Gathering the results (3.5) to (3.8) one finds

$$\lim_{t\to-\infty} \langle\psi(t) \mid \varphi(t)\rangle = \int \gamma^*(\alpha)\, c_+(\alpha)\, d\alpha, \quad (3.9)$$

and, in view of the expression (I.6.5) of the S-matrix,

$$\lim_{t\to+\infty} \langle\psi(t) \mid \varphi(t)\rangle = \int \gamma^*(\alpha)\, c_+(\alpha)\, d\alpha - 2\pi i \, \lambda \int [N(\alpha)\, N(\alpha')]^{\frac{1}{2}}$$

$$\delta\, [E(\alpha) - E(\alpha')]\, \langle\alpha| V - \lambda \{V R_{E(\alpha)+i0} V\}_{nd} |\alpha'\rangle\, \gamma^*(\alpha)\, c_+(\alpha')\, d\alpha\, d\alpha' =$$

$$= \int \gamma^*(\alpha)\, d\alpha \,\langle\alpha|S|\alpha'\rangle\, d\alpha'\, c_+(\alpha'). \quad (3.10)$$

One would find similarly by taking the lower sign in (3.1)

$$\lim_{t\to-\infty} \langle\psi(t) \mid \varphi(t)\rangle = \int \gamma^*(\alpha)\, d\alpha \,\langle\alpha|S^*|\alpha'\rangle\, d\alpha'\, c_-(\alpha'), \quad (3.11)$$

$$\lim_{t\to+\infty} \langle\psi(t) \mid \varphi(t)\rangle = \int \gamma^*(\alpha)\, c_-(\alpha)\, d\alpha. \quad (3.12)$$

We may incidentally remark that comparison of (3.9) and (3.11) for arbitrary $\gamma(\alpha)$ gives

$$c_+(\alpha) = \int \langle\alpha|\, S^*\, |\alpha'\rangle\, d\alpha'\, c_-(\alpha') \quad (3.13)$$

whereas (3.10) and (3.12) provide the inverse relation

$$c_-(\alpha) = \int \langle\alpha|\, S\, |\alpha'\rangle\, d\alpha'\, c_+(\alpha'). \quad (3.14)$$

Since the function $c_+(\alpha)$ or the function $c_-(\alpha)$ may be arbitrarily chosen the two last equations imply the unitarity of the S-matrix, a property which was not explicitly established in I.

It is now an easy matter to complete the proof of Equations (3.2). One assumes $\varphi(t)$ normalized to one and one successively selects for $\psi(t)$ the four vectors of form (3.3) appearing in (3.2). One then verifies that the norm of

$\psi(t)$ always approaches one for $t \to \pm\infty$; this follows readily from the asymptotic orthonormality of the states $|\alpha\rangle_{as}$ (last equation of Section 5 in I) and from the unitary character of the S-matrix. One finally establishes by means of Equations (3.9) to (3.12) that $\langle\psi(t) \mid \varphi(t)\rangle$ has the limit one for infinite times.

We shall end this section with a remark on the asymptotically stationary states $|\alpha\rangle_{as}$. The definition of these states in I, Equation (I.5.12), may have appeared rather arbitrary and found only a justification a posteriori in the fact that they provide a complete and consistent description for the asymptotic motion of wave packets. Now however new light is thrown on this definition by its close analogy with the expression (2.7) of the true stationary states $|\alpha\rangle_{\pm}$. The difference lies in the occurrence of the projection operator Y_a in front of each factor V, i.e. in a restriction of the set of states $|\alpha'\rangle$ coupled to the unperturbed state $|\alpha\rangle$. The restriction is to those states which play an effective role in the eigenvalue of diagonal parts for $|\alpha\rangle$. They are also the states which contribute to the properties of wave packets

$$\varphi = \int |\alpha\rangle_{\pm}\, d\alpha\, c(\alpha)$$

even for the most incoherent distribution of the phases of the amplitudes $c(\alpha)$, and they may therefore intuitively be pictured as the states $|\alpha'\rangle$ belonging to the "cloud" persistently attached to $|\alpha\rangle$ by virtue of the perturbation. It is an interesting and satisfactory result of the general theory that the restriction mentioned above results in the same asymptotically stationary states $|\alpha\rangle_{as}$ and thus in the same persistent cloud effects whether it is applied to the state $|\alpha\rangle_{+}$ with its outgoing nature of all scattered waves, or to the state $|\alpha\rangle_{-}$ with incoming scattered waves. We have here to do with a very significant fact which clarifies the physical meaning of the formal properties described in Section 4 of I.

4. *Perturbations without persistent effects.* It is obvious that the foregoing results apply in particular to the familiar case of perturbations which do not produce persistent effects because mathematically they do not give rise to any diagonal parts of the type defined in I, Section 2. These are the perturbations causing scattering and reaction processes only. For them one simply has to put in the results of I and of the foregoing sections

$$\mathcal{G}_l = 0,\ E(\alpha) = \varepsilon(\alpha),\ N(\alpha) = 1,\ |\alpha\rangle_{as} = |\alpha\rangle,$$

and to drop brackets of the type $\{\ldots\}_{nd}$. Although this case has been repeatedly studied in detail [3]) it may be worth noting that the method we used in the foregoing sections, when applied to it, gives an especially brief derivation of the perturbed stationary states and of the S-matrix. Our method is therefore of some interest also for ordinary collision theory.

5. *A simple type of perturbation with persistent effects.* The type of perturbation considered in the present section as illustration of the general formalism is amenable to an exact treatment in consequence of its very special mathematical structure. It has often been used on this ground as simplified model for various physical problems, in particular for resonance scattering and metastable states (theory of the line-width) [4]), and more recently by Lee [5]) for mass and coupling constant renormalization in quantum field theory *). We present this type of perturbation in a slightly more general form than usual. The generalization, which is mathematically trivial, amounts physically to the inclusion of recoil effects.

The unperturbed system of hamiltonian H is defined as having two continuous families of stationary states. The states of the first one, characterized by the presence of one particle (the V-particle of Lee), are labelled by its momentum $\mathbf{q}$ and are denoted by $|\mathbf{q}\rangle$. The states of the second family, denoted by $|\mathbf{q}, \mathbf{k}\rangle$, have two distinct particles present (the N- and θ-particles of Lee) of momenta $\mathbf{q}$ and $\mathbf{k}$. The unperturbed energy is defined by

$$H\,|\mathbf{q}\rangle = \varepsilon(\mathbf{q})\,|\mathbf{q}\rangle,\ H\,|\mathbf{q}, \mathbf{k}\rangle = \varepsilon(\mathbf{q}, \mathbf{k})\,|\mathbf{q}, \mathbf{k}\rangle. \tag{5.1}$$

One usually supposes $\varepsilon(\mathbf{q}, \mathbf{k})$ to be the sum of two one-particle energies, but this is irrelevant for the mathematical handling of the perturbation problem. The unperturbed stationary states $|\mathbf{q}\rangle$, $|\mathbf{q}, \mathbf{k}\rangle$, which correspond to the states $|\alpha\rangle$ of the general formalism, form two continuous families of dimensions 3 and 6 respectively. Orthonormality is expressed by

$$\left.\begin{aligned} &\langle\mathbf{q} \mid \mathbf{q}'\rangle = \delta(\mathbf{q} - \mathbf{q}'),\ \langle\mathbf{q}, \mathbf{k} \mid \mathbf{q}'\rangle = 0, \\ &\langle\mathbf{q}, \mathbf{k} \mid \mathbf{q}', \mathbf{k}'\rangle = \delta(\mathbf{q} - \mathbf{q}')\,\delta(\mathbf{k} - \mathbf{k}'). \end{aligned}\right\} \tag{5.2}$$

The perturbation V is defined by its matrix elements in the unperturbed representation:

$$\left.\begin{aligned} &\langle\mathbf{q}'\,|V|\,\mathbf{q}, \mathbf{k}\rangle = \langle\mathbf{q}, \mathbf{k}\,|V|\,\mathbf{q}'\rangle^* = v(\mathbf{q}, \mathbf{k})\ \delta(\mathbf{q} + \mathbf{k} - \mathbf{q}'), \\ &\langle\mathbf{q}\,|V|\,\mathbf{q}'\rangle = \langle\mathbf{q}, \mathbf{k}\,|V|\,\mathbf{q}', \mathbf{k}'\rangle = 0 \end{aligned}\right\} \tag{5.3}$$

It allows for emission of a θ-particle by a V-particle which at the same time transforms into a N-particle and for the inverse process, with conservation of momentum.

We now show that the results of I and of the present paper, when applied to this very special type of perturbation, give immediately the exact diagonalization of the hamiltonian $H + \lambda V$ and the exact expression of the S-matrix. One first notices that irreducible diagonal parts occur only for products VAV containing two factors V and that they have the value

$$\{VAV\}_{id}\,|\mathbf{q}'\rangle = |\mathbf{q}'\rangle \int A(\mathbf{q}, \mathbf{k})\,|v(\mathbf{q}, \mathbf{k})|^2\,\delta(\mathbf{q} + \mathbf{k} - \mathbf{q}')\,d\mathbf{q}\,d\mathbf{k},$$
$$\{VAV\}_{id}\,|\mathbf{q}, \mathbf{k}\rangle = 0.$$

$A(\mathbf{q}, \mathbf{k})$ is the eigenvalue for the state $|\mathbf{q}, \mathbf{k}\rangle$ of the operator A assumed to be

*) It is not clear whether Lee realized the very close resemblance of his field-theoretical model with the model introduced by Dirac for resonance scattering.

diagonal in the $|\mathbf{q}\rangle$, $|\mathbf{q}, \mathbf{k}\rangle$-representation. Consequently the operator $\mathcal{G}_l$ implicitly given by (I.3.13) can be calculated exactly and is found to have the following eigenvalues for $|\mathbf{q}'\rangle$ and $|\mathbf{q}, \mathbf{k}\rangle$:

$$\left.\begin{aligned} &\mathcal{G}_l(\mathbf{q}') = \int [\varepsilon(\mathbf{q}, \mathbf{k}) - l]^{-1} . |v(\mathbf{q}, \mathbf{k})|^2 . \delta(\mathbf{q} + \mathbf{k} - \mathbf{q}')\, d\mathbf{q}\, d\mathbf{k}, \\ &\mathcal{G}_l(\mathbf{q}, \mathbf{k}) = 0. \end{aligned}\right\} \tag{5.4}$$

The expression of the operators K_E and J_E follows immediately by application of the definition (I. 3.20). The perturbed energy values $E(\alpha)$ of the general theory are here $E(\mathbf{q}, \mathbf{k}) = \varepsilon(\mathbf{q}, \mathbf{k})$ and the root $E = E(\mathbf{q}')$ of the numerical equation

$$\varepsilon(\mathbf{q}') - E - \lambda^2 K_E(\mathbf{q}') = 0. \tag{5.5}$$

This root is supposed to be unique. The physically important condition $J_{E(\alpha)}(\alpha) = 0$, introduced in I, Section 4, to characterize the perturbations which give rise to self-energy and cloud effects as opposed to those producing dissipative effects, takes here the form

$$v(\mathbf{q}, \mathbf{k}) = 0 \text{ whenever } \mathbf{q} + \mathbf{k} = \mathbf{q}',\ \varepsilon(\mathbf{q}, \mathbf{k}) = E(\mathbf{q}'). \tag{5.6}$$

We assume it to be satisfied. It is instrumental in making our perturbation a meaningful model of field-theoretical interaction. When it is not satisfied one obtains a model for resonance scattering and metastable states [4]). The last important point to notice is that the non-diagonal part of any product $VA_1V \ldots A_nV$ ($A_1, \ldots A_n$ diagonal in the $|\mathbf{q}\rangle$, $|\mathbf{q}, \mathbf{k}\rangle$-representation) with more than two factors V ($n \geqslant 2$) vanishes. It is for this reason that our general formulae give in the case at hand a closed expression for the perturbed stationary states and for the S-matrix. The stationary states are found from (2.7)

$$\left.\begin{aligned} &|\mathbf{q}'\rangle_+ = |\mathbf{q}'\rangle_- = [N(\mathbf{q}')]^{\frac{1}{2}} \left[|\mathbf{q}'\rangle - \lambda \int |\mathbf{q}, \mathbf{k}\rangle . \frac{v^*(\mathbf{q}, \mathbf{k})\, \delta(\mathbf{q}+\mathbf{k}-\mathbf{q}')}{\varepsilon(\mathbf{q}, \mathbf{k}) - E(\mathbf{q}')} d\mathbf{q}\, d\mathbf{k} \right], \\ &|\mathbf{q}, \mathbf{k}\rangle_\pm = |\mathbf{q}, \mathbf{k}\rangle - \lambda v(\mathbf{q}, \mathbf{k})\, [\varepsilon(\mathbf{q} + \mathbf{k}) - \varepsilon(\mathbf{q}, \mathbf{k}) \mp i0 - \\ &\qquad\qquad - \lambda^2\, \mathcal{G}_{\varepsilon(\mathbf{q},\mathbf{k}) \pm i0}\, (\mathbf{q} + \mathbf{k})]^{-1} \\ &\left[|\mathbf{q} + \mathbf{k}\rangle - \lambda \int |\mathbf{q}', \mathbf{k}'\rangle \frac{v^*(\mathbf{q}', \mathbf{k}')\, \delta(\mathbf{q}' + \mathbf{k}' - \mathbf{q} - \mathbf{k})}{\varepsilon(\mathbf{q}', \mathbf{k}') - \varepsilon(\mathbf{q}, \mathbf{k}) \mp i0} d\mathbf{q}'\, d\mathbf{k}' \right], \end{aligned}\right\} \tag{5.7}$$

with

$$[N(\mathbf{q}')]^{-1} = 1 + \lambda^2 \int [\varepsilon(\mathbf{q}, \mathbf{k}) - E(\mathbf{q}')]^{-2}\, |v(\mathbf{q}, \mathbf{k})|^2\, \delta(\mathbf{q} + \mathbf{k} - \mathbf{q}')\, d\mathbf{q}\, d\mathbf{k}. \tag{5.8}$$

The asymptotically stationary states (I.5.12) simply reduce to

$$|\mathbf{q}'\rangle_{as} = |\mathbf{q}'\rangle_+ = |\mathbf{q}'\rangle_-,\ |\mathbf{q}, \mathbf{k}\rangle_{as} = |\mathbf{q}, \mathbf{k}\rangle. \tag{5.9}$$

Finally, for the S-matrix, the formula (I.6.5) gives

$$\left.\begin{aligned} &\langle \mathbf{q}\, |S|\, \mathbf{q}'\rangle = \delta(\mathbf{q} - \mathbf{q}'),\ \langle \mathbf{q}, \mathbf{k}\, |S|\, \mathbf{q}'\rangle = \langle \mathbf{q}'\, |S|\, \mathbf{q}, \mathbf{k}\rangle = 0, \\ &\langle \mathbf{q}, \mathbf{k}\, |S|\, \mathbf{q}', \mathbf{k}'\rangle = \delta(\mathbf{q} - \mathbf{q}')\, \delta(\mathbf{k} - \mathbf{k}') + 2\pi i\, \lambda^2\, \delta[\varepsilon(\mathbf{q}, \mathbf{k}) - \varepsilon(\mathbf{q}', \mathbf{k}')] \\ &\delta(\mathbf{q} + \mathbf{k} - \mathbf{q}' - \mathbf{k}')\ v^*(\mathbf{q}, \mathbf{k})\, v(\mathbf{q}', \mathbf{k}')\, [\varepsilon(\mathbf{q} + \mathbf{k}) - \varepsilon(\mathbf{q}, \mathbf{k}) - \\ &\qquad\qquad - \lambda^2\, \mathcal{G}_{\varepsilon(\mathbf{q},\mathbf{k}) + i0}(\mathbf{q} + \mathbf{k})]^{-1}. \end{aligned}\right\} \tag{5.10}$$

The perturbation problem is thus completely solved in terms of the root $E(\mathbf{q}')$ of the numerical equation (5.5). It is of course impossible to calculate this root explicitly for arbitrary forms of the functions $\varepsilon(\mathbf{q}')$, $\varepsilon(\mathbf{q}, \mathbf{k})$ and $v(\mathbf{q}, \mathbf{k})$.

6. *Preliminary remarks on the renormalization problem.* Since our general formalism will find its most important applications in quantum field theory one has to inquire as to the aspect it will give to the renormalization program which played such a central role in the successes of quantum electrodynamics[6]). No systematic study of this problem will be attempted here. We shall content ourselves with a few remarks, stressing one side of the problem on which our approach may eventually turn out to be more promising than the conventional ones.

The physical basis of the renormalization method in field theory lies in the fact that the interaction V inescapably affects all observations one can make on the field particles, so that we have no experimental access to what the theory calls the unperturbed system (hamiltonian H). Still, all the theory has to build upon is an hamiltonian $H + \lambda V$ composed of the term H belonging to this unobservable unperturbed system and a perturbation term V acting upon it. This remarkable situation *) has been met with by the remark that in view of the permanent presence of the interaction the constants, mass and charge, occurring in the two terms H and λV of the total hamiltonian are not necessarily equal to the corresponding measured quantities, so that a redefinition of them is required if one wants to use their measured values in comparing any theoretical prediction with experiment. Exploitation of this idea of mass and charge renormalization turned out to be possible and, beyond providing a method to circumvent mathematical divergence difficulties, it gave in quantum electrodynamics a brilliant explanation of new experimental facts. The formalism, either in the presentation of Dyson[7]) or in that of Källén[8]), and as far as electrodynamics is concerned, makes essential use of three so-called renormalization constants, one for the mass, one for the charge and a third one of more purely formal significance, the wave function renormalization constant. They are respectively called δm, Z_3 and Z_2 by Dyson, K, L and N by Källén. Dyson introduced an additional constant Z_1, but conjectured its identity with Z_2. The correctness of this conjecture was established by Ward[9]). All three constants δm, Z_3, Z_2 closely correspond to simple elements of the formalism developped in I and in the present paper. Z_3 and Z_2 are simply special cases of the coefficient $N(\alpha)$ introduced by (I.5.8); they are obtained by taking for $|\alpha\rangle$ a one-photon state or a one-electron state respectively. The mass renormalization δm appears in our non-covariant formalism as an energy renormalization when the unperturbed energy $\varepsilon(\alpha)$ is eliminated in terms of the perturbed energy $E(\alpha)$.

*) It is an interesting and unsolved problem to understand for which physical reasons the historical development has been such as to confront us with this situation.

One thus concludes (in contradiction with the too pessimistic statement at the end of I) that the renormalization program in its conventional form could be carried out on the basis of our equations as well as in the more conventional presentations.

There is however one aspect of the conventional renormalization scheme which is unsatisfactory on physical grounds and for the improvement of which our approach may offer new possibilities. While the conventional method duly avoids use of the unrenormalized values of mass and charge, it is not able to avoid completely the use of the unperturbed states $|\alpha\rangle$, although they are just as inaccessible to observation as the unrenormalized mass and charge values. It is true that in view of the so-called wave function renormalization $|\alpha\rangle$ enters the conventional formalism only through the combination $[N(\alpha)]^{\frac{1}{2}}\,|\alpha\rangle$, but despite its mathematical usefulness this combination has the drawback of corresponding to the same unobservable physical state as $|\alpha\rangle$ itself. Physically such states are "bare" particle states, whereas a consistent application of the renormalization idea would exclusively allow consideration of "dressed" particles, i.e. of particles surrounded by the clouds which the interaction permanently maintains around each of them. We now remark that it has been one of the main aims of I to give an explicit description of such cloud effects; this description is contained in the equation for the asymptotic stationary states $|\alpha\rangle_{as}$, Equation (I.5.12). The states $|\alpha\rangle_{as}$ occur as monochromatic components in the asymptotic motion of wave packets and they are thus observable, just as the plane wave states of a Schrödinger particle are observable even when an external potential is present in a limited region of space and produces ordinary scattering.

The asymptotically stationary states $|\alpha\rangle_{as}$ are the states which must be chosen instead of $|\alpha\rangle$ or $[N(\alpha)]^{\frac{1}{2}}\,|\alpha\rangle$ as basic representation for a more consistent development of the renormalization program, and the results of I and of the present paper, by the explicit attention they pay to the asymptotically stationary states, are likely to provide a more convenient starting point for this development than the conventional formulations of field theory. Here we can only mention this new standpoint of which we hope to work out the consequences elsewhere. We may however already remark that under this point of view the divergence difficulties will appear at least partly in a rather different form than in the formalisms of Dyson and Källén. The choice of $|\alpha\rangle_{as}$ as basic representation is very likely to remove some of the divergencies occurring in the conventional formulation, because it avoids consideration of Z_2. The divergencies here concerned are those originating from the fact that in a theory without cut-off the expansion of $|\alpha\rangle_{as}$ in the unperturbed states $|\alpha'\rangle$ cannot be expected to exist. The general situation in this respect will probably turn out to be analogous to what was established previously [10]) for a neutral scalar field interacting with a static point source. The states $|\alpha\rangle_{as}$ will probably span a separable Hilbert space S different from the separable Hilbert space S_0 spanned by the unperturbed states $|\alpha\rangle$, and one must expect the true stationary states $|\alpha\rangle_{\pm}$ to be contained in S rather than in S_0. For the understanding of these various remarks it may be good to have in mind that in field theory, for one-particle states, the $|\alpha\rangle_{as}$ must be identical with the true stationary states $|\alpha\rangle_{\pm}$ (themselves independent of the double sign). For many-particle states on the contrary $|\alpha\rangle_{as}$ should be essentially a product wave function of one-particle state vectors while the true stationary states $|\alpha\rangle_{\pm}$ will be much more involved since they contain all scattering and reaction effects.

Before closing these general and quite tentative considerations we have to mention a very recent paper by De Witt [2]) with an aim similar to ours, namely to extend conventional scattering theory to perturbations producing self-energy effects. Whereas the previous work in this direction, due to Pirenne and taken over by Gell-Mann and Goldberger [11]), payed attention to the energy shifts only, the paper of De Witt goes much further and introduces in addition a coefficient of "state vector renormalization", which is essentially our coefficient $N(\alpha)$. There is however no explicit discussion of the cloud effects modifying the motion of wave packets even for asymptotic times and manifesting themselves in our formalism through the fact that $|\alpha\rangle_{as}$ is not identical with $[N(\alpha)]^{\frac{1}{2}}\,|\alpha\rangle$, nor is mention made of the fact that the perturbation must satisfy special conditions (see I, in particular Section 4) in order for the conclusions of the paper to be valid. Still these conditions are very important, because for example they make all the difference between the behaviour of electrons in interaction with the photon field and the completely different (dissipative) behaviour of conduction electrons of a metal in interaction with the phonon field (field of elastic vibrations).

Received 6-2-56.

REFERENCES

1) Van Hove, L., Physica **21** (1955) 901.
2) De Witt, B. S., Phys. Rev. **100** (1955) 905.
3) Pauli, W., Meson Theory of Nuclear Forces, Interscience, New York (1946), chapter IV; Møller, C., Dan. mat. fys. Medd. **23** (1945) no. 1.
4) Dirac, P. A. M., The Principles of Quantum Mechanics, 3d ed., Clarendon Press, Oxford (1947), § 52, p. 201–204; Friedrichs, K. O., Comm. Appl. Math., **1** (1948) 361.
5) Lee, T. D., Phys. Rev. **95** (1954) 1329; Källén, G. and Pauli, W., Dan. mat. fys. Medd. **30** (1955) no. 7.
6) As recent review article on the renormalization method we quote Gunn, J. C., Rep. Progr. Phys. **18** (1955) 127.
7) Dyson, F. J., Phys. Rev. **75** (1949) 486 and 1736.
8) Källén, G., Helv. phys. Acta **25** (1952) 417.
9) Ward, J. C., Phys. Rev. **78** (1950) 182; Proc. Phys. Soc. **A 64** (1951) 54.
10) Van Hove, L., Physica **18** (1952) 145.
11) Pirenne, J., Helv. phys. Acta **21** (1948) 226; Gell-Mann, M. and Goldberger, M. L., Phys. Rev. **91** (1953) 398.

PERTURBATION THEORY OF LARGE QUANTUM SYSTEMS

by N. M. HUGENHOLTZ

Instituut voor theoretische fysica der Rijksuniversiteit, Utrecht, Nederland

Synopsis

The time-independent perturbation theory of quantum mechanics is studied for the case of very large systems, *i.e.* systems with large spatial dimensions (large volume Ω), and a large number of degrees of freedom. Examples of such systems are met with in the quantum theory of fields, solid state physics, the theory of imperfect gases and in the theory of nuclear matter. Only systems at or near the ground state (*i.e.*, systems at zero temperature) are treated in this paper. In the application of the conventional perturbation theory to such large quantum systems one encounters difficulties which are connected with the fact that even small perturbations produce large changes of the energy and wave function of the whole system. These difficulties manifest themselves through the occurrence of terms containing arbitrarily high powers of the volume Ω in the perturbation expansion of physical quantities. An extremely bad convergence of the perturbation expansion is the result.

For the analysis of the Ω-dependence of the terms in the expansion a new formulation of the time-independent perturbation theory is used, which was introduced by Van Hove. Making extensive use of diagrams to represent the different contributions to matrix elements it is possible to locate and separate the Ω-dependent terms, and to carry out partial summations in the original expansion. These separations and summations solve the above difficulties completely. Improved perturbation theoretical expressions are obtained for energies and wave functions of stationary states, as well as for the life-times of metastable states. All terms in these expressions are, in the limit of large Ω, either independent of Ω or proportional to Ω, corresponding to intensive or extensive physical quantities. The convergence of the improved perturbation expansions is no longer affected by the large magnitude of Ω.

CHAPTER I. INTRODUCTION

1. *The problem.* This paper is devoted to the perturbation theory of large quantum systems *i.e.*, quantum systems which have large spatial dimensions and a large number of degrees of freedom. The systems met with in the quantum theory of fields are, as is well known, of this type. Also in other branches of physics, such as quantum statistics and the Fermi gas model of heavy nuclei, one has to deal with such large systems. We shall in this paper only be interested in systems at or near the ground state. Our results are, therefore, only applicable to quantum systems at zero temperature.

The separation of the hamiltonian into an unperturbed part and a perturbation is not unique, but in most problems of interest there is a separation which presents itself in a most natural way. In quantum electrodynamics for example, the unperturbed system consists of the electron-positron field and the photon field without interaction. In the theory of an imperfect gas the unperturbed system will be taken as the ideal gas obtained by neglecting interparticle interactions.

In the application of perturbation theory to large quantum systems one encounters problems not met with in the usual perturbation theory of systems with a finite number of degrees of freedom. These problems are related to the following phenomena:

1. Self-energy and cloud effects of individual particles in excited states.
2. The perturbation of the system as a whole.

We shall discuss briefly the first point. The effects mentioned are well known in field theory. A state of one single electron is changed by the perturbation into a superposition of many different unperturbed states, where the one-electron-state is admixed with states containing one or more photons and electron-positron pairs. One usually says that the electron is surrounded by a cloud of photons and pairs. The self-energy of the electron manifests itself by a change of its mass. Also for a scattering state of two or more particles the interaction gives rise to the self-energy and cloud effects just mentioned, in addition to the directly observable scattering effects. While the latter are transient, *i.e.* take place (for general wave packets) within a finite time interval, the former are persistent effects which cause a permanent change of wave function and energy. Effects of this type are not limited to field theory, but occur also in many other systems.

Recently Van Hove [1]) made an extensive study of these phenomena. He developed a time-independent perturbation formalism which is adapted to the treatment of perturbations causing persistent effects. The developments in this paper are largely based on his work.

The effects just discussed concern the motion of one or more particles of the system, which is itself in a quantum state distinct from the ground state (the vacuum state of field theory). The self-energy is a shift caused by the perturbation in the distance between the energy level of the system in the state at hand and the ground state level. It is to be expected that such effects are independent of the volume Ω of the system, in the limit of $\Omega \rightarrow \infty$. For instance the self-energy of an electron is not appreciably changed if the fields are enclosed in a box of variable volume, at least for sufficiently large values of the volume.

The problems of the second type mentioned above, which form the subject of the present investigation, are connected with the overall shift of the energy levels, both of the ground state and of excited states. For large systems, as considered in this paper, one must expect that even weak perturbations give rise to large changes of the wave function and energy of the system. Such effects occur in field theory whenever virtual pair production from the ground state is possible. Disregarding surface effects one must expect on physical grounds that the energy of the ground state, both in the unperturbed and in the perturbed system, is proportional to the volume Ω of the system. This implies that the energy shift ΔE_0 caused by the perturbation is also proportional to Ω. One often uses the words *extensive* and *intensive* for quantities which are respectively proportional to and independent of the volume of the system. Using this terminology one can say that the energy shift ΔE_0 of the ground state is an extensive effect.

In studying states distinct from the ground state we have to deal with both types of phenomena mentioned above. For example, the total energy shift of a one-electron-state is the sum of the vacuum energy shift and the self-energy. Generally, the energy of an excited state can be written as the sum of two terms, one being the energy of the ground state, the other the excitation energy. In the limit $\Omega \to \infty$ the excitation energy is independent of Ω. Both terms are affected by the perturbation; hence the energy shift of an excited state must be the sum of an extensive and an intensive term. This expectation will be confirmed by our results. A separation of the same kind will be shown to exist for the change of the wave function of an excited state. This change is partly a consequence of the change of the ground state wave function, and involves in addition effects due to the excitation. The latter have an intensive character, while the change in the ground state wave function will be found extensive. It is a shortcoming of the conventional perturbation theory that these effects are not separated. It will be seen that this leads to serious difficulties. The expansion of matrix elements in powers of the perturbation contains terms with arbitrarily high powers of the volume Ω of the system, and this gives rise to an extremely bad convergence in the case of large systems.

It is the object of the present investigation to make a clear and complete separation between extensive and intensive effects. The hamiltonian of the system is written in the occupation number representation for the one-particle plane wave states, and we use diagrams to represent the different contributions to matrix elements, as is conventionally done in field theory. This appears to be a valuable tool for the analysis. Although the method and the developments of the following chapters are of a rather general nature and can be applied generally to field theoretical problems and to problems in quantum statistics, especially in solid state physics, the method will be illustrated mainly by considering the example of a Fermi gas with two-body interaction between the particles. This example is described in the next section. In a forthcoming paper our methods will be used for a discussion of the Fermi gas model of nuclear matter. The example adopted here will become there the main object of study. Chapter II contains an exposition of the perturbation formalism of Van Hove, which is based on a systematic use of the resolvent operator. Our exposition differs from the original presentation only in that extensive use is made of diagrams. In chapter III we investigate how the contributions to the resolvent, represented by different kinds of diagrams, depend on the volume Ω. This analysis shows that a separation is possible between Ω-dependent and Ω-independent quantities. The separation is carried through in chapters IV and V, for the energies and the wave functions of stationary states respectively. Explicit expressions in the form of improved perturbation expansions are derived. In the series expansions for intensive quantities all terms are independent of Ω, whereas all terms are proportional to Ω for extensive quantities.

In the last section of chapter V another phenomenon occurring in large systems is investigated. There are systems where no perturbed stationary states correspond in any simple way to the unperturbed excited states. Such systems are well known from statistical mechanics. Their most striking property is the occurrence of dissipative processes. In the case of small dissipation one can show the existence of metastable states. We shall derive explicit expressions for the life-time, energy and wave function of such states. The life-time will be found independent of Ω, in accordance with physical expectations. A very interesting example of such metastable states is encountered in the optical model description for the scattering of nucleons on heavy nuclei [2]) where a complex potential is introduced to account for the finite mean free path of nucleons in nuclear matter. This will be further analysed in the forthcoming paper already announced, where the present formalism will be applied to a system of interacting nucleons. It will be seen that the theory of Brueckner [3]) for the structure of nuclear matter can be considered as a special approximation to our general formalism. The latter will be helpful for getting new insight into the significance and limits of validity of Brueckner's method.

2. *The Fermi gas.* In this section we shall give a formulation of the N-particle problem, which is adapted to the treatment of a Fermi gas where both the number N and the volume Ω are large. This system will be used as a working example in the rest of the paper. For the interaction between the particles we take central two-body forces, and we shall neglect the spin of the particles. We enclose the whole system in a large cubic box with side L and volume $\Omega = L^3$, and we impose periodic boundary conditions. We have chosen these boundary conditions for mathematical convenience. Because we are particularly interested in large systems, the influence of surface effects is comparatively small.

The wave functions

$$\psi_k(x) = \Omega^{-\frac{1}{2}} \exp(ikx) \tag{2.1}$$

where the three components of k can have the values $2\pi n/L(n=0, \pm 1, \pm 2,\ldots)$, describing the motion of a single particle with momentum k *), form a complete orthonormal set of single particle states. A state of N identical particles moving independently of each other is determined by a series of occupation numbers N_k, each giving the number of particles in the one-particle state (2.1) with momentum k. These states form the basic set of the unperturbed system. In order to obtain a simple expression of the hamiltonian in this representation, we introduce the annihilation and creation operators η_k and η_k^* which obey in the case of Fermi particles the anti-commutation laws

$$\{\eta_k, \eta_l\} = \{\eta_k^*, \eta_l^*\} = 0 \text{ and } \{\eta_k, \eta_l^*\} = \delta_{kl}. \tag{2.2}$$

Using these operators the hamiltonian can be written

$$H = H_0 + V,$$

where

$$H_0 = \sum_k \tfrac{1}{2}(|k|^2/M)\, \eta_k^* \eta_k \tag{2.3}$$

and

$$V = \tfrac{1}{2}\, \Omega^{-1} \sum_{klmn} \delta_{Kr}\, (k + l - m - n)\, v(k - n) \eta_k^* \eta_l^* \eta_m \eta_n.$$

Here $v(k)$ is the Fourier-transform of the central two-body potential $v(r)$:

$$v(k) = \int d^3x\, v(r) \exp(-ikx), \tag{2.4}$$

and depends only on the modulus $|k|$ of k. The Kronecker symbol δ_{Kr} is equal to one if the argument is zero and vanishes otherwise. It expresses the fact that momentum is conserved in the interaction.

The creation operators η_k^* can be used to obtain simple expressions for the states of our basic set of unperturbed states. By $|0\rangle$ we denote the normalized state without any particles. It is determined by the condition that $\eta_k |0\rangle = 0$ for all k. A state of N particles with momenta $k_1, k_2, \ldots, k_N$ can be written

$$\eta_{k_1}^* \eta_{k_2}^* \cdots \eta_{k_N}^* |0\rangle. \tag{2.5}$$

The commutation rules (2.2) imply that this state vector is normalized to one and is antisymmetric in the N particles.

The formulation given thus far is not very suitable for our case. Of physical interest is the case where Ω and N are very large for a given value of the density $\varrho = N/\Omega$. In the limit $\Omega \to \infty$ one has a continuous spectrum and summations are replaced by integrations. The normalization of states must be changed as can be seen from (2.1) where $\psi_k(x)$ vanishes in the limit

*) We use no special notation to indicate vectors. The letters k, l, m, n are used for momenta, whereas in (2.1) and (2.4) x is a vector in configuration space. We put $\hbar = 1$ throughout this paper.

$\Omega \to \infty$. It seems therefore appropriate for a finite but large Ω to adopt another normalization of the wave vectors. We introduce the following new notations (L is the side of the cubic volume Ω)

$$\xi_k = (L/2\pi)^{3/2}\, \eta_k \text{ and } \delta(k-l) = (L/2\pi)^3\, \delta_{Kr}(k-l). \tag{2.6}$$

The function $\delta(k)$ of the discrete variable k goes over into the 3-dimensional delta-function of Dirac in the limit of $\Omega \to \infty$.

The commutation relations of ξ_k and ξ_k^* read

$$\{\xi_k, \xi_l\} = \{\xi_k^*, \xi_l^*\} = 0 \text{ and } \{\xi_k, \xi_l^*\} = \delta(k-l).$$

Introducing the notation

$$\textstyle\int_k = (2\pi/L)^3 \sum_k$$

the hamiltonian (2.3) reads

$$H = \textstyle\int_k (|k|^2/2M)\, \xi_k^*\xi_k + \frac{1}{2}(2\pi)^{-3} \int_{klmn} \delta(k+l-m-n)\, v(k-n)\, \xi_k^*\xi_l^*\xi_m\xi_n. \tag{2.7}$$

With this notation it is extremely simple to pass over to the limit of $\Omega \to \infty$, the only change being that the summation symbol $\int_k$ is replaced by the integration sign $\int d^3k$. The states of the unperturbed system will now also be expressed by means of the operators ξ_k^*. For a N-particle state one gets

$$\xi_{k_1}^*\, \xi_{k_2}^* \dots \xi_{k_N}^*\, |0\rangle, \tag{2.8}$$

which only differs from (2.5) by the normalization.

Obviously (2.8) is not very suitable for the case of a very large number of particles. Therefore we shall proceed in a different way. We draw in momentum space a sphere with centre in the origin and radius k_F and consider a normalized unperturbed N-particle state $|\varphi_0\rangle$, such that all one-particle states with momenta within the sphere are occupied, whereas there are no particles with momenta outside the sphere. This state $|\varphi_0\rangle$ is obviously the ground state of the unperturbed system of N particles. The sphere is often called the *Fermi sphere* and the set of particles occupying the states within this sphere we shall call the *Fermi sea,* in analogy with the Dirac sea of Dirac's hole theory for electrons and positrons.

The number N is a discontinuous function of the Fermi momentum k_F which we keep fixed and consider as a substitute for the density parameter. In the limit of $\Omega \to \infty$ we have however asymptotically

$$N = k_F^3 \Omega / 6\pi^2, \tag{2.9}$$

as follows from the fact that each one-particle state in momentum space occupies a volume $(2\pi)^3/\Omega$, $2\pi/L$ being the distance of the lattice points. The number of states within a sphere with the volume $\frac{4}{3}\pi k_F^3$ is then given by (2.9). Also the total kinetic energy ε_0 of $|\varphi_0\rangle$ is strictly speaking a discontinuous function of k_F. Again neglecting terms that vanish in the limit of $\Omega \to \infty$ one has however

$$\varepsilon_0 = k_F^5 \Omega / 20\pi^2 M. \tag{2.10}$$

We shall now characterize the states of the unperturbed system by comparing them with $|\varphi_0\rangle$. An arbitrary state of the basic system can be obtained from $|\varphi_0\rangle$ by removing a number of particles from the Fermi sea and adding some others with momenta outside the Fermi sphere. In other words one can get any state of the basic system by the application to the state $|\varphi_0\rangle$ of a number of annihilation operators ξ_m, with $|m| < k_F$, and of a number of creation operators ξ_k^* with $|k| > k_F$. We introduce the notation

$$|k_1 k_2 \ldots k_p \,;\, m_1 m_2 \ldots m_q > \, = \xi_{k_1}^* \xi_{k_2}^* \ldots \xi_{k_p}^* \xi_{m_1} \xi_{m_2} \ldots \xi_{m_q} |\, \varphi_0\rangle, \tag{2.11}$$

where

$$|k_i| > k_F \text{ and } |m_j| < k_F.$$

The conjugate wave function shall be denoted by

$$\langle m_q \ldots m_2 m_1 \,;\, k_p \ldots k_2 k_1|.$$

The state (2.11) differs from $|\varphi_0\rangle$ by the absence of q particles, with momenta $m_1, m_2, \ldots, m_q$, from the Fermi sea while there are p additional particles, with momenta $k_1, k_2, \ldots, k_p$, outside the Fermi sphere.

An unoccupied one-particle state will often be called a *hole*. By the energy and momentum of a hole we shall mean the energy and momentum of the missing particle, taken both with the opposite sign. Hence the energy carried by a hole is negative. In this terminology, which is selected in analogy to the hole theory of Dirac, the additional particles with momenta outside the Fermi sphere are briefly called particles. Thus the state (2.11) contains q holes and p particles. In this way we are led to a reinterpretation of the operators ξ and ξ^*.

For $|k| > k_F$, ξ_k annihilates a particle and ξ_k^* creates a particle.

For $|m| < k_F$, ξ_m creates a hole and ξ_m^* annihilates a hole.

Finally we shall study some different types of transitions which can be brought about by the interaction V. It is often convenient to have a more symmetrical expression for V than in (2.7).

One can write

$$V = \tfrac{1}{4} \textstyle\int_{l_1 l_2 l_3 l_4} v(l_1 l_2 l_3 l_4)\, \xi_{l_1}^* \xi_{l_2}^* \xi_{l_3} \xi_{l_4}, \tag{2.12}$$

where

$$v(l_1 l_2 l_3 l_4) = (2\pi)^{-3} (v(l_1 - l_4) - v(l_1 - l_3))\, \delta(l_1 + l_2 - l_3 - l_4).$$

The function $v(l_1 l_2 l_3 l_4)$ has the following symmetry properties

$$v(l_1 l_2 l_3 l_4) = -\, v(l_2 l_1 l_3 l_4) = v(l_3 l_4 l_1 l_2).$$

In (2.12) the summation is extended over all momenta $l_1 l_2 l_3 l_4$, both inside and outside the Fermi sphere.

We make the following convention. The letters m and k will be used for momenta inside and outside the Fermi sphere respectively.

Hence the expression

$$\tfrac{1}{4} \int_k v(k_1k_2k_3k_4)\ \xi^*_{k_1}\xi^*_{k_2}\xi_{k_3}\xi_{k_4}$$

differs from (2.12) by restricting the summation to momenta k such that $|k| > k_F$. This term describes the absorption of two particles and the emission of two other particles, a process which can be interpreted as the scattering of two particles. In exactly the same way the term

$$\tfrac{1}{4} \int_m v(m_1m_2m_3m_4)\ \xi^*_{m_1}\xi^*_{m_2}\xi_{m_3}\xi_{m_4}$$

gives rise to the scattering of two holes. Let us finally consider

$$\tfrac{1}{4} \int_{k_1k_2k_3m} v(k_1k_2k_3m)\ \xi^*_{k_1}\xi^*_{k_2}\xi_{k_3}\xi_{m},$$

where one particle is absorbed and two particles and a hole are emitted. This process can also be described in another way. A particle interacts with a particle in the Fermi sea, thereby removing it to a state outside the Fermi sphere. This leads to a state of two particles and one hole.

CHAPTER II. FORMULATION OF THE TIME-INDEPENDENT PERTURBATION METHOD BY MEANS OF DIAGRAMS

3. *Diagrams*. We consider a large but finite quantum system with a hamiltonian $H = H_0 + V$. The basic set of unperturbed states $|\alpha\rangle$ are eigenstates of H_0 with the eigenvalue ε_α. If the system is a gas of Fermi particles as was studied in section 2, the states $|\alpha\rangle$ are to be identified with the states $|k_1k_2 \ldots k_p\,;\, m_1m_2 \ldots m_q\rangle$ defined in (2.11), with arbitrary p and q. The unperturbed energy ε_α is then given by

$$\varepsilon_\alpha = \varepsilon_0 + \Sigma\, |k_j|^2/2M - \Sigma\, |m_i|^2/2M. \tag{3.1}$$

If $|\psi\rangle$ is some time-independent wave function then the wave function $|\psi(t)\rangle = U(t)|\,\psi\rangle$ with $U(t) = \exp\,(-iHt)$ solves the Schrödinger equation. Instead of the operator $U(t)$, we investigate, following Van Hove, a related time-independent operator, the *resolvent* $R(z)$, which depends on the complex number z. $R(z)$ is defined by

$$R(z) = (H - z)^{-1} = (H_0 + V - z)^{-1}, \tag{3.2}$$

and, because H is hermitian, $R(z)$ is a bounded operator for non-real z. The connection between $R(z)$ and $U(t)$ is given by the formula

$$U(t) = -\,(2\pi i)^{-1} \oint \mathrm{d}z\, R(z) \exp\,(-\,izt). \tag{3.3}$$

The path of integration is a contour around a sufficiently large portion of the real axis of the z-plane. It is to be described counterclockwise. Therefore we are only interested in the behaviour of $R(z)$ in the neighbourhood of the real axis.

From (3.2) follows

$$R(z) = (H_0 - z)^{-1} - (H_0 - z)^{-1} VR(z) = (H_0 - z)^{-1} - R(z)\, V(H_0 - z)^{-1}. \quad (3.4)$$

Iterating this formula one finds the series expansion:

$$R(z) = (H_0 - z)^{-1} - (H_0 - z)^{-1}\, V(H_0 - z)^{-1} + \\ + (H_0 - z)^{-1}\, V(H_0 - z)^{-1}\, V(H_0 - z)^{-1} - \ldots \quad (3.5)$$

In this paper the convergence of this series for z away from the real axis will be assumed. Whether this assumption is legitimate has to be investigated in each case.

For the calculation of matrix elements of $R(z)$ we represent the contributions to the various terms in (3.5) by diagrams. To be more specific, we shall turn to the case of the Fermi gas. Let us, as a simple example, consider the matrix element $\langle\beta\,|R(z)|\,\alpha\rangle$ between the initial state $|\alpha\rangle = |k_1\,;\,\rangle$ and the final state $|\beta\rangle = |k_2 k_3\,;\,m\rangle$, and see how one calculates the second order term in the expansion (3.5). Using (2.11), and (2.12) we get the expression

$$4^{-2} \int_{l_1 l_2 l_3 l_4} \int_{n_1 n_2 n_3 n_4} v(l_1 l_2 l_3 l_4)\, v(n_1 n_2 n_3 n_4) . \\ . \langle\varphi_0|\xi^*_m \xi_{k_3} \xi_{k_2} (H_0 - z)^{-1} \xi^*_{l_1} \xi^*_{l_2} \xi_{l_3} \xi_{l_4} (H_0 - z)^{-1} \xi^*_{n_1} \xi^*_{n_2} \xi_{n_3} \xi_{n_4} (H_0 - z)^{-1} \xi^*_{k_1} |\varphi_0\rangle, \quad (3.6)$$

with the summation symbols $\int_{l_1 l_2 l_3 l_4}$ introduced in section 2. The summation is extended over all momenta both inside and outside the Fermi sphere. The ground state to ground state matrix element in the integrand will only have a value different from zero provided (when reading from right to left) each particle or hole created in a virtual transition is reabsorbed in a later transition. In each non-vanishing contribution there must exist a one-to-one correspondence between creation and annihilation operators. Each associated pair consists of a creation operator and an annihilation operator belonging to the same particle or hole. Reading always from right to left the creation operator comes first.

We shall now see how one can represent such a contribution by a *diagram* †). Each interaction operator V is represented by a point (also called *vertex*). The operators ξ and ξ^* are represented by directed lines joining at this point. The direction is indicated by an arrow. If the direction of a line is pointing to the vertex, the line represents a ξ operator in this point, in the other case a ξ^* operator. The distinction between holes and particles is made in the following way. Lines directed to the left correspond to particles, lines directed to the right to holes. This results in the four possibilities shown

†) The use of diagrams is well known in field theory, where they were first introduced by Feynman [4]). Goldstone [5]) introduced them for the many particle problem. His diagrams are slightly different from the diagrams used here.

in the following table (the convention $|k| > k_F$, $|m| < k_F$ should be kept in mind)

Operator	Represented by
ξ_k	•←
ξ_m^*	•→
ξ_k^*	←•
ξ_m	→•

One sees that creation operators ξ_k^*, ξ_m (annihilation operators ξ_k, ξ_m^*) are represented by lines reaching the vertex from the left (right). Of the four lines joining at one point two and only two are directed towards that point.

Some diagrams representing different contributions to (3.6) are drawn in figure 1. Each diagram contains two points, the order from right to left

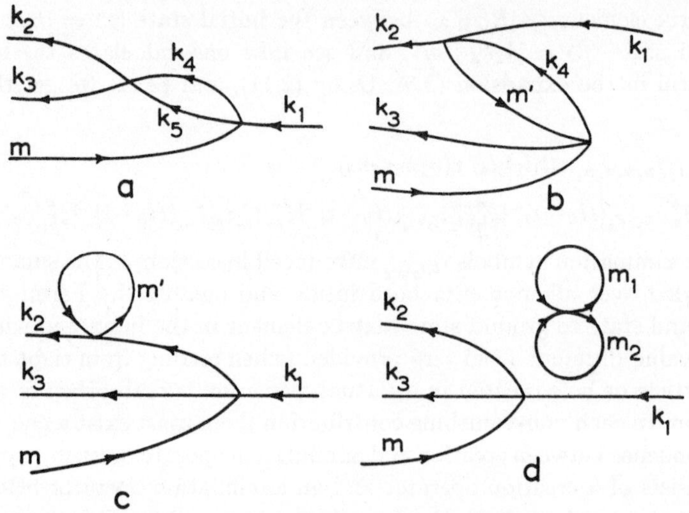

Fig. 1. Some second order diagrams contributing to the matrix element $\langle m;\, k_3 k_2\, |R(z)|\, k_1;\rangle$.

corresponding to the order of the V's in (3.6). A line joining two points corresponds to an associated pair of a creation and an annihilation operator. We call this an *internal line*. Lines running from a point towards the right or left edge of the diagram or from one edge of the diagram to the other correspond to associated pairs of which one or both belong to the initial or final state. Such lines are called *external lines*. All diagrams of figure 1 have two internal lines and four external lines.

Diagrams give a schematic picture of the transition process that takes place. In the diagram of fig. 1*a* the particle of the initial state interacts with the Fermi sea giving a hole and two particles. In the second transition these two particles are scattered on each other. The process represented by fig. 1*b* is different. The first interaction gives rise to the formation of two particles and two holes. In the second transition one particle and one hole are annihilated together with the particle of the initial state. Another particle is created.

Some remarks must be made regarding the diagrams of fig. 1, *c* and *d*. These give contributions to equation (3.6) with associated pairs of creation and annihilation operators belonging to the same interaction V. In V, reading from right to left, the ξ's precede the ξ^*'s. Therefore such associated pairs are possible for holes. In the diagrams they are represented by closed loops through a vertex point, the lines that represent the ξ_m^* and the ξ_m at the same point being the continuation of each other.

Before proceeding we introduce some definitions to be used frequently in the following. Diagrams that can be divided into two or more partial diagrams without cutting any lines are called *disconnected*. All other diagrams are *connected*. The diagrams shown in fig. 1*a*, *b* and *c* are obviously connected, whereas the diagram in *d* is disconnected. The connected parts, a disconnected diagram is composed of, will be called the *components* of the diagram. Diagrams without external lines will often be referred to as *ground state diagrams* and diagram components without external lines as *ground state components*. The diagram of fig. 1*d* has two components of which one is a ground state component.

We shall now show how one calculates the contribution of a given diagram. Let us take the diagram of fig. 1*a*. Putting in (3.6) $l_1 = k_2$, $l_2 = k_3$, $l_3 = n_2 = k_4$, $l_4 = n_1 = k_5$, $n_3 = m$ and $n_4 = k_1$ we find the expression

$$^1/_{16} \int_{k_4 k_5} v(k_2 k_3 k_4 k_5)\, v(k_5 k_4 m k_1)\,.$$

$$. \langle \varphi_0 | \xi_m^* \xi_{k_3} \xi_{k_2} (H_0 - z)^{-1} \xi_{k_2}^* \xi_{k_3}^* \xi_{k_4} \xi_{k_5} (H_0 - z)^{-1} \xi_{k_5}^* \xi_{k_4}^* \xi_m \xi_{k_1} (H_0 - z)^{-1} \xi_{k_1}^* | \varphi_0 \rangle. \quad (3.7)$$

The unperturbed energies of the initial, final and intermediate state can be obtained from (3.1). The last factor in (3.7) (without the energy denominators) is ± 1, the sign depending on the order of the operators ξ and ξ^*. Here the number of permutations necessary to bring the operators of associated pairs next to each other is even, hence we get a plus sign. One obtains identical contributions if one interchanges the role of the two ξ's or of the two ξ^*'s belonging to the same V. Hence a factor 4 must be added for each point, which gives a factor 16 in this example, exactly canceling the factor $^1/_{16}$. However each pair of equivalent lines, *i.e.* lines between the same two points and with the same direction, is counted twice, so that a factor $\frac{1}{2}$ must be added for each such pair. In our example the lines k_4 and k_5 are equivalent and the total factor is $\frac{1}{2}$. For the total contribution of the diagram of fig. 1*a* to

$$\langle m\ ;\ k_3 k_2 | R(z) |\ k_1\ ;\ \rangle$$

one finds

$$\tfrac{1}{2}\int_{k_4k_5} \frac{v(k_2k_3k_4k_5)\; v(k_5k_4mk_1)}{(\varepsilon_0 + k_2^2/2M + k_3^2/2M - m^2/2M - z)\,(\varepsilon_0 + k_4^2/2M + k_5^2/2M - m^2/2M - z)\,(\varepsilon_0 + k_1^2/2M - z)}.$$

This example suffices to indicate how one calculates matrix elements of the resolvent (3.5) to any order in the perturbation. One draws all possible diagrams of the given order and one adds their contributions, each of which is calculated in the way shown.

A remark must still be made concerning the Pauli principle for intermediate states. The various particles must have different momenta and the same must hold for holes. Thus, for the example treated above, the term with $k_4 = k_5$ should be excluded in the summation. However $v(k_2k_3k_4k_5)$ and $v(k_5k_4k_1m)$ are antisymmetric in k_4 and k_5 so that the term with $k_4 = k_5$ would automatically give no contribution and we are justified in dropping the restriction on the summation. It has been remarked by Wick [6]) that this holds quite generally for Fermi particles and that for Bose particles one is similarly allowed to forget the modifications in the production and absorption matrix elements which occur when more than one boson is in a given state. Quite generally, the errors made if one does not take into account the influence of the Fermi or Bose statistics on intermediate states with particles of equal momenta, cancel each other exactly.

We shall now introduce the important concept of *diagonal diagrams*. In fig. 2 different diagrams are drawn describing the interaction of two particles. Momentum is conserved in each elementary interaction. One will therefore have the relation $k_1 + k_2 = k_3 + k_4$ in all diagrams. In the diagrams *c* and *d* however one has $k_1 = k_3$ and $k_2 = k_4$. These diagrams are called diagonal because their contributions contain the factors $\delta^3(k_1 - k_3)\, \delta^3(k_2 - k_4)$. We shall in general call a diagram of the matrix element $\langle\beta\,|R(z)|\,\alpha\rangle$ diagonal if the states $|\alpha\rangle$ and $|\beta\rangle$ contain the same numbers of particles and holes, and if the contribution of the diagram to $\langle\beta\,|R(z)|\,\alpha\rangle$ contains the factor $\delta(\alpha-\beta)$, where $\delta(\alpha - \beta)$ is the product of the 3-dimensional δ-functions for the momenta of all particles and holes, as defined by (2.6).

Diagonal diagrams play a very important part in the theory of large systems. This is shown by the following consideration. Diagonal diagrams give contributions only to diagonal matrix elements of the resolvent $R(z)$, whereas non-diagonal diagrams contribute both to its diagonal and non-diagonal matrix elements. Comparing now the contributions of a diagonal and a non-diagonal diagram to some diagonal element $\langle\alpha\,|R(z)|\,\alpha\rangle$, one finds that the contribution of the first diagram is larger than that of the second by at least one factor Ω. This is an immediate consequence of the fact that the contribution of a diagonal diagram contains more δ-factors than the contribution of a non-diagonal one. According to (2.6) each δ-factor gives rise to a factor $\Omega/8\pi^3$. The origin of this extra factor Ω must be sought in the much larger number of intermediate states occurring in the contributions of diagonal diagrams.

There exist essentially three types of diagonal diagrams. In the first place diagrams without external lines, the so-called ground state diagrams, are diagonal. They contribute to the diagonal element $\langle\varphi_0 |R(z)| \varphi_0\rangle$. Secondly all diagrams contributing to matrix elements $\langle\ ;\ k_2 |R(z)| k_1\ ;\ \rangle$ between one-particle states are diagonal. Each contribution contains the factor $\delta^3(k_1 - k_2)$ which results from conservation of momentum. The diagrams of this type have one external particle line at each end. Also the diagrams with one external hole line at each end are diagonal. These three types of diagrams correspond in field theory with vacuum diagrams and self-energy diagrams. We have learned from the examples of fig. 2 that disconnected diagrams, the components of which belong to the categories just mentioned, are also diagonal. It is easily established that no other diagonal diagrams exist.

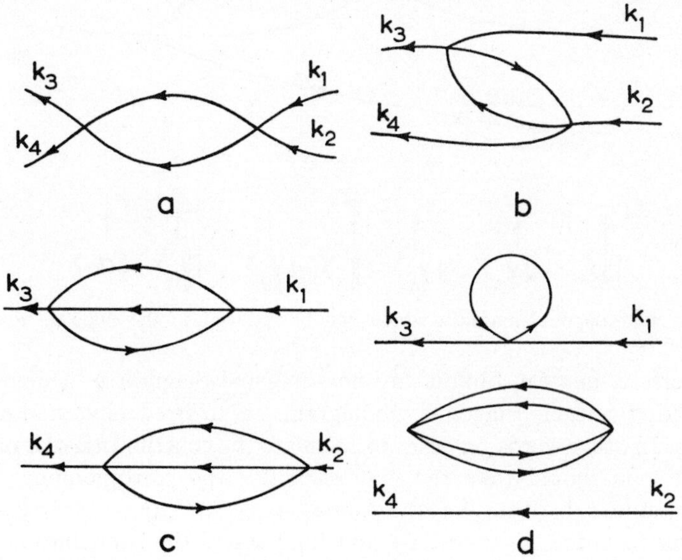

Fig. 2. Some diagonal and non-diagonal diagrams of the matrix element $\langle\ ;\ k_4k_3 |R(z)| k_1k_2;\rangle$

Each matrix element $\langle\beta |R(z)| \alpha\rangle$ can unambiguously be written as

$$\langle\beta |R(z)| \alpha\rangle = D_\alpha(z)\ \delta(\beta - \alpha) + F_{\beta\alpha}(z), \tag{3.8}$$

where the first term is the sum of the contributions of all diagonal diagrams. It is of course only present when the states $|\alpha\rangle$, $|\beta\rangle$ involve the same numbers of particles and holes. The operator $D(z)$, with matrix elements $\langle\beta |D(z)| \alpha\rangle = D_\alpha(z)\ .\ \delta(\beta - \alpha)$, is called the *diagonal part* of $R(z)$.

4. *The reduction of diagrams.* Let us consider as an example the non-diagonal diagram shown in fig. 3. It is of the 6th order, so that there are five intermediate states, indicated in the figure. These intermediate states cannot all be varied independently. According to the arguments which were used in section 3 in connection with the diagonal diagrams, it is seen that the intermediate state $|\gamma_4\rangle$ is related to $|\beta\rangle$ by the factor $\delta(\beta - \gamma_4)$. Also the states $|\gamma_1\rangle$ and $|\gamma_3\rangle$ are connected by a factor $\delta(\gamma_1 - \gamma_3)$. When cut at the intermediate states $|\gamma_1\rangle$, $|\gamma_3\rangle$, and $|\gamma_4\rangle$, the diagram falls apart into four parts, two of which are diagonal. Removing the diagonal parts, to be called *diagonal subdiagrams,* and joining the remaining pieces, one gets exactly the diagram *a* of fig. 1. The process of elimination of diagonal subdiagrams is called the *reduction* of a diagram. If a diagram cannot be reduced, as for example diagram *a* of fig. 1, we call it *irreducible.*

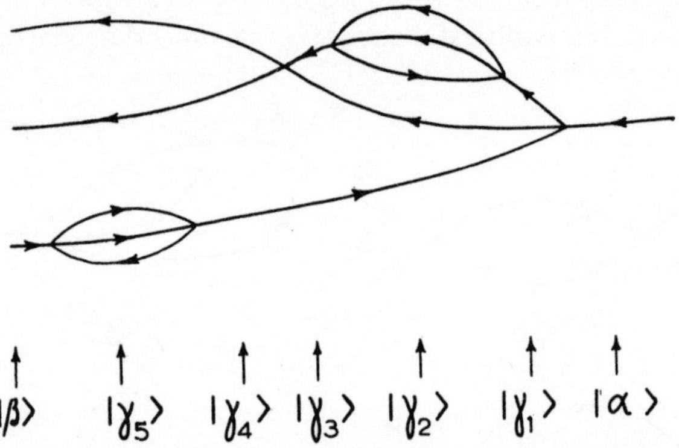

Fig. 3. A non-diagonal diagram which can be reduced to the diagram *a* of fig. 1..

Conversely, one can obtain any non-diagonal diagram in a unique way by inserting suitable diagonal subdiagrams in an irreducible non-diagonal diagram. In other words, in order to calculate the contribution of a reducible diagram, one should take the expression for the corresponding reduced diagram, and substitute for the factors $(\varepsilon_\alpha - z)^{-1}$, $(\varepsilon_\gamma - z)^{-1}$, $(\varepsilon_\beta - z)^{-1}$ belonging to initial, intermediate and final states the contributions of the appropriate diagonal diagrams, without the δ-factor. The sum of the contributions of all non-diagonal diagrams of $\langle\beta\,|R(z)|\,\alpha\rangle$ is obtained by taking the sum of the contributions of all irreducible non-diagonal diagrams and substituting for the factors $(\varepsilon_\alpha - z)^{-1}$, $(\varepsilon_\gamma - z)^{-1}$ and $(\varepsilon_\beta - z)^{-1}$ the functions $D_\alpha(z)$, $D_\gamma(z)$, and $D_\beta(z)$ defined by (3.8). We can express this simply by the formula

$$\{R(z)\}_{nd} = [-D(z)\; V\, D(z) + D(z) V\, D(z)\; V\, D(z) - \ldots\ldots]_{ind}.$$

The subscript *nd* indicates the non-diagonal part of $R(z)$, whereas *ind* means restriction to the contributions of all irreducible non-diagonal diagrams.

For $R(z)$ itself we find

$$R(z) = D(z) + [- D(z)\, V\, D(z) + D(z)\, V\, D(z)\, V\, D(z) - \ldots\ldots]_{ind}. \quad (4.1)$$

Having discussed the reduction of non-diagonal diagrams, we now go over to an analysis of the diagonal ones. We want to derive a formula which expresses $D(z)$ in terms of irreducible diagrams. To that end we give a unique prescription how to reduce a diagonal diagram. We make the following convention. The reduced diagonal diagram is obtained by removing all diagonal subdiagrams not containing the first vertex (from the right) of the original diagram. The contribution of any diagonal diagram of $\langle\beta\,|R(z)|\,\alpha\rangle$ can now again be derived unambiguously from the reduced diagram by replacing the factors $(\varepsilon_\beta - z)^{-1}$, $(\varepsilon_\gamma - z)^{-1}$ by the contributions of the appropriate diagonal diagrams, the factor $(\varepsilon_\alpha - z)^{-1}$ being left unaltered. This leads to the following formula for $D(z)$:

$$D(z) = (H_0 - z)^{-1} + D(z)\,[-V + V\,D(z)\,V - -V\,D(z)\,V\,D(z)\,V + \ldots]_{id}\,(H_0 - z)^{-1}. \quad (4.2)$$

The subscript *id* means that only contributions of irreducible diagonal diagrams should be taken.

The second term in the right-hand side of (4.2) contains only diagonal factors. The order of factors is therefore immaterial and the result is independent of the way we defined the reduction of diagonal diagrams.

Let us define a diagonal operator $G(z)$ by

$$G(z) = [- V + V\,D(z)\,V - V\,D(z)\,V\,D(z)\,V + \ldots]_{id}. \quad (4.3)$$

Substituting (4.3) in (4.2) one gets

$$D(z) = (H_0 - z)^{-1} + D(z)\,G(z)\,(H_0 - z)^{-1}$$

or

$$D(z) = (H_0 - z - G(z))^{-1}. \quad (4.4)$$

This is one of the basic equations of Van Hove (compare formulae (3.12), (3.15) of H I). It was derived here by an alternative method. For the sake of comparison a remark must be made on the fact that in H I (section 2) an assumption had to be made on the occurrence of $\delta(\gamma_i - \gamma_k)$ factors for the intermediate states. It was assumed that, whenever one has two pairs of intermediate states $|\gamma_j\rangle$, $|\gamma_k\rangle$ and $|\gamma_l\rangle$, $|\gamma_m\rangle$ related by the factors $\delta(\gamma_j - \gamma_k)$ and $\delta(\gamma_l - \gamma_m)$, the order, in which these four intermediate states occur in the matrix element, is never such that the states of one pair are separated by only one state of the other pair. In the present work, where diagonal parts of operators are described by means of diagrams, the assumption is automatically satisfied. It is an immediate consequence of the structure of the diagrams.

5. *Energies and wave functions of stationary states.* From (4.4), the operators $G(z)$ and $D(z)$ being diagonal in the $|\alpha\rangle$ representation, their eigenvalues $G_\alpha(z)$ and $D_\alpha(z)$ for some state $|\alpha\rangle$ are related by the equation

$$D_\alpha(z) = (\varepsilon_\alpha - z - G_\alpha(z))^{-1}. \tag{5.1}$$

It has been shown in H I that the numerical functions $G_\alpha(z)$, $D_\alpha(z)$ are both holomorphic for non-real z and satisfy the inequalities

$$Im\, D_\alpha(z) > 0 \text{ and } Im\, G_\alpha(z) \geqslant 0 \text{ for } Im\, z > 0. \tag{5.2}$$

The fact that the hamiltonian H is a hermitian operator implies the relations

$$R(z^*) = R^*(z),\ D_\alpha(z^*) = D^*_\alpha(z),\ G_\alpha(z^*) = G^*_\alpha(z). \tag{5.3}$$

$G_\alpha(z)$ and $D_\alpha(z)$ have singularities only on the real axis, where for a finite system they have a large number of poles. The analytical behaviour in the neighbourhood of the real axis becomes however very simple in the asymptotic limit of large Ω, *i.e.* if one neglects all effects which tend to zero for $\Omega \to \infty$.

We shall study the functions $G_\alpha(z)$ and $D_\alpha(z)$ in this approximation. From the definition (4.3) of $G(z)$, where in our approximation all sums over intermediate states are replaced by integrals, one can conclude that $G_\alpha(z)$ has no poles but has finite discontinuities for z crossing the real axis in all points of certain intervals which usually depend on α. In most cases these points of discontinuity cover a portion of the real axis from a finite number on up to $+\infty$.

Let x be a point on the real axis, and $\eta > 0$, then the real functions $K_\alpha(x)$ and $J_\alpha(x)$ are defined by

$$\lim_{\eta\to 0} G_\alpha(x + i\eta) = K_\alpha(x) + iJ_\alpha(x). \tag{5.4}$$

According to (5.3) a similar equation holds with i replaced by $-i$. Equation (5.2) implies

$$J_\alpha(x) \geqslant 0. \tag{5.5}$$

It is clear that $J_\alpha(x) = 0$ in those points of the real axis where $G_\alpha(z)$ is regular. The points x where $J_\alpha(x) > 0$ are the points where $G_\alpha(z)$ has a finite discontinuity for z crossing the real axis. In these points $D_\alpha(z)$ has also a finite discontinuity for z crossing the real axis.

In contrast to $G_\alpha(z)$, the function $D_\alpha(z)$ may have poles even in the limit of $\Omega \to \infty$. This will be the case if the equation $\varepsilon_\alpha - z - G_\alpha(z) = 0$ has a solution. This solution must necessarily be real and hence we consider the equation

$$\varepsilon_\alpha - x - K_\alpha(x) = 0. \tag{5.6}$$

Equation (5.6) has at least one root, and in most applications only one. We suppose such to be the case and call this root E_α. A necessary and sufficient condition for E_α to be a pole of $D_\alpha(z)$ is that $J_\alpha(x) = 0$ for x in the neighbourhood of E_α. In section 14 we shall investigate the case $J_\alpha(E_\alpha) \neq 0$, but for the time being we shall suppose that $J_\alpha(x) = 0$ for x near E_α.

An important difference between $D_\alpha(z)$ and the corresponding function in the unperturbed system, $(\varepsilon_\alpha - z)^{-1}$, is the shift of the pole from ε_α to E_α, *i.e.* by an amount $G_\alpha(E_\alpha) = K_\alpha(E_\alpha)$. It was shown in H I and we shall derive again that E_α is the energy of a stationary state which arises from $|\alpha\rangle$ through the influence of the perturbation. As we have seen the pole E_α is not the only singularity of $D_\alpha(z)$; $D_\alpha(z)$ has the same interval (or intervals) of discontinuity as $G_\alpha(z)$, formed of all points x where $J_\alpha(x) > 0$. It is evident that E_α is not such a point.

It might be of interest to compare the situation just described with what would be found if one took into account all corrections which vanish for $\Omega \to \infty$. In an exact treatment of a large but finite system one would find a very dense but discrete energy spectrum. $D_\alpha(z)$ would have a large number of poles and no other singularities. All these poles except one, which becomes E_α in the limiting case of large Ω, would be very densely distributed on the real axis, with a separation less than $k_F M^{-1}\Omega^{-\frac{1}{3}}$. The behaviour of $D_\alpha(z)$ at a distance from the real axis large compared to the separation of the poles would be approximately the same as in the limit of $\Omega \to \infty$, when the poles merge together into a line of discontinuity. One can say that the function $D_\alpha(z)$ in the limit of $\Omega \to \infty$ gives a good description of the corresponding quantity in the finite case if one is interested in a kind of average behaviour over energy intervals large compared to $k_F M^{-1}\Omega^{-\frac{1}{3}}$, or in the motion of the system over time intervals short compared to $M\Omega^{\frac{1}{3}}/k_F$.

Returning to the limiting case $\Omega \to \infty$ we shall now derive a formula for the wave function of a stationary state, on the basis of our assumption that $D_\alpha(z)$ has a pole at $z = E_\alpha$. Calculating the matrix element $\langle\beta|R(z)|\alpha\rangle$ by means of (4.1) one finds

$$\langle\beta|R(z)|\alpha\rangle = \langle\beta|[1 + D(z)\{-V + V D(z) V - \ldots\}_{ind}]|\alpha\rangle D_\alpha(z). \quad (5.7)$$

Of the two factors on the right-hand side the second one has a pole in E_α, while in general the first factor has a finite discontinuity if z crosses the real axis at E_α. Hence one can define two residues of $\langle\beta|R(z)|\alpha\rangle$ in E_α, one for the upper half plane and one for the lower half plane, by

$$\Re^{\pm}_{E_\alpha}[\langle\beta|R(z)|\alpha\rangle] = \lim_{z\to E_\alpha}(z - E_\alpha)\langle\beta|R(z)|\alpha\rangle,$$

where the plus sign must be chosen if z approaches E_α from above, and the minus sign if z approaches E_α from below. Taking the residue of both sides of equation (5.7) one finds

$$\Re^{\pm}_{E_\alpha}[\langle\beta|R(z)|\alpha\rangle] =$$
$$= -N_\alpha\langle\beta|[1 + D(E_\alpha \pm i0)\{-V + V D(E_\alpha \pm i0) V - \ldots\}_{ind}]|\alpha\rangle,$$

where $N_\alpha = (1 + G'_\alpha(E_\alpha))^{-1}$. The quantity $-N_\alpha$ is the residue of $D_\alpha(z)$ in E_α.

We shall now prove that the states defined by

$$\int d\beta\, |\beta\rangle \,.\, \Re^{\pm}_{E\alpha}\,[\langle\beta\, |R(z)|\, \alpha\rangle] = \Re^{\pm}_{E\alpha}[R(z)\, |\alpha\rangle]$$

are stationary states with the energy E_α.From the definition (3.2) of $R(z)$ one derives easily

$$R(z) - R(z') = (z - z')\, R(z)\,.\, R(z'). \tag{5.8}$$

By application of this operator relation to the state $|\alpha\rangle$, an equation is obtained where both sides, as functions of z', have a pole of the type just considered. Equating the residues $\Re^{+}_{E\alpha}$ or $\Re^{-}_{E\alpha}$ of both sides and dividing by $z - E_\alpha$ one finds

$$R(z)\, \Re^{\pm}_{E\alpha}\,[R(z')\, |\alpha\rangle] = \frac{1}{E_\alpha - z}\, \Re^{\pm}_{E\alpha}\,[R(z')\, |\alpha\rangle]\,.$$

Substituting in (3.3) one concludes immediately

$$U(t)\, \Re^{\pm}_{E\alpha}[R(z)\, |\alpha\rangle] = \exp\,(-\, iE_\alpha t)\,.\, \Re^{\pm}_{E\alpha}\,[R(z)\, |\alpha\rangle].$$

The states $\Re^{\pm}_{E\alpha}\,[R(z)\, |\alpha\rangle]$ are not yet properly normalized. In H II the normalization constant is shown to be $N_\alpha^{-\frac{1}{2}}$. The stationary states are therefore given by

$$|\psi_\alpha\rangle^{\pm} = -\, N_\alpha^{-\frac{1}{2}}\, \Re^{\pm}_{E\alpha}\,[R(z)\, |\alpha\rangle] =$$

$$= N_\alpha^{\frac{1}{2}}\,[1 + D(E_\alpha \pm i0)\{-\, V + V\, D(E_\alpha \pm i0)\, V - \ldots\}_{ind}]\, |\alpha\rangle. \tag{5.9}$$

In the case that the states $|\psi_\alpha\rangle^{+}$ and $|\psi_\alpha\rangle^{-}$ are different, they describe scattering with outgoing and ingoing waves respectively. More details are given in H II, where it is moreover proved that, provided $J_\alpha(E_\alpha) = 0$ for all states $|\alpha\rangle$, the set of states $|\psi_\alpha\rangle^{+}$ form a complete orthonormal set, and the states $|\psi_\alpha\rangle^{-}$ as well. This is not necessarily the case if there exist states $|\alpha\rangle$ for which $J_\alpha(E_\alpha) \neq 0$, *i.e.* for which the only singularities of $D_\alpha(z)$ are finite discontinuities.

CHAPTER III. SEPARATION METHOD FOR THE Ω-DEPENDENT PARTS OF THE DIAGRAMS

6. *Ω-dependence of the diagram contributions.* As explained in the introduction, one is often interested in the way the different physical quantities vary with the volume Ω of the system, at least asymptotically for large Ω. In the last chapter a method was studied to calculate energies and wave functions for the case of large Ω. However the formulae derived there are not very suitable for analysing the dependence on Ω of observable quantities. Although for example we expect on physical grounds that the energy differ-

ence $E_\alpha - E_{\alpha'}$ between two low-lying states must become independent of Ω for large Ω (intensive quantity), it will not be easy to derive such a conclusion from the fact that the perturbed energy is the root of (5.6). The origin of this difficulty must be found in the rather complicated Ω-dependence of $D_\alpha(z)$ and $G_\alpha(z)$, which we shall investigate presently. We restrict ourselves throughout to states $|\alpha\rangle$ differing from the unperturbed ground state by the presence of a finite number of excited particles and holes.

We go back to the series expansion (3.5) for $R(z)$ and see how the contributions of the different diagrams of $\langle\beta\,|R(z)|\,\alpha\rangle$ depend on Ω. All energy denominators contain a term proportional to Ω, for the unperturbed energy ε_α can be written as the sum of two terms $\varepsilon_\alpha = \varepsilon_0 + \varepsilon_\alpha'$, where the ground state energy ε_0 is proportional to Ω according to (2.10) and ε_α', the sum of the unperturbed energies of the additional particles and holes, is independent of Ω. Henceforth we shall consider $\langle\beta\,|R(\varepsilon_0 + z)|\,\alpha\rangle$ instead of $\langle\beta\,|R(z)|\,\alpha\rangle$; the denominators of this new expression do not depend on Ω.

We consider now the contributions to $\langle\beta\,|R(\varepsilon_0 + z)|\,\alpha\rangle$ of different types of diagrams and study their Ω-dependence. Let us take first a connected diagram with external lines. As remarked before, the conservation of momentum is expressed by a factor $\delta(K_\alpha - K_\beta)$ in the contribution of the diagram, where K_α and K_β are the total momenta of the states $|\alpha\rangle$ and $|\beta\rangle$. If we now replace the summation by an integration we get an expression independent of Ω (see section 3). The terms one should add to correct for the replacement of the summation by an integration tend to zero for $\Omega \to \infty$. Such terms will be neglected as before.

Next we take a connected ground state diagram, *i.e.* a connected diagram without external lines. As always there is a δ-function for each point, expressing the conservation of momentum in each elementary transition. In the present case, however, through the absence of external lines, one of these δ-functions is dependent on the others. This gives rise to a factor $\delta(0)$, which by (2.6) leads to a factor $\Omega/8\pi^3$. If, in the remaining expression, we replace the sums by integrals we get again an expression independent of Ω, except for correction terms which vanish for $\Omega \to \infty$. However we have the factor Ω multiplying not only the integral but also the correction terms, which cannot be all neglected in this case. Hence we conclude that a connected ground state diagram gives a contribution containing a main term proportional to Ω and possibly other terms which, although not all negligible, are small compared to the main term for large Ω.

These considerations are easily extended to more complex diagrams containing one or more ground state components: they exhibit a Ω-dependence such that the highest power of Ω is equal to the number of ground state components. Consequently it is clear that all matrix elements of $R(\varepsilon_0 + z)$ contain terms with arbitrarily high powers of Ω.

7. *Decomposition of diagrams.* After having located the Ω-dependence in the contributions of the diagrams our next task is to make a separation between the Ω-dependent and the Ω-independent parts of a diagram. We must clearly base such a separation on the distinction between the different components of the diagram. We shall derive a formula which makes it possible to express the contribution of each disconnected diagram in terms of the contributions of its components.

Consider two diagrams A and B with or without external lines and denote their contributions to $R(z)$ by $\langle\alpha'|A(z)|\alpha\rangle$ and $\langle\beta'|B(z)|\beta\rangle$. The states $|\alpha\rangle$, $|\alpha'\rangle$, $|\beta\rangle$, and $|\beta'\rangle$ contain certain numbers (possibly zero) of particles and holes. They can be obtained from the state $|\varphi_0\rangle$, which describes the

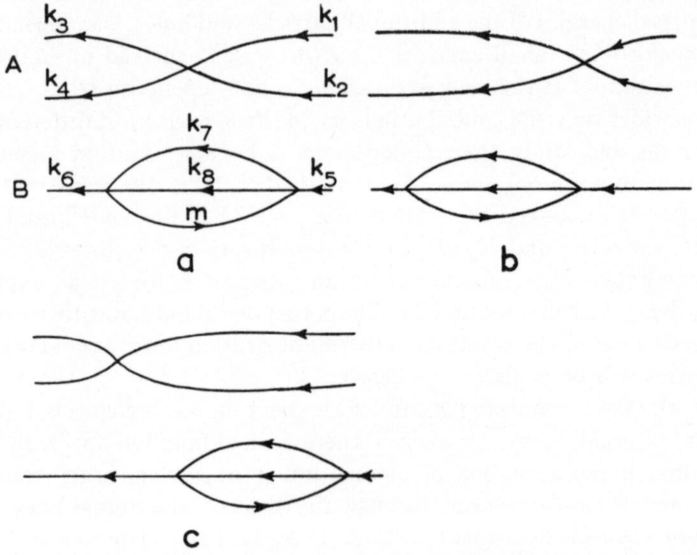

Fig. 4. This figure shows the three ways in which two diagrams of the first and second order in V can be combined to form a diagram of order three.

unperturbed Fermi sea, by applying to $|\varphi_0\rangle$ products of creation operators ξ_k^* and ξ_m for particles and holes respectively. We suppose that $|\alpha\rangle$ and $|\beta\rangle$ do not contain particles or holes with identical momenta. It is then possible to define a state $|\alpha\beta\rangle$ containing all the particles and holes of $|\alpha\rangle$ and $|\beta\rangle$ together. We define $|\alpha\beta\rangle$ as the state obtained, when one applies to $|\beta\rangle$ all the creation operators which must be applied to $|\varphi_0\rangle$ in order to give $|\alpha\rangle$, and in the same order. The notation $\langle\beta\alpha|$ is used for the conjugate of $|\alpha\beta\rangle$. For the states $|\alpha'\rangle$ and $|\beta'\rangle$ we make the same assumption as for $|\alpha\rangle$, $|\beta\rangle$, and we define $|\alpha'\beta'\rangle$ in exactly the same way.

The two given diagrams can be combined in various ways to form a composite diagram. If n and m are the numbers of vertices of A and B, the composite diagrams have $m+n$ vertices. The various composite diagrams differ by the order in which the points of the two original diagrams A and B occur from right to left, the number of possibilities being $(n+m)!/n!m!$. Figure 4 shows the three possible ways in which two diagrams A and B of order one and two in V respectively can be taken together to form a composite diagram. The sum of the contributions to $\langle\beta'\alpha'|R(z)|\alpha\beta\rangle$ of all composite diagrams found in this way we shall denote by $\langle\beta'\alpha'|C(z)|\alpha\beta\rangle$.

The important point is now that a simple relation exists between $\langle\beta'\alpha'|C(z)|\alpha\beta\rangle$ and the contributions $\langle\alpha'|A(z)|\alpha\rangle$ and $\langle\beta'|B(z)|\beta\rangle$ of the original diagrams A and B to the resolvent. It is expressed by the equation

$$\langle\beta'\alpha'|C(z)|\alpha\beta\rangle = -(2\pi i)^{-1}\oint \mathrm{d}\zeta\, \langle\alpha'|A(z-\zeta)|\alpha\rangle\langle\beta'|B(\varepsilon_0+\zeta)|\beta\rangle. \tag{7.1}$$

The path of integration is a contour encircling all singular points of the integrand on the real axis, but not encircling the singular points situated on the straight line through z parallel to the real axis. It is to be described counterclockwise.

Before deriving (7.1), we note that the integral in the right-hand side is a type of convolution integral, taken in the complex plane. We shall encounter such convolutions very often and it is therefore convenient to introduce a special notation for them. Let $f(z)$ and $g(z)$ be two functions, holomorphic for non-real z, for which $zf(z)$ and $zg(z)$ are bounded for $|z|\to\infty$. The symbol $f(z) * g(z)$ indicates another function of z, defined by

$$f(z) * g(z) = -(2\pi i)^{-1}\oint \mathrm{d}\zeta\, f(z-\zeta)\, g(\zeta), \tag{7.2}$$

with a path of integration as defined above. Using the property that $zf(z)$ and $zg(z)$ are bounded for large $|z|$, one can deform the path of integration into a contour encircling the straight line through z parallel to the real axis. This leads to the equation

$$f(z) * g(z) = g(z) * f(z). \tag{7.3}$$

With our new notation (7.1) reads

$$\langle\beta'\alpha'|C(\varepsilon_0+z)|\alpha\beta\rangle = \langle\alpha'|A(\varepsilon_0+z)|\alpha\rangle * \langle\beta'|B(\varepsilon_0+z)|\beta\rangle. \tag{7.4}$$

We start now the proof of the relation (7.1) which constitutes the basic tool for all the derivations in the following sections.

We first establish the validity of (7.1) for the simple diagrams of fig. 4. The states $|\alpha\rangle$, $|\alpha'\rangle$, $|\beta\rangle$, and $|\beta'\rangle$ are denoted by $|k_1k_2\,;\,\rangle$, $|k_3k_4\,;\,\rangle$, $|k_5\,;\,\rangle$, and $|k_6\,;\,\rangle$ respectively.

According to the rules of section 3 one finds

$$\langle\,;\,k_4k_3|A(z+\varepsilon_0)|k_1k_2\,;\,\rangle = -v(k_4k_3k_1k_2)(\varepsilon'_{\alpha'}-z)^{-1}(\varepsilon'_{\alpha}-z)^{-1}, \tag{7.5}$$

$$\begin{aligned}\langle\,;\,k_6|B(z+\varepsilon_0)|k_5\,;\,\rangle = \tfrac{1}{2}\textstyle\int_{k_7k_8m} v(k_6mk_7k_8)\, v(k_7k_8k_5m)\,.\\ .\,(\varepsilon'_{\beta'}-z)^{-1}(\varepsilon'_{\beta_1}-z)^{-1}(\varepsilon'_{\beta}-z)^{-1}.\end{aligned} \tag{7.6}$$

The energies in the denominators are the excitation energies of the states as compared with the energy ε_0 of $|\varphi_0\rangle$. Diagram *a* of fig. 4 gives the contribution

$$- \tfrac{1}{2} \int_{k_7 k_8 m} v(k_6 m k_7 k_8)\, v(k_4 k_3 k_1 k_2)\, v(k_7 k_8 k_5 m)\, .$$
$$(\varepsilon'_{\alpha'} + \varepsilon'_{\beta'} - z)^{-1} (\varepsilon'_{\alpha'} + \varepsilon'_{\beta_1} - z)^{-1} (\varepsilon'_{\alpha} + \varepsilon'_{\beta_1} - z)^{-1} (\varepsilon'_{\alpha} + \varepsilon'_{\beta} - z)^{-1}.$$

In writing down this equation we made essential use of the remark in section 3 concerning intermediate states with two or more particles in the same plane wave state. The diagrams *b* and *c* give the same expression except for the energy denominators. The sum of the products of energy factors in the expressions for *a*, *b* and *c* is easily calculated. After some simple algebraic manipulations one gets

$$(\varepsilon'_{\alpha} - \varepsilon'_{\alpha'})^{-1} (\varepsilon'_{\alpha'} + \varepsilon'_{\beta'} - z)^{-1} (\varepsilon'_{\alpha'} + \varepsilon'_{\beta_1} - z)^{-1} (\varepsilon'_{\alpha'} + \varepsilon'_{\beta} - z)^{-1} +$$
$$+ (\varepsilon'_{\alpha'} - \varepsilon'_{\alpha})^{-1} (\varepsilon'_{\alpha} + \varepsilon'_{\beta'} - z)^{-1} (\varepsilon'_{\beta} + \varepsilon'_{\beta_1} - z)^{-1} (\varepsilon'_{\alpha} + \varepsilon'_{\beta} - z)^{-1},$$

which again is equal to

$$(\varepsilon'_{\beta'} - z)^{-1} (\varepsilon'_{\beta_1} - z)^{-1} (\varepsilon'_{\beta} - z)^{-1} * (\varepsilon'_{\alpha} - z)^{-1} (\varepsilon'_{\alpha'} - z)^{-1}$$

as follows immediately from our definition (7.2) of convolution.
For the sum of the contributions of the diagrams *a*, *b*, and *c* of fig. 4 we find using (7.5) and (7.6)

$$\langle\, ;\, k_6 k_4 k_3\, |C(\varepsilon_0 + z)|\, k_1 k_2 k_5\, ;\, \rangle = - \tfrac{1}{2} \int_{k_7 k_8 m} v(k_6 m k_7 k_8)\, .$$
$$. v(k_4 k_3 k_1 k_2)\, v(k_7 k_8 k_5 m)\, [(\varepsilon'_{\alpha'} - z)^{-1} (\varepsilon'_{\alpha} - z)^{-1} * (\varepsilon'_{\beta'} - z)^{-1} (\varepsilon'_{\beta_1} - z)^{-1} (\varepsilon'_{\beta} - z)^{-1}] =$$
$$= \langle\, ;\, k_4 k_3\, |A(z + \varepsilon_0)|\, k_1 k_2\, ;\, \rangle * \langle\, ;\, k_6\, |B(z + \varepsilon_0)|\, k_5\, ;\, \rangle,$$

which proves equation (7.1) for the special case considered.

This simple example shows that to prove equation (7.1) it is sufficient to establish the corresponding equation for the products of energy factors only. In the case of our example this equation could be proved by a direct calculation, which however cannot easily be extended to the general case. It is more convenient to proceed by induction. The products of energy factors corresponding to the two diagrams *A* and *B* can be written in the form

$$\Pi_{k=0}^{n} (a_k - z)^{-1} \text{ and } \Pi_{l=0}^{m} (b_l - z)^{-1}$$

where

$$a_0 = \varepsilon'_{\alpha},\ a_n = \varepsilon'_{\alpha'},\ b_0 = \varepsilon'_{\beta},\ b_m = \varepsilon'_{\beta'},$$

while $a_k (k = 1, 2, \ldots, n-1)$ and $b_l (l = 1, 2, \ldots, m-1)$ are the excitation energies of the intermediate states of *A*, and *B* relative to the ground state energy ε_0. We introduce ordered products of $n + m + 1$ factors

$$(a_k + b_l - z)^{-1}\ (k = 0, \ldots, n\ ;\ l = 0, \ldots, m)$$

with the following property: if $(a_k + b_l - z)^{-1}$ and $(a_{k'} + b_{l'} - z)^{-1}$ are consecutive factors, the first being to the left, one has either $k = k'$, $l = l' + 1$ or $k = k' + 1$, $l = l'$. The number of products which can be constructed according to this rule is $(n + m)!/n!m!$ and we shall denote their sum by $\Phi(a_n \dots a_1 a_0; b_m \dots b_1 b_0)$. The first factor from the left of each ordered product will always be $(a_n + b_m - z)^{-1}$, the last one to the right $(a_0 + b_0 - z)^{-1}$. The second factor will be either $(a_n + b_{m-1} - z)^{-1}$ or $(a_{n-1} + b_m - z)^{-1}$. In the first case the product can be written as $(a_n + b_m - z)^{-1}$ multiplied by an ordered product of factors $(a_k + b_l - z)^{-1}$ ($\mathrm{k} = 0, \dots, n$; $l = 0, \dots, m - 1$). For the sum of all products of this kind, we find therefore $(a_n + b_m - z)^{-1} \, . \, \Phi(a_n \dots a_1 a_0 \, ; \, b_{m-1} \dots b_1 b_0)$. In exactly the same way we get for the sum of all products with $(a_{n-1} + b_m - z)^{-1}$ as the second factor the expression $(a_n + b_m - z)^{-1} \, . \, \Phi(a_{n-1} \dots a_1 a_0 \, ;$ $b_m \dots b_1 b_0)$. These results taken together give the reduction formula

$$\Phi(a_n \dots a_0 \, ; \, b_m \dots b_0) = (a_n + b_m - z)^{-1} \, [\Phi(a_{n-1} \dots a_0 \, ; \, b_m \dots b_0) + \\ + \Phi(a_n \dots a_0 \, ; \, b_{m-1} \dots b_0)]. \quad (7.7)$$

Let us define the quantity $\Psi(a_n \dots a_0 \, ; \, b_m \dots b_0)$ by the formula

$$\Psi(a_n \dots a_0 \, ; \, b_m \dots b_0) = \Pi_{k=0}^{n} \, (a_k - z)^{-1} * \Pi_{l=0}^{m} (b_l - z)^{-1}.$$

The equation we want to prove is then simply

$$\Phi = \Psi. \quad (7.8)$$

We show first that (7.7) is satisfied by Ψ as well as by Φ. Indeed

$$(a_n + b_m - z)^{-1} \, [\Psi(a_{n-1} \dots a_0 \, ; \, b_m \dots b_0) + \Psi(a_n \dots a_0 \, ; \, b_{m-1} \dots b_0)] =$$

$$= - \, (2\pi i)^{-1} \oint \mathrm{d}\zeta \frac{1}{a_n + b_m - z} \left(\frac{1}{b_m - \zeta} + \frac{1}{a_n - z + \zeta} \right) \frac{1}{a_{n-1} - z + \zeta} \cdots$$

$$\cdots \frac{1}{a_0 - z + \zeta} \cdot \frac{1}{b_{m-1} - \zeta} \cdots\cdots \frac{1}{b_0 - \zeta} = \Psi \, (a_n \dots a_0 \, ; \, b_m \dots b_0).$$

On the other hand the definitions of Φ and Ψ imply immediately

$$\Phi(a_0 \, ; \, b_l \dots b_0) = \Psi(a_0 \, ; \, b_l \dots b_0),$$

$$\Phi(a_k \dots a_0 \, ; \, b_0) = \Psi(a_k \dots a_0 \, ; \, b_0).$$

By induction we can now conclude to the validity of (7.8), thus completing the proof of equation (7.1).

In the appendix A1 another derivation of (7.1) will be discussed. It is based on a comparison with a system consisting of two completely uncoupled subsystems, a situation for which equation (7.1) is a direct consequence of the additivity of the energies.

Chapter IV. The separation of ground state diagrams. Calculation of energies

8. *The integral equation for* $D_0(z)$. We consider a matrix element $\langle\alpha'|R(z)|\alpha\rangle$ of $R(z)$ and suppose that $|\alpha\rangle$ and $|\alpha'\rangle$ are not both identical with $|\varphi_0\rangle$. This means that the contributing diagrams contain external lines. Each diagram consists of one or more components (*i.e.* connected parts) with external lines and possibly some components without external lines. The sum of the contributions to $\langle\alpha'|R(z)|\alpha\rangle$ of all diagrams $\bar{A}$ which do not contain ground state components, will be denoted by $\langle\alpha'|\bar{R}(z)|\alpha\rangle$. Each diagram of $\langle\alpha'|R(z)|\alpha\rangle$ can be obtained in an unambiguous way from a diagram $\bar{A}$ of $\langle\alpha'|\bar{R}(z)|\alpha\rangle$ by the addition of a ground state diagram A_0. The contribution to $\langle\alpha'|R(\varepsilon_0+z)|\alpha\rangle$ of all diagrams one can form from $\bar{A}$ and A_0 is, according to (7.4), expressed by

$$\langle\alpha'|\bar{A}(\varepsilon_0+z)|\alpha\rangle * A_0(\varepsilon_0+z),$$

where $\langle\alpha'|\bar{A}(z)|\alpha\rangle$ is the contribution of $\bar{A}$ to $\langle\alpha'|\bar{R}(z)|\alpha\rangle$ and $A_0(z)$ is the contribution of A_0 to $\langle\varphi_0|R(z)|\varphi_0\rangle \equiv D_0(z)$.

One clearly gets the total value of $\langle\alpha'|R(\varepsilon_0+z)|\alpha\rangle$ by summing over all possible diagrams $\bar{A}$ and A_0. This gives the formula

$$\langle\alpha'|R(\varepsilon_0+z)|\alpha\rangle = \langle\alpha'|\bar{R}(\varepsilon_0+z)|\alpha\rangle * D_0(\varepsilon_0+z). \tag{8.1}$$

We have seen in section 6 that diagrams not containing ground state components give contributions which, for large volume Ω, are independent of Ω, whereas ground state diagrams are Ω-dependent. The importance of (8.1) is due to the fact that it gives in the resolvent a complete separation between Ω-dependent and Ω-independent quantities.

We shall study now the dependence on Ω of the ground state expectation value $D_0(z)$ of the resolvent. $D_0(z)$ is, by definition, the sum of the contributions of all ground state diagrams. As discussed in section 6 these contributions contain arbitrarily high powers of Ω. In order to investigate the explicit Ω-dependence of $D_0(z)$, we derive for this function a simple integral equation which will enable us to calculate it using only connected ground state diagrams.

In the second of the operator equations (3.4) we take on both sides the diagonal element for the state $|\varphi_0\rangle$ and replace z by ε_0+z. We find

$$D_0(\varepsilon_0+z) = -1/z + \langle\varphi_0|R(\varepsilon_0+z)V|\varphi_0\rangle . 1/z,$$

or, summing over intermediate states,

$$D_0(\varepsilon_0+z) = -1/z + D_0(\varepsilon_0+z)\langle\varphi_0|V|\varphi_0\rangle/z + \\ + 1/z \textstyle\int' \langle\varphi_0|R(\varepsilon_0+z)|\alpha\rangle\langle\alpha|V|\varphi_0\rangle.$$

The summation is extended over all states $|\alpha\rangle \neq |\varphi_0\rangle$. This equation can be transformed by applying (8.1) to the matrix element $\langle\varphi_0|R(\varepsilon_0+z)|\alpha\rangle$. One finds after elementary manipulations

$$D_0(\varepsilon_0+z) = -z^{-1}[1 + D_0(\varepsilon_0+z) * (z^{-1}\langle\varphi_0|V|\varphi_0\rangle - \\ -\int'\langle\varphi_0|\bar{R}(\varepsilon_0+z)|\alpha\rangle\langle\alpha|V|\varphi_0\rangle)] = \\ = -z^{-1}[1 - D_0(\varepsilon_0+z) * z^{-1}\bar{G}_0(\varepsilon_0+z)]. \quad (8.2)$$

The function $\bar{G}_0(z)$ is defined by

$$\bar{G}_0(z) = \langle\varphi_0|[-V + V(H_0-z)^{-1}V - \ldots\ldots]_C|\varphi_0\rangle, \quad (8.3)$$

where the subscript C means that only connected ground state diagrams contribute to $\bar{G}_0(z)$. Equation (8.2) is an integral equation for $D_0(z)$ which, by (7.2), can be written in the more explicit form

$$zD_0(\varepsilon_0+z) = -1 - (2\pi i)^{-1}\oint d\zeta\,\zeta^{-1}\bar{G}_0(\varepsilon_0+\zeta)\,D_0(\varepsilon_0+z-\zeta). \quad (8.4)$$

The path of integration is, according to (7.2), a contour around that portion of the real axis, which contains all the singularities of the first factor in the integrand. It is described counterclockwise and it is chosen in such a way that it does not cross the line through the point z parallel to the real axis.

As we shall see below, (8.4) can be solved explicitly. It expresses $D_0(\varepsilon_0+z)$ in terms of the function $\bar{G}_0(\varepsilon_0+z)$, which is much simpler since it involves connected diagrams only. In particular the definition (8.3) implies that $\bar{G}_0(\varepsilon_0+z)$ contains a main term proportional to the volume Ω of the system, and other terms which, for large Ω, are small compared to the first.

The connected ground state diagrams contributing to (8.3) contain in general diagonal subdiagrams. With the methods of section 4 we derive an expression for $\bar{G}_0(z)$ in terms of irreducible diagrams only. Starting from irreducible ground state diagrams one can construct all diagrams occurring in (8.3) in an unambiguous way by inserting suitable diagonal subdiagrams between any pair of successive points. These diagonal subdiagrams should not contain any ground state components. This suggests considering for each state $|\alpha\rangle \neq |\varphi_0\rangle$ the sum $\bar{D}_\alpha(z)$ of the contributions to $D_\alpha(z)$ of all diagonal diagrams which do not contain ground state components. Using this definition we obtain the following expression for $\bar{G}_0(z)$:

$$\bar{G}_0(z) = \langle\varphi_0|[-V + V\bar{D}(z)V - V\bar{D}(z)V\,\bar{D}(z)V + \ldots]_{idC}|\varphi_0\rangle. \quad (8.5)$$

The subscript *idC* means that, in calculating the right-hand side, one should limit oneself to irreducible connected ground state diagrams.

9. *Solution of the integral equation.* It is our aim to solve explicitly the integral equation (8.4) for $D_0(\varepsilon_0+z)$ in the limiting case of large systems. To that end we shall first discuss briefly some properties of the function $\bar{G}_0(\varepsilon_0+z)$ for this limiting case.

All terms in $\bar{G}_0(\varepsilon_0+z)$ except the term proportional to Ω will be neglected.

This means in particular that we replace in (8.5) all sums over intermediate states by integrals. In this approximation, from (8.5), the function $\bar{G}_0(\varepsilon_0+z)$ has no poles. Its only singularities are the points of a cut along the real axis from a point B up to $+\infty$. In each point of this cut the function has a finite discontinuity for z crossing the real axis. The function can, in most practical cases, be continued analytically across the cut, from above and from below. B plays then the role of a branch point.

We shall assume, as is consistent with the fact that $|\varphi_0\rangle$ is the ground state and has an energy ε_0, that B lies on the positive real axis or at the origin. In the latter case a further assumption will be made, concerning the real function

$$\bar{J}_0(x) = -\tfrac{1}{2}i \lim_{\eta\to 0} [\bar{G}_0(x+i\eta) - \bar{G}_0(x-i\eta)],\ \eta > 0, \tag{9.1}$$

namely

$$|\bar{J}_0(\varepsilon_0 + x)| < A \,.\, x^{\alpha+1}, \text{ for } x > 0, \tag{9.2}$$

where A and α are positive constants.

If we write

$$\bar{G}_0(\varepsilon_0 + z) = -\langle\varphi_0\,|V|\,\varphi_0\rangle + g(z),$$

the function $g(z)$ has, according to (8.5), the property that $zg(z)$ is bounded for large $|z|$. This implies that the path of integration C in Cauchy's formula

$$g(z) = (2\pi i)^{-1} \int_C \mathrm{d}\zeta\, g(\zeta)(\zeta - z)^{-1} \text{ for non-real } z,$$

can be deformed into a contour around the singular points of $g(z)$ on the positive real axis. One finds in this way using (9.1)

$$\bar{G}_0(\varepsilon_0 + z) = \pi^{-1} \int_0^\infty \mathrm{d}\xi\, \bar{J}_0(\varepsilon_0 + \xi)(\xi - z)^{-1} - \langle\varphi_0|V|\,\varphi_0\rangle, \tag{9.3}$$

and, taking the derivative at both sides,

$$\bar{G}_0'(\varepsilon_0 + z) = \pi^{-1} \int_0^\infty \mathrm{d}\xi\, \bar{J}_0(\varepsilon_0 + \xi)(\xi - z)^{-2}. \tag{9.4}$$

As an immediate consequence of our assumptions we see that both $\bar{G}_0(\varepsilon_0 + z)$ and its first derivative exist at the origin.

The validity of the assumptions we made to reach these conclusions must of course be established in each special case. One can however easily see that the assumption that the branch point B is situated on the negative real axis would lead to unphysical results. In the case that $\bar{G}_0(\varepsilon_0 + z)$ has negative singularities, equation (8.4) can only be solved by a function $D_0(\varepsilon_0 + z)$ having singularities extending to $-\infty$. This would correspond to a perturbed energy spectrum without lower bound, a situation not realized in actual physical systems. In quantum electrodynamics the branch point B is at the point $z = 2m$ (m is the observable mass of the electron), corresponding to the lowest energy necessary for the creation of an electron-positron pair and a photon. For a Fermi gas with interaction, the case considered as main example in the present paper, B is at the origin with $\alpha > 0$, as will be shown in the forthcoming paper already announced.

To reduce (8.4) to a simpler form we introduce the function

$$h(z) = (\bar{G}_0(\varepsilon_0 + z) - \bar{G}_0(\varepsilon_0))z^{-1} \tag{9.5}$$

which, under our assumptions, has no singularities except for a cut on the positive real axis, from B to $+\infty$. At the origin it has the well-defined value $h(0) = \bar{G}_0'(\varepsilon_0)$. Substituting (9.5) in (8.4) we find

$$z \,.\, D_0(\varepsilon_0 + z) = -1 - \bar{G}_0(\varepsilon_0)\, D_0(\varepsilon_0 + z) - (2\pi i)^{-1} \oint d\zeta\, h(\zeta)\, D_0(\varepsilon_0 + z - \zeta)$$

which, by the substitution $z \to z - \bar{G}_0(\varepsilon_0)$ can be written

$$zD_0(\varepsilon_0 - \bar{G}_0(\varepsilon_0) + z) = -1 - (2\pi i)^{-1} \oint d\zeta\, h(\zeta)\, D_0(\varepsilon_0 - \bar{G}_0(\varepsilon_0) + z - \zeta).$$

If we introduce the notation

$$f(z) = D_0(\varepsilon_0 - \bar{G}_0(\varepsilon_0) + z) \tag{9.6}$$

our integral equation is reduced to the simple form

$$zf(z) = -1 - (2\pi i)^{-1} \oint d\zeta\, h(\zeta)\, f(z - \zeta). \tag{9.7}$$

Both $h(z)$ and the desired solution $f(z)$ have the property that $zh(z)$ and $zf(z)$ remain bounded for $|z| \to \infty$, which means that according to (7.3) the equation can be written in the equivalent form

$$zf(z) = -1 - (2\pi i)^{-1} \oint d\zeta\, h(z - \zeta)\, f(\zeta). \tag{9.8}$$

The second term on the right-hand side tends to zero for $|z| \to \infty$. This gives the relation

$$-(2\pi i)^{-1} \oint dz\, f(z) = 1, \tag{9.9}$$

which also follows from (3.3) by taking the expectation value for $|\varphi_0\rangle$ and putting $t = 0$.

To solve equation (9.7) we proceed in the following way. It can be shown that (9.7) has at most one solution $f(z)$ belonging to the class of functions which are holomorphic outside the real axis and bounded for large $|z|$. A proof will be given in appendix A2. If we now can find a function $f(z)$ of the class mentioned which solves (9.7) we are certain that it is the only one. From a physical point of view we are not interested in other solutions if they exist.

Equation (9.7) suggests a solution of the form

$$f(z) = -N_0/z + \psi(z), \tag{9.10}$$

where the function $\psi(z)$, just as $h(z)$, has no other singularities than a cut on the positive real axis running from B to $+\infty$ †). We shall show that a solution of the form (9.10) exists and we shall determine N_0 and $\psi(z)$. The relations (5.3) imply $h(z^*) = h(z)^*$ and $\psi(z^*) = \psi(z)^*$. Consequently the functions $p(x)$ and $\varphi(x)$, defined by

$$2\pi i\, p(x) = \lim_{\eta \to 0} [h(x + i\eta) - h(x - i\eta)],\ \eta > 0 \tag{9.11}$$

$$2\pi i\, \varphi(x) = \lim_{\eta \to 0} [\psi(x + i\eta) - \psi(x - i\eta)],\ \eta > 0 \tag{9.12}$$

are real. They vanish for $x < B$. Furthermore, from (5.2), $\varphi(x) \geqslant 0$, while (9.1) and (9.5), imply

$$p(x) = \bar{J}_0\, (\varepsilon_0 + x)/x. \tag{9.13}$$

It will be sufficient for us to determine $\varphi(x)$. The function $\psi(z)$ will then follow by application of Cauchy's theorem. Substituting (9.10) in (9.8) one finds, using (9.12),

$$-N_0 + z\psi(z) = -1 + N_0\, h(z) + \int_0^\infty \mathrm{d}\xi\, h(z - \xi)\, \varphi(\xi)$$

which by (9.11) and (9.12) can be reduced to the following integral equation for $\varphi(x)$:

$$x\varphi(x) = N_0\, p(x) + \int_0^x \mathrm{d}\xi\, p(x - \xi)\, \varphi(\xi). \tag{9.14}$$

This equation is solved by means of a Laplace transformation. If one defines

$$\hat{\varphi}(s) = \int_0^\infty \varphi(x)\, e^{-sx} \mathrm{d}x,\ \hat{p}(s) = \int_0^\infty p(x)\, e^{-sx}\, \mathrm{d}x,$$

(9.14) can be transformed into

$$-\frac{d}{\mathrm{d}s}\, \hat{\varphi}(s) = N_0\, \hat{p}(s) + \hat{p}(s)\, .\, \hat{\varphi}(s). \tag{9.15}$$

The general solution of this linear first order differential equation is

$$\hat{\varphi}(s) = -N_0 + C \exp\,(-\int \hat{p}(s)\, \mathrm{d}s),$$

where C is an arbitrary constant. The indefinite integral in the exponent can be taken equal to $-\int_0^\infty p(x)\, x^{-1} \exp\,(-sx)\, \mathrm{d}x$. For $\hat{\varphi}(s)$ to be the Laplace-transform of a function $\varphi(x)$ the following condition must be satisfied: $\lim_{s \to \infty} \hat{\varphi}(s) = 0$. It implies $C = N_0$ and gives us the following expression for $\hat{\varphi}(s)$:

$$\hat{\varphi}(s) = N_0 \left[\exp\left(\int_0^\infty \frac{p(x)}{x}\, e^{-sx}\, \mathrm{d}x\right) - 1\right]. \tag{9.16}$$

Whether this function $\hat{\varphi}(s)$ is the Laplace-transform of a solution $\varphi(x)$ of

†) In the case $B = 0$, the origin is not a proper pole of $f(z)$. We shall however continue to call such a point a pole, provided the function $\varphi(x)$, defined in (9.12) has near the origin the behaviour $\varphi(x) = O(x^{\alpha - 1})$ with $\alpha > 0$. As seen from (9.19) this condition is fulfilled.

(9.14) depends on the behaviour of $p(x)$ near the origin. It will be shown in appendix A3 that a sufficient condition for this to hold is

$$|p(x)| = \mathrm{O}(x^{\alpha}),\ \alpha > 0. \tag{9.17}$$

Equation (9.17) however follows immediately from (9.13) and (9.2) and is thus always satisfied under our assumptions. For $\varphi(x)$ one has the expression

$$\varphi(x) = (2\pi i)^{-1}\, x^{-1} \int_{-i\infty+\delta}^{+i\infty+\delta} \hat{\varphi}'(s)\, e^{sx}\, \mathrm{d}s,\ \delta > 0 \tag{9.18}$$

which is independent of δ. It is also shown in A3 that the behaviour of $\varphi(x)$ near the origin is given by

$$\varphi(x) = \mathrm{O}(x^{\alpha-1}),\ \alpha > 0 \tag{9.19}$$

(see footnote on page 508).

The constant N_0 must still be determined. Substituting (9.10) in (9.9) and using (9.12) one finds

$$\int_0^{\infty} \varphi(x)\, \mathrm{d}x = 1 - N_0. \tag{9.20}$$

Remembering that $\int_0^{\infty} \varphi(x)\, \mathrm{d}x = \hat{\varphi}(0)$ one obtains from (9.16) and (9.20)

$$N_0 = \exp\left(- \int_0^{\infty} p(x)\, x^{-1}\, \mathrm{d}x\right)$$

or, from (9.13) and (9.4),

$$N_0 = \exp\left(- \bar{G}_0'(\varepsilon_0)\right). \tag{9.21}$$

Finally, Cauchy's theorem gives rise to the following expression of $\psi(z)$ in terms of $\varphi(x)$

$$\psi(z) = \int_0^{\infty} \mathrm{d}\xi\, \varphi(\xi)(\xi - z)^{-1}. \tag{9.22}$$

By direct substitution it is now easily shown that (9.10) actually represents a solution of (9.7) if for N_0 and $\psi(z)$ we adopt the expressions just found. The solution of the integral equation (8.4) is now completed. The result reads, by (9.6),

$$D_0(z) = \frac{\exp\left(- \bar{G}_0'(\varepsilon_0)\right)}{\varepsilon_0 - \bar{G}_0(\varepsilon_0) - z} + \int_0^{\infty} \mathrm{d}\xi \frac{\varphi(\xi)}{\xi - z + \varepsilon_0 - \bar{G}_0(\varepsilon_0)} \tag{9.23}$$

where $\varphi(x)$, by (9.18) and (9.16), is explicitly expressed in terms of $p(x) = \bar{J}_0(\varepsilon_0 + x)/x$. It also contains the factor $N_0 = \exp\left(- \bar{G}_0'(\varepsilon_0)\right)$.

Equation (9.23) gives an explicit expression for $D_0(z)$ in terms of $\bar{G}_0(\varepsilon_0)$, $\bar{G}_0'(\varepsilon_0)$ and $\bar{J}_0(\varepsilon_0 + x)$, quantities which, for large Ω, are all proportional to Ω. Let us analyse our results in more detail, in particular for the pole of $D_0(z)$.

As shown in section 5 the pole of $D_0(z)$ is the energy E_0 of the perturbed ground state $|\psi_0\rangle$. From (9.23) we obtain its expression in very simple terms

$$E_0 = \varepsilon_0 - \bar{G}_0\,(\varepsilon_0). \tag{9.24}$$

As was to be expected the energy shift $\Delta E_0 = - \bar{G}_0(\varepsilon_0)$ and consequently the perturbed energy E_0 are proportional to Ω for large Ω. This important result is established to general order in the perturbation. It will be commented upon later. On the basis of (8.3) the energy shift can be written

$$\Delta E_0 = \\ = -\langle\varphi_0|[-V+V(H_0-\varepsilon_0)^{-1}V-V(H_0-\varepsilon_0)^{-1}V(H_0-\varepsilon_0)^{-1}V+\ldots]_C|\varphi_0\rangle. \quad (9.25)$$

This formula was recently derived by Goldstone [5]), who used an adiabatic switching-on of the interaction and a time-dependent perturbation method. A slightly different formula is obtained by summing the contributions of all diagrams that can be reduced to the same irreducible form, thus replacing (8.3) by (8.5). It reads

$$\Delta E_0 = - \langle\varphi_0|[-V+V\,\bar{D}(\varepsilon_0)V-V\bar{D}(\varepsilon_0)V\bar{D}(\varepsilon_0)V+\ldots]_{\iota dC}|\varphi_0\rangle. \quad (9.26)$$

One should note that the ground state energy shift is the only quantity for which the Ω-dependence was studied before to general order in the perturbation. The argument used to this end by Goldstone does not extend to the investigation of other quantities. As we shall see in the following, our method is of much greater generality.

The residue of the function $D_0(z)$ at its pole is $-N_0$. The Ω-dependence of this quantity is not linear but, as follows from (9.21), exponential. This is in accordance with the remark in section 8 that terms of arbitrarily high powers in Ω occur in the expansion of $D_0(z)$. As seen from equation (5.9) the factor $N_0^{\frac{1}{2}}$ is a normalization constant for the wave function $|\psi_0\rangle$. In fact, N_0 is the probability that one finds the actual ground state $|\psi_0\rangle$ in the state $|\varphi_0\rangle$. That this factor should decrease exponentially with the size of the system can be understood on the basis of the same general arguments sometimes used to explain why the total energy of a large system is proportional to its volume. One subdivides the system in a large number of identical cells, themselves large enough for the interactions across cell boundaries to be negligible. Just as the total energy is then approximately the sum of the energies of the individual cells and consequently proportional to the size of the system, the total wave function takes the form of a product and must therefore depend exponentially on the size.

10. *Energies of excited states.* We shall now turn to the determination of $D_\alpha(z)$ for a state different from the ground state. Taking in (8.1) the diagonal element for a state $|\alpha\rangle \neq |\varphi_0\rangle$ one finds

$$D_\alpha(\varepsilon_0 + z) = \bar{D}_\alpha(\varepsilon_0 + z) * D_0(\varepsilon_0 + z), \quad (10.1)$$

where, as defined in section 8, $\bar{D}_\alpha(z)$ is the sum of the contributions to $D_\alpha(z)$ of all diagrams which do not contain ground state components. This equation determines $D_\alpha(\varepsilon_0 + z)$ in terms of $D_0(\varepsilon_0 + z)$ and $\bar{D}_\alpha(\varepsilon_0 + z)$, thus leading us to a study of the function $\bar{D}_\alpha(\varepsilon_0 + z)$.

Applying the methods of section 4 and taking into account that only diagrams without ground state components are involved, we derive, in exactly the same way as (4.2), the formula

$$\bar{D}_\alpha(\varepsilon_0 + z) = (\varepsilon_\alpha' - z)^{-1} + (\varepsilon_\alpha' - z)^{-1}[-V + V\bar{D}(\varepsilon_0 + z)V - \ldots]_{idL}(\alpha)\bar{D}_\alpha(\varepsilon_0 + z),$$

where $\varepsilon_\alpha' = \varepsilon_\alpha - \varepsilon_0$.

The subscript *idL* means that only irreducible diagonal diagrams without ground state components contribute. The L stands for "linked clusters", an expression used by Brueckner, e.a., to indicate contributions from diagrams without ground state components. Defining

$$\bar{G}_\alpha(\varepsilon_0 + z) = [-V + V\bar{D}(\varepsilon_0 + z)V - \ldots]_{idL}(\alpha) \tag{10.2}$$

one obtains for $\bar{D}_\alpha(\varepsilon_0 + z)$ the expression

$$\bar{D}_\alpha(\varepsilon_0 + z) = (\varepsilon_\alpha' - z - \bar{G}_\alpha(\varepsilon_0 + z))^{-1}, \tag{10.3}$$

which has just the same form as (5.1).

The considerations of section 6 tell us that $\bar{G}_\alpha(\varepsilon_0 + z)$ and $\bar{D}_\alpha(\varepsilon_0 + z)$, being defined by means of diagrams without ground state components, have a finite limit for $\Omega \to \infty$. We see here clearly the important advance made with respect to chapter II. While in the developments of chapter II we were forced to keep Ω finite in order to avoid the occurrence of infinite quantities, we can here in the expressions of $\bar{D}_\alpha(\varepsilon_0 + z)$ and $\bar{G}_\alpha(\varepsilon_0 + z)$ carry out completely the limit $\Omega \to \infty$. In this limit $\bar{G}_\alpha(\varepsilon_0 + z)$ has no poles as can be concluded from (10.2). There will be one or more cuts in the complex plane along the real axis. Exactly as for $D_\alpha(z)$ and $G_\alpha(z)$ we have

$$\bar{G}_\alpha(z^*) = \bar{G}_\alpha(z)^* \text{ and } \bar{D}_\alpha(z^*) = \bar{D}_\alpha(z)^*.$$

If we define the real functions $\bar{K}_\alpha(x)$ and $\bar{J}_\alpha(x)$ of the real variable x by the equation

$$\lim_{\eta\to 0} \bar{G}_\alpha(x + i\eta) = \bar{K}_\alpha(x) + i\bar{J}_\alpha(x)\ ;\ \eta > 0, \tag{10.4}$$

the above relations imply

$$\lim_{\eta\to 0} \bar{G}_\alpha(x - i\eta) = \bar{K}_\alpha(x) - i\bar{J}_\alpha(x)\ ;\ \eta > 0, \tag{10.5}$$

The singular points of $\bar{G}_\alpha(\varepsilon_0 + z)$ on the real axis are the points where $\bar{J}_\alpha(\varepsilon_0 + x) \neq 0$. Equation (10.3) shows that these points will also be singularities of $\bar{D}_\alpha(\varepsilon_0 + z)$. In addition $\bar{D}_\alpha(\varepsilon_0 + z)$ can have a pole, when the equation

$$\varepsilon_\alpha' - x - \bar{K}_\alpha(\varepsilon_0 + x) = 0 \tag{10.6}$$

has a root in the neighbourhood of which $\bar{J}_\alpha(\varepsilon_0 + x) = 0$. Equation (10.6) has at least one and in most cases it has only one root $\bar{E}_\alpha$; for simplicity we assume the latter to be the case. The present section, as well as sections 12 and 13 hereafter, deal with the case that this point $\bar{E}_\alpha$is a pole of $\bar{D}_\alpha(\varepsilon_0 + z)$. For $\bar{E}_\alpha$ to be a true pole of $\bar{D}_\alpha(\varepsilon + z)$ one must have $\bar{J}_\alpha(\varepsilon_0 + x) = 0$ in a neighbourhood of $\bar{E}_\alpha$. This condition is, however, too strong for our purpose. It will be enough to assume that $\bar{J}_\alpha$ satisfies for small x the relation

$$\bar{J}_\alpha(\varepsilon_0 + \bar{E}_\alpha + x) = O(|x|^{1+\alpha}) \text{ with } \alpha > 0. \tag{10.7}$$

Under this circumstance we still call $\bar{E}_\alpha$ a pole of the function $\bar{D}_\alpha(\varepsilon_0 + z)$. The condition (10.7) is sufficient for the finiteness of $\bar{G}_\alpha(\varepsilon_0 + z)$ and its derivative $\bar{G}'_\alpha(\varepsilon_0 + z)$ at $\bar{E}_\alpha$. From (10.6) and (10.7) we also notice

$$\bar{E}_\alpha = \varepsilon'_\alpha - \bar{G}_\alpha(\varepsilon_0 + \bar{E}_\alpha). \tag{10.8}$$

The residue of $\bar{D}_\alpha(\varepsilon_0 + z)$ at $\bar{E}_\alpha$ we denote by $-\bar{N}_\alpha$. It follows easily from (10.3) that

$$\bar{N}_\alpha^{-1} = 1 + \bar{G}'_\alpha(\varepsilon_0 + \bar{E}_\alpha). \tag{10.9}$$

Equation (10.1) enables us to express the pole $E_\alpha - \varepsilon_0$ and the residue $-N_\alpha$ of $D_\alpha(\varepsilon_0+z)$ in the corresponding quantities of $\bar{D}_\alpha(\varepsilon_0+z)$ and $D_0(\varepsilon_0+z)$. We must simply add up the poles of $\bar{D}_\alpha(\varepsilon_0 + z)$ and $D_0(\varepsilon_0 + z)$ to find the pole of $D_\alpha(\varepsilon_0 + z)$, whereas the residue of $D_\alpha(\varepsilon_0 + z)$ is minus the product of the residues of $\bar{D}_\alpha(\varepsilon_0 + z)$, and $D_0(\varepsilon_0 + z)$. This leads to the equations

$$N_\alpha = N_0 \cdot \bar{N}_\alpha, \tag{10.10}$$

and

$$E_\alpha = E_0 + \bar{E}_\alpha. \tag{10.11}$$

It can furthermore be shown that the relation (10.7) implies that the discontinuity of $\bar{D}_\alpha(\varepsilon_0 + z)$ at a point x of the real axis in the neighbourhood of $\bar{E}_\alpha$ behaves like $O(|x - \bar{E}_\alpha|^{\alpha-1})$ and that by (10.1) the same holds for the discontinuity of $D_\alpha(z)$ in the neighbourhood of E_α. We shall forgo the proof. These facts imply that we are justified in calling $\bar{E}_\alpha$ and E_α poles (see the footnote on page 508).

The inequality (5.2) for $D_\alpha(z)$ and $D_0(z)$ implies that both $N_\alpha$and N_0 are positive quantities. Hence (10.10) shows that also $\bar{N}_\alpha > 0$.

We shall now discuss the physical significance of the result (10.11). In section 5 we saw that the pole E_α of $D_\alpha(z)$ represents the energy of the perturbed states $|\psi_\alpha\rangle^\pm$ which, through the influence of the perturbation, originate from the unperturbed state $|\alpha\rangle$ with energy ε_α. Equation (10.11) shows that $\bar{E}_\alpha$ represents the energy of the system in the state $|\psi_\alpha\rangle^\pm$ as compared with the energy E_0 of the perturbed ground state $|\psi_0\rangle$, *i.e.* $\bar{E}_\alpha$ is the excitation energy of $|\psi_\alpha\rangle^\pm$. From the Ω-independence of $\bar{D}_\alpha(\varepsilon_0 + z)$, the energy $\bar{E}_\alpha$ is independent of the size of the system, in agreement with physical expectation. We thus see that $\bar{E}_\alpha$ is not only a convenient auxiliary quantity, but that it also has a simple and direct physical meaning. In field theory in particular, where the true (perturbed) energy E_0 of the vacuum is not measurable, $\bar{E}_\alpha$ is the only energy of physical interest.

An important remark must be added concerning the case where the state $|\alpha\rangle$ involves several particles or holes. The diagonal diagrams contributing to $\bar{D}_\alpha(\varepsilon_0 + z)$ for such states are not connected. An example is shown in figure 2. The diagram c represents a contribution to $\bar{D}_\alpha(\varepsilon_0 + z)$ where $|\alpha\rangle$ is a state of two particles. As seen in section 3 the diagonal diagrams of states containing several particles and holes are always composed of diagonal diagrams of one-particle-states and one-hole-states. Let us, to be more explicit, take the state $|\alpha\rangle = |k_1 k_2\ ;\ \rangle$, and consider $\bar{D}_\alpha(\varepsilon_0 + z)$. Each diagram is composed of a diagonal diagram of the state $|k_1\ ;\ \rangle$, and a diagonal diagram of $|k_2\ ;\ \rangle$. Applying (7.4), and summing over all possible diagrams one gets

$$\bar{D}_\alpha(\varepsilon_0 + z) = \bar{D}_{k_1}(\varepsilon_0 + z) * \bar{D}_{k_2}(\varepsilon_0 + z), \tag{10.12}$$

where $\bar{D}_k(\varepsilon_0 + z)$ denotes the function $\bar{D}_\gamma(\varepsilon_0 + z)$ for $|\gamma\rangle = |k\ ;\ \rangle$. Repeating the arguments which led to (10.10) and (10.11) one finds from (10.12)

$$\bar{N}_\alpha = \bar{N}_{k_1} \bar{N}_{k_2},\quad \bar{E}_\alpha = \bar{E}_{k_1} + \bar{E}_{k_2}. \tag{10.13}$$

The last equation expresses the additivity of the perturbed excitation energies of the two particles. It is clear that our argument extends to states with an arbitrary number of particles and holes.

Chapter V. The perturbed wave functions

11. *The wave function of the ground state.* In this and the following sections we are concerned with the application of the considerations of chapter III to the calculation of wave functions. We have learned in section 5 that to each unperturbed state $|\alpha\rangle$, such that $D_\alpha(z)$ has a pole E_α, can be associated two perturbed stationary states $|\psi_\alpha\rangle^\pm$ respectively characterized by the outgoing and incoming nature of the scattered waves. For such a state $|\alpha\rangle$, according to (5.7), the matrix element $\langle\beta\,|R(z)|\,\alpha\rangle$ can be written as a product of two factors. The second factor is $D_\alpha(z)$ and has a pole E_α, whereas the first factor has a cut on the real axis running from a point B to $+\infty$. For most states $|\alpha\rangle$, $B < E_\alpha$ and E_α is not a proper pole of the function $\langle\beta\,|R(z)|\,\alpha\rangle$. Instead of one, there are two residues in such a point E_α defined by

$$\mathfrak{R}^\pm_{E_\alpha}\left[\langle\beta\,|R(z)|\,\alpha\rangle\right] = \lim_{z\to E_\alpha}(z - \mathrm{E}_\alpha)\,\langle\beta\,|R(z)|\,\alpha\rangle,$$

where the plus (minus) sign must be chosen if z approaches E_α from the upper (lower) half of the complex plane. It is clear that both residues coincide if $E_\alpha < B$. Using this, slightly more general, definition of the residue we found in section 5 that the wave functions

$$|\psi_\alpha\rangle^\pm = -\,N_\alpha^{-\frac{1}{2}}\,\mathfrak{R}^\pm_{E_\alpha}\left[R(z)\,|\alpha\rangle\right] \tag{11.1}$$

are normalized eigenfunctions of $H = H_0 + V$.

We now write this equation in an alternative form. We define the operator

$$A_\alpha(z) = \int_\beta \langle\beta\,|R(z)|\,\alpha\rangle \,.\, A_\beta, \tag{11.2}$$

where A_β is for each $|\beta\rangle$ the ordered product of creation operators such that $A_\beta\,|\varphi_0\rangle = |\beta\rangle$. Applying (11.2) to $|\varphi_0\rangle$ we get the equality

$$A_\alpha(z)\,|\varphi_0\rangle = R(z)\,|\alpha\rangle. \tag{11.3}$$

$A_\alpha(z)$ contains the factor $D_\alpha(z)$ which has a pole at $z = E_\alpha$. We define the residues $\Re^{\pm}_{E_\alpha}[A_\alpha(z)]$ of $A_\alpha(z)$ (in the extended sense defined above) by taking the residues of each matrix element in the expansion (11.2). We then define the operators O^+_α and O^-_α

$$O^\pm_\alpha = -\,N_\alpha^{-\frac{1}{2}}\,\Re^{\pm}_{E_\alpha}\,[A_\alpha(z)], \tag{11.4}$$

where $-N_\alpha$ is as usual the residue of $D_\alpha(z)$ in E_α.

From (11.4) and (11.3) the formula (11.1) can be written

$$|\psi_\alpha\rangle^\pm = O^\pm_\alpha\,|\varphi_0\rangle. \tag{11.5}$$

The purpose of this section is to achieve a far-reaching simplification of (11.4) by means of the results of chapter III.

We study first the ground state wave function $|\psi_0\rangle$. Equation (5.7) for $|\alpha\rangle = |\varphi_0\rangle$ reads

$$\langle\beta\,|R(z)|\,\varphi_0\rangle = \langle\beta|[1 + \{-D(z)\,V + D(z)\,V\,D(z)\,V - \ldots\}_{ind}]\,|\varphi_0\rangle\,D_0(z). \tag{11.6}$$

The intermediate states $|\gamma\rangle$ occurring in (11.6) are also intermediate states in the expression for $G_0(z)$, which one obtains from (4.3) by taking the diagonal matrix element for $|\varphi_0\rangle$. Furthermore, according to section 5, the fact that E_0 is a pole of $D_0(z)$ implies that $G_0(z)$ is single-valued at the point E_0. This requires, as was shown in H I, that for none of the intermediate states $|\gamma\rangle$ under consideration the cut of $D_\gamma(z)$ would extend through E_0. Consequently the cut of the first factor on the right-hand side of (11.6) does not extend through E_0. In other words $E_0 \leqslant B$. Accordingly the matrix element $\langle\beta\,|R(z)|\,\varphi_0\rangle$ and the operator

$$A_0(z) = \int_\beta \langle\beta\,|R(z)|\,\varphi_0\rangle\,A_\beta$$

have only one residue, whether calculated from the upper half or the lower half of the z-plane. Hence

$$|\psi_0\rangle = O_0\,|\varphi_0\rangle, \tag{11.7}$$

where

$$O_0 = -\,N_0^{-\frac{1}{2}}\,\Re_{E_0}\,[A_0(z)]. \tag{11.8}$$

$A_0(z)$ can be written

$$A_0(z) = D_0(z) + \int{}'\,\langle\beta\,|R(z)|\,\varphi_0\rangle\,A_\beta, \tag{11.9}$$

where the sum extends over all states $|\beta\rangle$ except $|\varphi_0\rangle$. Replacing z by $\varepsilon_0 + z$ and applying (8.1) to the matrix element $\langle\beta\,|R(\varepsilon_0 + z)|\,\varphi_0\rangle$ we obtain the formula

$$A_0(\varepsilon_0 + z) = \bar{A}_0(\varepsilon_0 + z) * D_0(\varepsilon_0 + z), \tag{11.10}$$

where $\bar{A}_0(\varepsilon_0 + z)$ is defined by

$$\bar{A}_0(\varepsilon_0 + z) = -1/z + \textstyle\int' \langle\beta\,|\bar{R}(\varepsilon_0 + z)|\,\varphi_0\rangle\, A_\beta. \tag{11.11}$$

The matrix element $\langle\beta\,|\bar{R}(\varepsilon_0 + z)|\,\varphi_0\rangle$ for $|\beta\rangle \neq |\varphi_0\rangle$ was defined in section 8 as the sum of the contributions to $\langle\beta\,|R(\varepsilon_0 + z)|\,\varphi_0\rangle$ of all diagrams, which do not contain ground state components.

Applying the methods of section 4 it is easy to express $\langle\beta\,|\bar{R}(\varepsilon_0 + z)|\,\varphi_0\rangle$ in terms of irreducible diagrams only. One finds, remembering that $|\beta\rangle \neq |\varphi_0\rangle$,

$$\langle\beta\,|\bar{R}(\varepsilon_0 + z)|\,\varphi_0\rangle =$$

$$= \langle\beta|\,[-\bar{D}(\varepsilon_0+z)\,V + \bar{D}(\varepsilon_0+z)\,V\bar{D}(\varepsilon_0+z)\,V - \ldots]_{iL}\,|\varphi_0\rangle\,(-z)^{-1}, \tag{11.12}$$

where the subscript iL means that one should take only irreducible diagrams without ground state components. Instead of the factor D_0 at the extreme right of (11.6), one finds in (11.12) the factor $(-z)^{-1}$. This shows that $\langle\beta\,|\bar{R}(\varepsilon_0 + z)\,|\varphi_0\rangle$ has a pole in the origin, and the same holds true for $\bar{A}_0(\varepsilon_0 + z)$, as seen from (11.11). From (11.10) $A_0(\varepsilon_0 + z)$ is obtained by convolution of $\bar{A}_0(\varepsilon_0 + z)$ and $D_0(\varepsilon_0 + z)$. The latter functions have poles at $z = 0$ and $z = E_0 - \varepsilon_0$, and these poles determine the pole of $A_0(\varepsilon_0 + z)$ at $E_0 - \varepsilon_0$. Consequently the residue of $A_0(\varepsilon_0 + z)$ at its pole $E_0 - \varepsilon_0$ is simply minus the product of the residues of $\bar{A}_0(\varepsilon_0 + z)$, and $D_0(\varepsilon_0 + z)$. This gives the formula

$$\mathfrak{R}_{E_0}\,[A_0(z)] = N_0\,\mathfrak{R}_0\,[\bar{A}_0(\varepsilon_0 + z)]. \tag{11.13}$$

Defining the operator $\bar{O}_0$ by

$$\bar{O}_0 = -\,\mathfrak{R}_0\,[\bar{A}_0(\varepsilon_0 + z)], \tag{11.14}$$

we get from (11.8) and (11.13)

$$O_0 = N_0^{\frac{1}{2}}\,.\,\bar{O}_0. \tag{11.15}$$

This formula already presents an important simplification with respect to (11.8), inasmuch as the definition of $\bar{O}_0$ only involves diagrams without ground state components.

Equation (11.15) is equivalent to a result derived recently by Goldstone [5]). To show the equivalence we write (11.11) in a more explicit form using (3.5).

$$\bar{A}_0(\varepsilon_0 + z)\,|\varphi_0\rangle =$$

$$=[1-(H_0-\varepsilon_0-z)^{-1}\,V+(H_0-\varepsilon_0-z)^{-1}\,V(H_0-\varepsilon_0-z)^{-1}\,V-\ldots]_L\,|\varphi_0\rangle\,(-z)^{-1}$$

which, together with (11.14) and (11.15), gives

$$|\psi_0\rangle = N_0^{\frac{1}{2}}\,[1 - (H_0-\varepsilon_0)^{-1}V + (H_0-\varepsilon_0)^{-1}V(H_0-\varepsilon_0)^{-1}V - \ldots]_L|\varphi_0\rangle. \quad (11.16)$$

The subscript L excludes diagrams with ground state components. This equation is, except for the normalization factor $N_0^{\frac{1}{2}}$, identical with eq. (3.2) of Goldstone's paper.

We now proceed to derive a still simpler expression for O_0. We notice that the diagrams occurring in the definition of $\bar{A}_0(\varepsilon_0 + z)$ are, in general, not connected. They can be composed of an arbitrary number of components, each of which has external lines at the left end. We define the operator

$$\tilde{A}_0(\varepsilon_0 + z) = \textstyle\int_\beta' \langle\beta|\, \tilde{R}(\varepsilon_0 + z)|\, \varphi_0\rangle\, A_\beta, \quad (11.17)$$

where $\langle\beta\,|\tilde{R}(\varepsilon_0 + z)|\,\varphi_0\rangle$ is the sum of all connected diagrams contributing to the matrix element $\langle\beta\,|R(\varepsilon_0 + z)|\,\varphi_0\rangle$, for $|\beta\rangle \neq |\varphi_0\rangle$. In exactly the same way as (11.12) we derive for $|\beta\rangle \neq |\varphi_0\rangle$ the formula

$$\langle\beta\,|\tilde{R}(\varepsilon_0 + z)|\,\varphi_0\rangle =$$

$$= \bar{D}_\beta(\varepsilon_0 + z)\,\langle\beta\,|[-V + V\bar{D}(\varepsilon_0 + z)V - \ldots]_{iC}|\,\varphi_0\rangle\,(-z)^{-1}, \quad (11.18)$$

where the subscript iC means that one sums over the contributions of irreducible connected diagrams only. As we see $\langle\beta\,|\tilde{R}(\varepsilon_0 + z)|\,\varphi_0\rangle$ has a pole in the origin, and by (11.17) the same holds for $\tilde{A}_0(\varepsilon_0 + z)$. We now define the operator $\tilde{O}_0$ by

$$\tilde{O}_0 = -\,\Re_0\,[\tilde{A}_0(\varepsilon_0 + z)]. \quad (11.19)$$

Just as before for O_0 and $\bar{O}_0$, the residue is unique. Using (11.17) and (11.18) we can write (11.19) in a more explicit form

$$\tilde{O}_0 = \textstyle\int_\beta' \langle\beta\,|[-\bar{D}(\varepsilon_0)\,V + \bar{D}(\varepsilon_0)\,V\,\bar{D}(\varepsilon_0)\,V - \ldots]_{iC}\,|\varphi_0\rangle\,.\,A_\beta, \quad (11.20)$$

where the sum is extended over all states $|\beta\rangle \neq |\varphi_0\rangle$.

Only connected diagrams contribute to $\tilde{O}_0$. This class of diagrams is much smaller than the class of all diagrams without ground state components, which we had to use in the expression of $\bar{O}_0$. Still, as we shall see now, $\bar{O}_0$ can be expressed very simply in terms of $\tilde{O}_0$. We write

$$\bar{A}_0(\varepsilon_0 + z) = \textstyle\sum_{\nu=0}^{\infty} A_\nu, \quad (11.21)$$

where A_ν is the sum of the contributions of all diagrams of $\bar{A}_0(\varepsilon_0 + z)$ containing exactly ν components. From (11.11) and (11.17) follows immediately that $A_0 = -\,z^{-1}$ and $A_1 = \tilde{A}_0\,(\varepsilon_0 + z)$. Let us calculate A_2. Consider all diagrams which are composed of a diagram of $\langle\beta'\,|\tilde{R}(\varepsilon_0 + z)|\,\varphi_0\rangle$ and a diagram of $\langle\beta''\,|\tilde{R}(\varepsilon_0 + z)|\,\varphi_0\rangle$. These diagrams have two components and their contribution to A_2 is given by

$$\langle\beta'\,|\tilde{R}(\varepsilon_0 + z)|\,\varphi_0\rangle * \langle\beta''\,|\tilde{R}(\varepsilon_0 + z)|\,\varphi_0\rangle\,A_{\beta'}A_{\beta''},$$

as follows immediately from the fundamental formula (7.4). Summing this expression over all states $|\beta'\rangle$ and $|\beta''\rangle$ distinct from $|\varphi_0\rangle$ we get

$$A_2 = \tfrac{1}{2}\tilde{A}_0(\varepsilon_0 + z) * \tilde{A}_0(\varepsilon_0 + z).$$

The factor $\frac{1}{2}$ arises from the fact that in the summation over $|\beta'\rangle$ and $|\beta''\rangle$ each diagram of A_2 is counted twice. The diagrams of A_3 can be obtained by the combination of a diagram of A_2 with a diagram of A_1. Another factor $\frac{1}{3}$ must be added to compensate for redundant counting and one gets

$$A_3 = \tfrac{1}{6}\tilde{A}_0(\varepsilon_0 + z) * \tilde{A}_0(\varepsilon_0 + z) * \tilde{A}_0(\varepsilon_0 + z).$$

Continuing in the same way we get generally

$$A_\nu = (\nu!)^{-1}\, \tilde{A}_0(\varepsilon_0 + z) * \tilde{A}_0(\varepsilon_0 + z) * \ldots\ldots * \tilde{A}_0(\varepsilon_0 + z),$$

with ν factors $\tilde{A}_0(\varepsilon_0 + z)$ in the convolution. If we now take the residue in $z = 0$ of each term in the expansion (11.21) we find

$$\bar{O}_0 = 1 + \tilde{O}_0 + \tilde{O}_0^2/2! + \tilde{O}_0^3/3! + \ldots\ldots,$$

a result which reduces to the compact form

$$\bar{O}_0 = \exp\,(\tilde{O}_0). \tag{11.22}$$

Inserting this in (11.15) we obtain the important result

$$O_0 = N_0^{\frac{1}{2}} \exp\,(\tilde{O}_0) = \exp\,(-\tfrac{1}{2}\bar{G}_0'(\varepsilon_0) + \tilde{O}_0), \tag{11.23}$$

where $\tilde{O}_0$ is given by (11.20) and where the value (9.21) of N_0 has been used.

The derivations of (11.15) and (11.23) are actually valid for a finite but very large volume Ω. The operators $\bar{O}_0$ and $\tilde{O}_0$ are defined by means of diagrams which do not contain ground state components.

In section 6 we have shown that the contributions of such diagrams have a finite limit for $\Omega \to \infty$. This means that in the expansion of $\bar{O}_0\,|\varphi_0\rangle$ or of $\tilde{O}_0^\nu\,|\varphi_0\rangle$, $\nu = 1, 2, \ldots$, in unperturbed states all coefficients have a finite limit. Owing however to the large number of terms in the expansion the norm of $\tilde{O}_0^\nu\,|\varphi_0\rangle$ is large as $\Omega^{\nu/2}$, while the norm of $\bar{O}_0\,|\varphi_0\rangle$ is exponentially large for $\Omega \to \infty$. As seen from (11.15) this behaviour is compensated in (11.23) by the normalization factor $N_0^{\frac{1}{2}}$, which approaches zero exponentially in the limit $\Omega \to \infty$. In fact we saw before that $\bar{G}_0'(\varepsilon_0)$ is proportional to Ω for large Ω.

12. *Wave functions of excited states.* Having determined O_0 in terms of contributions of connected diagrams we turn to an analysis of $O_\alpha^\pm$ where $|\alpha\rangle \neq |\varphi_0\rangle$ is a state such that $D_\alpha(z)$ has a pole E_α. $O_\alpha^\pm$ is defined by (11.4). Let us consider an arbitrary diagram of $\langle\beta\,|R(\varepsilon_0 + z)|\,\alpha\rangle$. It contains one or more components with external lines at the right end, and other components without such lines. Diagrams composed only of components of the latter type give contributions to $\langle\beta'\,|R(\varepsilon_0 + z)|\,\varphi_0\rangle$. On the other hand we

can take together all diagrams of $\langle\beta''\,|R(\varepsilon_0+z)|\,\alpha\rangle$, all components of which have one or more external lines at their right end. The sum of the contributions of these diagrams we denote by $\langle\beta''\,|\hat{R}(\varepsilon_0+z)|\,\alpha\rangle$.

Consider all diagrams which are composed of a diagram of $\langle\beta'|\,R(\varepsilon_0+z)\,|\varphi_0\rangle$ and a diagram of $\langle\beta''\,|\hat{R}(\varepsilon_0+z)|\,\alpha\rangle$. These diagrams contribute to the matrix element $\langle\beta'\beta''\,|R(\varepsilon_0+z)|\,\alpha\rangle$ where $|\beta'\beta''\rangle = A_{\beta'}\,.\,A_{\beta''}|\,\varphi_0\rangle$. Their contribution is, as follows immediately from (7.4),

$$\langle\beta'\,|R(\varepsilon_0+z)|\,\varphi_0\rangle * \langle\beta''\,|\hat{R}(\varepsilon_0+z)|\,\alpha\rangle. \tag{12.1}$$

The operator $A_\alpha(\varepsilon_0+z)$, defined by (11.2), can now be written

$$A_\alpha(\varepsilon+z) = \textstyle\int_{\beta'\beta''}\langle\beta'\beta''\,|R(\varepsilon_0+z)|\alpha\rangle\,A_{\beta'}A_{\beta''} =$$
$$= \textstyle\int_{\beta'\beta''}\langle\beta'\,|R(\varepsilon_0+z)|\,\varphi_0\rangle * \langle\beta''\,|\hat{R}(\varepsilon_0+z)|\,\alpha\rangle\,A_{\beta'}A_{\beta''}. \tag{12.2}$$

Defining the operator

$$\hat{A}_\alpha(\varepsilon_0+z) = \textstyle\int_\beta\langle\beta|\hat{R}(\varepsilon_0+z)|\,\alpha\rangle\,A_\beta \tag{12.3}$$

we obtain for equation (12.2) the simple form

$$A_\alpha(\varepsilon_0+z) = \hat{A}_\alpha(\varepsilon_0+z) * A_0(\varepsilon_0+z). \tag{12.4}$$

We must now study the matrix element $\langle\beta\,|\hat{R}(\varepsilon_0+z)|\,\alpha\rangle$ in somewhat more detail. All diagrams with ground state components are excluded from its definition. By the methods of section 4 we can easily express $\langle\beta\,|\hat{R}(\varepsilon_0+z)\,|\alpha\rangle$ in terms of contributions of irreducible diagrams. The formula we obtain reads

$$\langle\beta\,|\hat{R}(\varepsilon_0+z)|\,\alpha\rangle =$$
$$\langle\beta|[1+\{-\bar{D}(\varepsilon_0+z)\,V+\bar{D}(\varepsilon_0+z)\,V\,\bar{D}(\varepsilon_0+z)\,V-\ldots\}_{indR}]\,|\alpha\rangle\,\bar{D}_\alpha(\varepsilon_0+z), \tag{12.5}$$

where $|\alpha\rangle \neq |\varphi_0\rangle$. The subscript *indR* indicates restriction to irreducible non-diagonal diagrams, all components of which have at least one external line at the right-hand side. We see, from (12.5), that $\langle\beta\,|\hat{R}(\varepsilon_0+z)|\,\alpha\rangle$ contains the factor $\bar{D}_\alpha(\varepsilon_0+z)$, which has a pole $\bar{E}_\alpha$. The other factor on the right-hand side of (12.5) has a cut along the real axis; in most cases this factor is double-valued at the point $\bar{E}_\alpha$, giving exactly the same situation as met before with $\langle\beta\,|R(\varepsilon_0+z)|\,\alpha\rangle$. In (12.2) we have the convolution

$$\langle\beta'\,|R(\varepsilon_0+z)|\,\varphi_0\rangle * \langle\beta''\,|\hat{R}(\varepsilon_0+z)|\,\alpha\rangle.$$

The residue of this expression at its pole $E_\alpha - \varepsilon_0$ is

$$\mathfrak{R}^{\pm}_{\bar{E}_\alpha-\varepsilon_0}[\langle\beta'\,|R(\varepsilon_0+z)|\,\varphi_0\rangle * \langle\beta''|\,\hat{R}(\varepsilon_0+z)\,|\alpha\rangle] =$$
$$= -\,\mathfrak{R}^{\pm}_{\bar{E}_\alpha}[\langle\beta''\,|\hat{R}(\varepsilon_0+z)|\,\alpha\rangle]\,\mathfrak{R}_{E_0-\varepsilon_0}[\langle\beta'\,|R(\varepsilon_0+z)|\,\varphi_0\rangle],$$

where we have used $\bar{E}_\alpha = E_\alpha - E_0$. Inserting this in (12.2) we find with the definitions (11.2) and (12.3)

$$\mathfrak{R}^{\pm}_{\bar{E}_\alpha}[A_\alpha(z)] = \mathfrak{R}^{\pm}_{\bar{E}_\alpha}[\hat{A}_\alpha(\varepsilon_0+z)]\,.\,\mathfrak{R}_{E_0}[A_0(z)]. \tag{12.6}$$

If we now define the operators $\hat{O}_\alpha^\pm$ by

$$\hat{O}_\alpha^\pm = -\,\bar{N}_\alpha^{-\frac{1}{2}}\,\mathfrak{R}_{\bar{E}_\alpha}^\pm[\hat{A}_\alpha(\varepsilon_0 + z)], \tag{12.7}$$

where $-\bar{N}_\alpha$ is the residue of $\bar{D}_\alpha(\varepsilon_0 + z)$ in $\bar{E}_\alpha$, we obtain, using (10.10), the important result

$$O_\alpha^\pm = \hat{O}_\alpha^\pm \,.\, O_0. \tag{12.8}$$

$O_\alpha^\pm$ and O_0 were defined by (11.4) and (11.8). Applying the operator equation (12.8) to $|\varphi_0\rangle$ we get

$$|\psi_\alpha\rangle^\pm = \hat{O}_\alpha^\pm\, |\psi_0\rangle. \tag{12.9}$$

This equation shows clearly the physical meaning of $\hat{O}_\alpha^\pm$. It "creates" the state $|\psi_\alpha\rangle^\pm$ from the actual (perturbed) ground state $|\psi_0\rangle$. It is the analogue, for the perturbed system, of the operator A_α which creates $|\alpha\rangle$ from $|\varphi_0\rangle$ in absence of the interaction. The importance of the operator $\hat{O}_\alpha^\pm$ is further stressed by considering the case of large systems. From the definition (12.7) and from the fact that in the calculation of $\bar{D}_\alpha(\varepsilon_0 + z)$ and $\hat{A}_\alpha(\varepsilon_0 + z)$ only diagrams without ground state components are involved, we conclude that $\hat{O}_\alpha^\pm$ has a finite limit for $\Omega \to \infty$. Although for an infinitely large system a proper expansion of $|\psi_0\rangle$ in unperturbed states strictly speaking no longer exists (remember the vanishing of N_0 for $\Omega \to \infty$ in (11.15)), the operator $\hat{O}_\alpha^\pm$, which describes the change of $|\psi_0\rangle$ introduced by the presence of particles outside the Fermi sphere and holes inside it, keeps a simple and meaningful form.

Throughout this paper we have often used a terminology inspired by the special problem of a gas of Fermi particles with interaction. As mentioned before, however, all results are of a quite general nature and are applicable to a broad range of problems. Up till now we investigated states $|\alpha\rangle$ for which the function $D_\alpha(z)$ has a pole. As will be shown elsewhere, in the theory of the Fermi gas with interaction strictly speaking no such state except $|\varphi_0\rangle$ exists. Low-lying states satisfy however this requirement with a very good approximation and the results of the present section will provide us with an excellent starting point for their study. In the quantum theory of fields, on the other hand, all states $|\alpha\rangle$ satisfy the requirement that $D_\alpha(z)$ has a pole and the whole discussion of this section is immediately applicable.

We end this section with a remark concerning one-particle-states. Let $|\alpha\rangle$ be a state differing from the unperturbed ground state $|\varphi_0\rangle$ by the presence of one single particle. Taking e.g. the case of interacting meson and nucleon fields, $|\varphi_0\rangle$ is the free vacuum and $|\alpha\rangle$ would be for example a one-nucleon-state. We denote this state by $|k\rangle$, k referring to the momentum of the particle. From (12.5) we see that the diagrams contributing to $\langle\beta\,|\hat{R}(\varepsilon_0 + z)|\,k\rangle$ are connected and have one external line at the right end. As is easily seen the intermediate states in (12.5) are the same as those occurring in the expression (10.2) for $\bar{G}_\alpha(\varepsilon_0 + z)$ if we take $|\alpha\rangle = |k\rangle$. By our assumption $\bar{D}_k(\varepsilon_0 + z)$ has a pole $\bar{E}_k$, a fact which requires that $\bar{G}_k(\varepsilon_0 + z)$ be single-valued at the point $\bar{E}_k$, *i.e.*, that the cut of $\bar{G}_k$ does not go through $\bar{E}_k$. As shown in H I, this has the consequence that the same property holds for all functions $\bar{D}_\gamma(\varepsilon_0 + z)$ belonging to states $|\gamma\rangle$ which occur as intermediate states in (10.2). We conclude that also $\langle\beta\,|\hat{R}(\varepsilon_0 + z)|\,k\rangle$, and by (12.3) $\hat{A}_k(\varepsilon_0 + z)$ are single-valued in $\bar{E}_k$. Thus we have shown that to each single particle state $|k\rangle$, such that $D_k(z)$ has a pole, the operators $\hat{O}_k^+$ and $\hat{O}_k^-$ are identical. The expression (12.9) reduces to a single stationary state

$$|\psi_k\rangle = \hat{O}_k\,|\psi_0\rangle. \tag{12.10}$$

If $|\alpha\rangle$ is a state of more than one free particle or hole the states $|\psi_\alpha\rangle^+$ and $|\psi_\alpha\rangle^-$ will in general be different. They correspond to scattering states with outgoing and incoming scattered waves respectively. This was shown in H II by an investigation of the asymptotic behaviour of wave packets for large times.

13. *Asymptotically stationary states*. In this section we shall briefly consider in the light of the diagram analysis, the theory of asymptotically stationary states as developed by Van Hove in H I and H II. It will appear that these states can be expressed very simply by means of the operators $\hat{O}_k$ introduced in the last section.

Let $|\alpha\rangle = \xi_{k_1}^* \xi_{k_2}^* \ldots\ldots \xi_{k_p}^* \,|\varphi_0\rangle$ be an unperturbed p-particle state and assume that the function $D_\alpha(z)$ has a pole E_α. Consider the state $|\psi_\alpha\rangle^{as}$ defined by

$$|\psi_\alpha\rangle^{as} = \hat{O}_{k_1}\hat{O}_{k_2} \ldots \hat{O}_{k_p}\,|\psi_0\rangle. \tag{13.1}$$

As will be shown hereafter, this state is identical with the asymptotically stationary state $|\alpha\rangle_{as}$ defined by Van Hove in H I (equation 5.12). The physical meaning of $|\psi_\alpha\rangle^{as}$ is particularly clear in field theory. It is a state of p "dressed" particles without mutual interaction. In meson-theory for example it would represent a physical situation where one has e.g., p nucleons with their surrounding cloud of mesons and nucleon-antinucleon pairs, moving independently of each other in plane wave states. Such a state is clearly not stationary, and a wave function $|\psi(t)\rangle^{as}$, defined as a linear combination

$$|\psi(t)\rangle^{as} = \textstyle\int_\alpha c_\alpha \exp\,(-iE_\alpha t)\,|\psi_\alpha\rangle^{as}, \tag{13.2}$$

is not a solution of the Schrödinger equation. It does however approach such a solution for large $|t|$. Indeed, considering the two wave functions

$$|\psi(t)\rangle^{\pm} = \textstyle\int_\alpha c_\alpha \exp\,(-iE_\alpha t)\,|\psi_\alpha\rangle^{\pm} \tag{13.3}$$

which obviously verify the Schrödinger equation, one has the following relations

$$\lim_{t\to-\infty} \mid |\psi(t)\rangle^{as} - |\psi(t)\rangle^{+}| = 0,$$
$$\lim_{t\to+\infty} \mid |\psi(t)\rangle^{as} - |\psi(t)\rangle^{-}| = 0.$$

The bars refer to the norm of the wave functions enclosed. These formulae are identical with (3.2) in H II.

All we want to do here is to establish the identity of the states (13.1) with the states $|\alpha\rangle_{as}$ in H I. From the definition (13.1) of $|\psi_\alpha\rangle^{as}$ we derive, using (12.7), (12.3) and (11.8),

$$|\psi_\alpha\rangle^{as} = -N_\alpha^{-\frac{1}{2}}\,\Re_{E\alpha-\varepsilon_0}\,[\textstyle\int_{\beta_0\beta_1\ldots\beta_p} |\beta_0\beta_1\ldots\beta_p\rangle \cdot$$
$$\langle\beta_0\,|R(\varepsilon_0+z)|\,\varphi_0\rangle * \langle\beta_1\,|\hat{R}(\varepsilon_0+z)|\,k_1\rangle * \ldots\ldots * \langle\beta_p\,|\hat{R}(\varepsilon_0+z)|\,k_p\rangle].$$

This again can be written

$$|\psi_\alpha\rangle^{as} = -N_\alpha^{-\frac{1}{2}}\,\Re_{E_\alpha}\,[R'(z)\,|\alpha\rangle], \tag{13.4}$$

where $\langle\beta\,|R'(z)|\,\alpha\rangle$ for arbitrary $|\beta\rangle$ is the sum of the contributions to $\langle\beta\,|R(z)|\,\alpha\rangle$ of all diagrams, each component of which has at most one external line at its right end. We shall call such diagrams *completely disconnected.* Substituting (4.1) in (13.4) and taking the residue in E_α one finds

$$|\psi_\alpha\rangle^{as} = N_\alpha^{\frac{1}{2}}\,[1 - D(E_\alpha)\,V + D(E_\alpha)\,V\,D(E_\alpha)\,V - \ldots]_{iD}\,|\alpha\rangle. \tag{13.5}$$

The subscript iD indicates that in calculating $|\psi_\alpha\rangle^{as}$ one should limit oneself to irreducible non-diagonal diagrams which are completely disconnected. Comparing equation (13.5) with equation (5.12) of H I one sees that they are equivalent. The projection operators Y_α in (5.12) of H I were intended to limit the intermediate states to those states which contribute to $D_\alpha(z)$. In the language of diagrams this means that only completely disconnected diagrams should be taken. The identity of the states $|\psi_\alpha\rangle^{as}$ defined in (13.1) with the states $|\alpha\rangle_{as}$ in H I is thereby established.

14. *Metastable states.* Up till now we have considered states $|\alpha\rangle$ such that $D_\alpha(z)$ has a pole in E_α. This value E_α is a root of the equation

$$\varepsilon_\alpha - x - K_\alpha(x) = 0, \tag{14.1}$$

where ε_α is the unperturbed energy and $K_\alpha(x)$ is defined by (5.4). If $J_\alpha(x)$, also defined by (5.4), vanishes in a neighbourhood of E_α (or if this quantity approaches zero sufficiently fast for $x \to E_\alpha$) the states $|\psi_\alpha\rangle^{\pm}$ defined by

$$|\psi_\alpha\rangle^{\pm} = N_\alpha^{\frac{1}{2}}\,[1 - D(E_\alpha \pm io)\,V + D(E_\alpha \pm io)\,V\,D(E_\alpha \pm io)\,V - \ldots]_i\,|\alpha\rangle, \tag{14.2}$$

where $N_\alpha^{-1} = 1 + K'_\alpha(E_\alpha)$, are stationary states.

We already mentioned that in field theory the above condition is always fulfilled. There are however many quantum mechanical systems where for some or all of the states $|\alpha\rangle \neq |\varphi_0\rangle$, one has $J_\alpha(E_\alpha) \neq 0$. By (5.5) $J_\alpha(E_\alpha)$ is then positive. Under such conditions it is still possible to define states $|\psi_\alpha\rangle^\pm$ by the relation (14.2), but these states have in general no simple physical meaning. However in the special case that $J_\alpha(E_\alpha)$ is very small, we shall see that $|\psi_\alpha\rangle^+$ still approximately behaves as a stationary state. States of this type will be called *metastable*. They are frequently encountered in the many-particle systems of statistical mechanics and play also an important role in the theory of nuclear matter. They are investigated in the present section.

According to (5.1) we can write

$$D_\alpha(z)^{-1} = \varepsilon_\alpha - z - G_\alpha(z).$$

At the point $z = E_\alpha + io$ we have $D_\alpha^{-1}(E_\alpha + io) = -\,iJ_\alpha(E_\alpha)$. We expand $D_\alpha^{-1}(z)$ in a power series of $(z - E_\alpha)$ for z in the neighbourhood of $E_\alpha + io$ and obtain in this way an analytic continuation of $D_\alpha^{-1}(z)$ from the upper to the lower half of the complex plane. Thus, to first order,

$$D_\alpha^{-1}(z) = -\,iJ_\alpha(E_\alpha) + (E_\alpha - z)(1 + G'_\alpha(E_\alpha + io)).$$

$J_\alpha(x)$ is assumed to be small for x near E_α. We put accordingly

$$G'_\alpha(E_\alpha + io) = K'_\alpha(E_\alpha)$$

and find

$$D_\alpha^{-1}(z) = N_\alpha^{-1}\,[E_\alpha - iN_\alpha J_\alpha(E_\alpha) - z], \tag{14.3}$$

with

$$N_\alpha^{-1} = 1 + K'_\alpha(E_\alpha).$$

Equation (14.3) shows that $D_\alpha(z)$, if continued analytically from above to below the real axis, has a pole

$$F_\alpha = E_\alpha - iN_\alpha J_\alpha(E_\alpha). \tag{14.4}$$

The time-dependent wave function corresponding to $|\psi_\alpha\rangle^+$ is, according to (3.3), given by

$$U(t)\,|\psi_\alpha\rangle^+ = (2\pi i)^{-1} \int_{-\infty+io}^{+\infty+io} \mathrm{d}\zeta\, R(\zeta)\, e^{-i\zeta t}\, |\psi_\alpha\rangle^+, \tag{14.5}$$

where we assume $t > 0$. This leads us to a study of the matrix element $\langle\beta\,|R(\zeta)|\,\psi_\alpha\rangle^+$ for arbitrary $|\beta\rangle$ and $\operatorname{Im}\zeta > 0$. If we apply both sides of (5.8) to the state $|\alpha\rangle$, putting $z = \zeta$, $z' = E_\alpha + io$, we get after some simple manipulations using (14.2),

$$\langle\beta\,|R(\zeta)|\,\psi_\alpha\rangle^+ =$$
$$= N_\alpha^{\frac{1}{2}}(\zeta - E_\alpha)^{-1}\,\langle\beta\,|R(\zeta)|\,\alpha\rangle\, D_\alpha^{-1}(E_\alpha + io) - (\zeta - E_\alpha)^{-1}\,\langle\beta|\psi_\alpha\rangle^+. \tag{14.6}$$

We have seen that $D_\alpha^{-1}(E_\alpha + io) = -\,iJ_\alpha(E_\alpha)$, a quantity assumed to be small. Nonetheless, owing to the singularity at $\zeta = E_\alpha$, the first term on the right-hand side cannot be neglected when inserting (14.6) in (14.5). Equation (14.6) can be rewritten as

$$\begin{aligned}\langle\beta\,|R(\zeta)|\,\psi_\alpha\rangle^+ = &- iJ_\alpha(E_\alpha)\,.\,N_\alpha^{\frac{1}{2}}\,.\,(\zeta - E_\alpha)^{-1}\,[\langle\beta\,|R(\zeta)\,D^{-1}(\zeta)|\,\alpha\rangle - \\ &- \langle\beta\,|R(E_\alpha + io)\,D_\alpha^{-1}(E_\alpha + io)|\,\alpha\rangle]\,D_\alpha(\zeta) + \\ &+ D_\alpha(\zeta)(\zeta - E_\alpha)^{-1}[D^{-1}(E_\alpha + io) - D_\alpha^{-1}(\zeta)]\,.\,\langle\beta|\psi_\alpha\rangle^+. \quad (14.7)\end{aligned}$$

It is now legitimate to drop the first term in the right-hand side. The second term no longer has a singularity at $\zeta = E_\alpha$, but its analytical continuation in the lower half of the ζ-plane has a pole at $\zeta = F_\alpha = E_\alpha - iN_\alpha J_\alpha(E_\alpha)$. Neglecting terms of the order of $J_\alpha(E_\alpha)$ we are left with

$$\langle\beta\,|R(\zeta)|\,\psi_\alpha\rangle^+ = (\zeta - E_\alpha + iN_\alpha J_\alpha(E_\alpha))^{-1}\,\langle\beta|\psi_\alpha\rangle^+, \text{ for } \operatorname{Im}\zeta > 0.$$

If we substitute this approximate result in (14.5) we find, for positive t large of order $J_\alpha(E_\alpha)^{-1}$ and arbitrary $|\beta\rangle$,

$$\langle\beta\,|U(t)|\,\psi_\alpha\rangle^+ = \exp\,(-\,iE_\alpha t - N_\alpha J_\alpha(E_\alpha)t)\,\langle\beta|\psi_\alpha\rangle^{+\,*)}. \quad (14.8)$$

This equation shows that $|\psi_\alpha\rangle^+$ is a metastable state with an energy E_α and a mean life-time $T_\alpha = 1/N_\alpha J_\alpha(E_\alpha) = 1/\Gamma_\alpha$. The quantity Γ_α plays for our case of continuous spectra a role analogous to the level width of discrete spectra. Just as we derived (14.8) we could establish for $t < 0$

$$\langle\beta|\,U(t)\,|\psi_\alpha\rangle^- = \exp\,(-\,iE_\alpha t + N_\alpha J_\alpha(E_\alpha)t)\,\langle\beta\,|\psi_\alpha\rangle^-,$$

a formula which however has little physical interest.

Before commenting upon the significance of (14.8) we shall derive, along the lines of sections 10 and 12, simpler expressions for Γ_α and $|\psi_\alpha\rangle^+$. In section 10 we introduced the function $\bar{D}_\alpha(\varepsilon_0 + z)$ which was defined by means of diagrams without ground state components. It was established that the validity of the equation $\bar{J}_\alpha(\varepsilon_0 + x) = 0$ for x in a neighbourhood of $\bar{E}_\alpha$ ($\bar{E}_\alpha$ was the root of equation (10.6)) implies $J_\alpha(x) = 0$ in a neighbourhood of E_α. In the case considered here we have clearly $\bar{J}_\alpha(\varepsilon_0 + \bar{E}_\alpha) \neq 0$, and, as we shall see below, $\bar{J}_\alpha(\varepsilon_0 + \bar{E}_\alpha)$ is positive but small. Using (9.23) and (10.1) we can write

$$D_\alpha(\varepsilon_0 + z) = N_0(E_0 - \varepsilon_0 - z)^{-1} * \bar{D}_\alpha(\varepsilon_0 + z) + \psi(\varepsilon_0 - E_0 + z) * \bar{D}_\alpha(\varepsilon_0 + z).$$

To study the singular behaviour of $D_\alpha(z)$ obtained by analytical continuation in the neighbourhood of E_α the second term on the right-hand side can be neglected and we have approximately

$$D_\alpha(z) = N_0\,\bar{D}_\alpha(\varepsilon_0 - E_0 + z) \text{ for } |z - E_\alpha| \text{ small.} \quad (14.9)$$

*) It is essential for the validity of this equation that $|\beta\rangle$ is a state with only a finite number of particles and holes.

Taking the value at $z = E_\alpha = E_0 + \bar{E}_\alpha$ we get

$$-iJ_\alpha(E_\alpha) = -iN_0\bar{J}_\alpha(\varepsilon_0 + \bar{E}_\alpha).$$

This gives the important formula

$$\Gamma_\alpha \equiv N_\alpha J_\alpha(E_\alpha) = \bar{N}_\alpha \bar{J}_\alpha(\varepsilon_0 + \bar{E}_\alpha), \tag{14.10}$$

which expresses the life-time Γ_α^{-1} in terms of diagrams without ground state components. In particular we conclude that Γ_α is independent of the volume Ω of the system, since both $\bar{N}_\alpha$ and $\bar{J}_\alpha(\varepsilon_0 + \bar{E}_\alpha)$ have this property.

The wave function $|\psi_\alpha\rangle^+$, defined by (14.2), can be written

$$|\psi_\alpha\rangle^+ = O_\alpha^+ \, |\varphi_0\rangle,$$

where

$$O_\alpha^+ = N_\alpha^{\frac{1}{2}} A_\alpha(E_\alpha + io)\, D_\alpha^{-1}(E_\alpha + io). \tag{14.11}$$

The operator $A_\alpha(z)$ was defined in section 11 by (11.2). According to (12.4) we have

$$A_\alpha(\varepsilon_0 + z) = \hat{A}_\alpha(\varepsilon_0 + z) * A_0(\varepsilon_0 + z).$$

Following exactly the same arguments as in the derivation of (14.9) we find

$$A_\alpha(z) = -\,\Re_{E_0}[A_0(z)]\, .\, \hat{A}_\alpha(\varepsilon_0 - E_0 + z), \text{ for } |z - E_\alpha| \text{ small.}$$

Substituting this expression in (14.11), one obtains, using (11.8) and (14.9),

$$O_\alpha^+ = \hat{O}_\alpha^+ \, . \, O_0, \quad |\psi_\alpha\rangle^+ = \hat{O}_\alpha^+ \, |\psi_0\rangle \tag{14.12}$$

with

$$\hat{O}_\alpha^+ = -\, i\bar{J}_\alpha(\varepsilon_0 + \bar{E}_\alpha)\, \bar{N}_\alpha^{\frac{1}{2}}\, \hat{A}_\alpha(\varepsilon_0 + \bar{E}_\alpha + io).$$

Notice that this formula, which only has an approximate validity, is exactly of the same form as (12.8).

Examples of metastable states in systems with continuous spectra, in the sense defined here, are actually well known. We mention only one, the so-called cloudy-crystal-ball model of heavy nuclei, which is meant to describe the scattering of nucleons at low energies [2]). The imaginary part of the potential, introduced in the model to describe the "absorption" of the incident nucleon in nuclear matter, (leading to compound nucleus formation) corresponds to our quantity Γ_α. In a forthcoming paper, which will deal with the application of the Fermi gas model to the problem of nuclear structure, we shall have opportunity to come back to this point in greater detail. Let us only mention here that in the Fermi gas model, states containing in addition to the Fermi sea one particle with momentum k are metastable in our sense (small Γ_α) when k is near the Fermi momentum k_F. Application of (10.12) shows immediately that states containing more additional particles are then also metastable. Furthermore it is easy to verify the approximate validity of (10.13) for the case at hand. This formula expresses now the excitation energy of a state containing several additional particles as the sum of the excitation energies of the single particles, whereas the inverse life-time of the total state becomes the sum of the individual inverse life-times. Also the considerations concerning asymptotically stationary states are approximately valid for metastable cases. The asymptotically stationary states are essential for the description of scattering processes. In H I and H II they are used to establish a formula for the S-matrix. If one is interested in collision processes in dissipative systems (e.g., collisions between two additional nucleons in nuclear matter) one can apply this S-matrix formalism provided the life-time of the metastable states is long compared to the time in which the collision takes place.

Chapter VI. Conclusion

15. *Summary of results.* We have now come to the end of our analysis and we shall briefly summarize what has been achieved. Our starting point was the resolvent operator $R(z)$ from which one can derive most of the desired information, such as energies and wave functions of stationary states and life-times of metastable states. The resolvent was expanded in powers of the perturbation, as shown in (3.5). The different contributions to each term in (3.5) were analysed by means of diagrams. In section 6 we investigated the dependence of these contributions upon the volume Ω (or the total number of particles) of the system under consideration. We found that diagrams containing a certain number n of ground state components give, in the limit of $\Omega \to \infty$, a contribution proportional to Ω^n, whereas in the same limit all other diagrams give finite contributions. Because diagrams containing any number of ground state components contribute to $R(z)$, the straight perturbation expansion (3.5) has terms with arbitrarily high powers of Ω. Clearly such an expansion is extremely inadequate for the application to large systems.

The analysis of chapters III and IV showed how this important difficulty can be overcome. On the basis of a general theorem (expressed by (7.4)) we derived the basic formula (8.1) which expresses an arbitrary matrix element $\langle\beta|R(z)|\alpha\rangle$ by means of a convolution integral involving the unperturbed ground state matrix element $\langle\varphi_0|R(z)|\varphi_0\rangle = D_0(z)$ and the matrix element $\langle\beta|\bar{R}(z)|\alpha\rangle$. The latter differs from $\langle\beta|R(z)|\alpha\rangle$ in this respect that the only diagrams contributing to $\langle\beta|\bar{R}(z)|\alpha\rangle$ are those without ground state components. Consequently $\langle\beta|\bar{R}(z)|\alpha\rangle$ is, in the limit of $\Omega \to \infty$, finite and independent of Ω. The whole Ω-dependence is thereby isolated in $D_0(z)$.

To investigate $D_0(z)$ we derived by a new application of (8.1) the integral equation (8.4). This equation can be solved explicitly, the solution being given by (9.23). It expresses $D_0(z)$ in terms of the function $\bar{G}_0(z)$. According to its definition (8.3), only connected ground state diagrams contribute to $\bar{G}_0(z)$, so that it is, for large Ω, simply proportional to Ω.

Two quantities of physical interest can be derived from $D_0(z)$. They are the pole E_0 of this function, giving the perturbed energy of the ground state, and the residue $-N_0$ in this pole. The factor $N_0^{\frac{1}{2}}$ plays the role of a normalization factor in the expansion of the exact ground state wave function $|\psi_0\rangle$ in unperturbed states. The values of E_0 and N_0 are given by (9.24) and (9.21). We see that these expressions involve only the values of $\bar{G}_0(z)$ and of its derivative at $z = \varepsilon_0$, both proportional to Ω (ε_0 is the unperturbed ground state energy). Two of our intermediate formulae, (9.25) and (11.16), which we used for the shift $\Delta E_0 = E_0 - \varepsilon_0$ of the ground state energy and for the wave function $|\psi_0\rangle$ were found recently by Goldstone [5]) who derived them from a time-dependent perturbation method originally introduced by Gell-Mann and Low [7]). These expressions differ considerably from our final formulae (9.26) and (11.23). The simplicity of (11.23) as compared to (11.16) lies in the fact that the former involves only connected diagrams. In addition the reduction of the diagrams to their irreducible form (using the method introduced by Van Hove in H I) makes our formulae much more suitable for the application to infinitely large systems. The perturbed ground state wave function is obtained by application to its unperturbed analogue of the operator (11.23) involving the exponential of a very simple operator $\tilde{O}_0$.

Going over to the consideration of excited states (*i.e.*, for the example of a Fermi gas, of states differing from the ground state by the presence of some additional particles and some holes), the main results of this paper are expressed by (10.11) and (12.9). The importance of these formulae can be expressed by saying that the excitation energy $\bar{E}_\alpha$ and the operator $\hat{O}_\alpha^\pm$ have a finite and simple limit for $\Omega \to \infty$. $\bar{E}_\alpha$ is the perturbed energy difference between excited and ground state, while $\hat{O}_\alpha^\pm$ is the operator which transforms the perturbed ground state wave function into the perturbed wave function of the excited state. As a further result we might mention formula (13.1) which gives a very concise and transparent expression for the asymptotically stationary states as defined by Van Hove in H I and H II. These states play an important role in the theory of collisions.

A striking property of many systems with a large number of degrees of freedom is the existence of dissipative effects. For systems with an excitation energy of the order of the total number of particles, these effects are responsible for the trend towards thermal equilibrium; they were studied extensively by Van Hove [8]). Also for smaller excitation energies (a situation corresponding to zero-temperature) such dissipative effects can play an important role. One aspect of them has been investigated here: the case of metastable states, *i.e.* of states which would be stationary were it not that they show, as a result of the perturbation, an exponential decay with a long life-time. Such states have been studied in section 14. An important example is provided by a slow nucleon penetrating into nuclear matter and traveling a considerable distance before the compound nucleus is formed.

16. *Final remarks.* At the start of our investigation we assumed the convergence of the expansion (3.5) of $R(z)$ in powers of the perturbation, at least for z non-real. Our final results are still expressed as series expansions but the latter differ from the original expansion by the fact that a number of partial summations have been performed explicitly. This circumstance manifests itself clearly in our results, inasmuch as the class of diagrams contributing to the final expressions is very much smaller than the class contributing to the original ones. We have therefore every reason to believe that the convergence of our resulting expressions is much better. We know in particular that this convergence is no longer affected in any way by the large size of the system and its large number of degrees of freedom. The question under what condition on the strength and form of the two-body potential our final series converge is however unsolved. Let us devote a few comments to this difficult point.

Let us take a large vessel, with volume Ω, filled with a gas of interacting Fermi particles. Considering the ground state of the system we distinguish the following cases.

1. The particles are distributed homogeneously throughout the vessel, exerting a pressure on the walls. This situation certainly occurs whenever the forces are repulsive, but also partly attractive forces can obviously give rise to it. For not too singular forces it is to be expected that our expansions converge.

2. The particles are bound together by their mutual interaction, thus occupying only a part Ω' of the volume Ω. The volume Ω' and the energy are proportional to the number N of particles, as will be the case for saturating forces. A large nucleus of volume Ω' enclosed in a vessel of volume $\Omega > \Omega'$ is an example of the case considered here. For such a system the perturbation theory, even in case of convergence, is not strictly valid: the state $|\psi_0\rangle$, obtained by perturbation of the unperturbed ground state, would then not represent the state of lowest energy. If, however, we reduce the vessel to a volume $\leqslant \Omega'$, thus increasing the particle density, we are back to the first case.

3. In contrast with case 2, the forces may be such that the ground state corresponds to a particle density and an energy density increasing with the total number of particles. This corresponds to non-saturating forces. For such forces the perturbation method will break down completely.

Another remark concerns the normalization factor $N_0^{\frac{1}{2}}$ in (11.23). This factor has the simple form exp $(-\ \overline{G}_0'(\varepsilon_0))$. The exponent is proportional to Ω and consequently N_0 approaches zero in the limit of $\Omega \to \infty$. Consequently, if this limit is actually carried out, all expansion coefficients are zero and a proper expansion of $|\psi_0\rangle$ in unperturbed states is no longer possible. Another way of stating this remarkable fact is to say that the ground state $|\psi_0\rangle$ as well as any other eigenstate $|\psi_\alpha\rangle^\pm$ of the total hamiltonian, become orthogonal to all unperturbed states $|\alpha\rangle$ in the limit $\Omega \to \infty$. This is connected with the fact that in this limit the system has infinitely many degrees of freedom (*e.g.*, infinitely many particles), so that the set of basic vectors spanning the Hilbert space of its state vectors is no longer countable. In this non-separable Hilbert space many separable subspaces can be formed. On the one hand, the unperturbed ground state $|\varphi_0\rangle$, and all unperturbed states $|\alpha\rangle$ differing from $|\varphi_0\rangle$ by excitation of a finite number of particles (and holes) span a separable Hilbert space. On the other hand a separable Hilbert space is formed by the perturbed states $|\psi_0\rangle$ and $|\psi_\alpha\rangle^\pm$. The vanishing of N_0 for $\Omega = \infty$ implies that these separable Hilbert spaces are orthogonal to each other. As was remarked by Van Hove [9]), a similar situation occurs also in field theories where the vacuum is not affected by the perturbation (no pair creation). It is then caused by ultra-violet divergencies. In such theories it is irrelevant whether the volume in the configuration space is finite or not, the essential fact is the occurrence of divergencies in momentum integrations, *i.e.*, the occurrence of an infinite "effective" volume in momentum space.

Finally some words must be said on the relation of the present investigation to the formalism of current field theory. Applying our formalism to field theory, one would be tempted to identify the function $\overline{D}_k(\varepsilon_0 + z)$, being the diagonal element of $R(\varepsilon_0 + z)$ for a state of one particle with momentum k, calculated with omission of all disconnected diagrams, with the Fourier transform of the one-particle propagation function $\Delta'_F(x, t)$ as introduced by Dyson [10]). This, however, is not generally true. One can show that the identity exists only in those theories where the free vacuum is not affected by the perturbation. It can nevertheless be established that the singularities of both quantities, which determine the mass renormalization of the particle, are the same [11]).

Acknowledgements. The author is glad to acknowledge his indebtedness to Professor L. Van Hove who not only suggested many of the ideas underlying this investigation but also assisted the author with advice and valuable criticism during all stages of this work. The author also profited from discussions with other members of the Institute for Theoretical Physics in Utrecht, in particular Dr. N. G. van Kampen and Mr. Th. W. Ruijgrok.

This work is part of the research program of the "Stichting voor Fundamenteel Onderzoek der Materie", which is financially supported by the Netherlands Organization for pure scientific Research (Z.W.O.).

Appendices

Appendix 1. An alternative proof of equation (7.1) can be obtained by comparison with the case of a system composed of two completely independent subsystems. The hamiltonian H of the total system can be written

$$H = H_1 + H_2,$$

where H_1 and H_2 are the hamiltonians of the two independent subsystems. We shall denote the resolvent operators by $R(z)$, $R_1(z)$ and $R_2(z)$. They are commuting operators.

If one multiplies the identity

$$H - z = (H_1 - \zeta) + (H_2 - z + \zeta)$$

by the product $R(z)\, R_1(\zeta)\, R_2(z - \zeta)$ one gets

$$R_1(\zeta)\, R_2(z - \zeta) = R(z)\, (R_1(\zeta) + R_2(z - \zeta)).$$

Taking $Im\ z \neq 0$ and integrating on both sides over the variable ζ along the path defined in section 7 eq. (7.2) one obtains the formula

$$-(2\pi i)^{-1} \oint d\zeta\, R_1(\zeta)\, R_2(z-\zeta) = R(z)[-(2\pi i)^{-1} \oint d\zeta\, R_1(\zeta) - (2\pi i)^{-1} \oint d\zeta R_2(z-\zeta)].$$

The second term on the right-hand side is zero, owing to the fact that $R(z - \zeta)$ has no singularities on the real ζ-axis. The first term within the brackets is equal to one, as one sees from (3.3) by putting $t = 0$. We are left with

$$R(z) = R_1(z) * R_2(z), \tag{A1.1}$$

where we used the notation introduced in section 7.

Suppose now that the two subsystems are identical though independent systems of the type studied in this paper. As an example one could think of two vessels of equal volume filled with the same number of identical Fermi particles. The hamiltonians are $H_1 = H_1^0 + V_1$ and $H_2 = H_2^0 + V_2$. The total resolvent $R(z)$ can be expanded in powers of $V = V_1 + V_2$

$$R(z) = \frac{1}{H_1^0 + H_2^0 - z} - \frac{1}{H_1^0 + H_2^0 - z} (V_1 + V_2) \frac{1}{H_1^0 + H_2^0 - z} + \ldots\ldots$$

and the contributions to the different terms can again be represented by diagrams. Consider such an arbitrary diagram. It contains two different kinds of vertices corresponding to V_1 and V_2. The diagram falls apart into two subdiagrams A' and B' which contain all vertices of systems 1 and 2 respectively. A' and B' are not connected with each other, there being no lines joining a vertex of system 1 with a vertex of system 2. Together with this diagram we consider all diagrams which can be obtained from this one by changing the positions of the vertices of A' with respect to B'. The contributions of these diagrams differ only by the energy denominators. Let us denote the sum by $\langle\alpha'\beta'|C'(z)|\alpha\beta\rangle$ where $|\alpha\rangle$ and $|\alpha'\rangle$ are the initial and final state of system 1, $|\beta\rangle$ and $|\beta'\rangle$ of system 2. If we denote the contribution of A' to $R_1(z)$ by $\langle\alpha'|A'(z)|\alpha\rangle$ and the contribution of B' to $R_2(z)$ by $\langle\beta'|B'(z)|\beta\rangle$, application of (A1.1) gives immediately the formula

$$\langle\alpha'\beta'|C'(z)|\alpha\beta\rangle = \langle\alpha'|A'(z)|\alpha\rangle * \langle\beta'|B'(z)|\beta\rangle. \tag{A1.2}$$

It is valid for two uncoupled systems and must not be confused with (7.4). We can however use (A1.2) to establish the validity of (7.4) by means of the following argument. Let us take the diagrams A' and B' identical with A and B of section 7. The quantities $\langle\alpha'|A'(z)|\alpha\rangle$ and $\langle\beta'|B'(z)|\beta\rangle$ are then formally identical with $\langle\alpha'|A(z)|\alpha\rangle$ and $\langle\beta'|B(z)|\beta\rangle$ of section 7. Let us now compare $\langle\alpha'\beta'|C'(z)|\alpha\beta\rangle$ with $\langle\beta'\alpha'|C(z)|\alpha\beta\rangle$. Although these quantities clearly have different meanings, the only formal difference is the fact that in the latter the energy ε_0 of the unperturbed ground state is counted only once and not twice in the energy denominators. This difference can be compensated for by substituting $z - \varepsilon_0$ for z in $\langle\beta'\alpha'|C(z)|\alpha\beta\rangle$. This leads to the formula

$$\langle\beta'\alpha'|C(z-\varepsilon_0)|\alpha\beta\rangle = \langle\alpha'|A(z)|\alpha\rangle * \langle\beta'|B(z)|\beta\rangle,$$

an alternative form of (7.4) or (7.1).

Appendix 2. It will be shown in this appendix that the integral equation (9.7) has at most one solution $f(z)$ which is holomorphic outside the real axis and bounded for large $|z|$. It is sufficient to prove that the homogeneous equation

$$zf(z) = -(2\pi i)^{-1} \oint \mathrm{d}\zeta\, h(\zeta)\, f(z-\zeta)$$

has no such solution $f(z)$.

By (9.11) this equation can be written

$$zf(z) = \int_0^\infty \mathrm{d}\xi\, p(\xi)\, f(z-\xi). \tag{A2.1}$$

We shall make use of the fact that the integrals

$$L = \int_0^\infty |p(x)|\, \mathrm{d}x \quad \text{and} \quad M = \int_0^\infty \frac{|p(x)|}{x}\, \mathrm{d}x \tag{A2.2}$$

are convergent. These properties of $p(x)$ are an immediate consequence of (9.13) and (9.2). We choose an arbitrary point z, not on the real axis, for which $Re\, z < 0$. The tunction $f(z+a)$ of the real variable a is bounded; consequently there exists a positive number $N(z)$ such that

$$|f(z+a)| < N(z) \quad \text{for all } a.$$

Iterating equation (A2.1) n times, one obtains

$$f(z) = \frac{1}{z}\int_0^\infty \mathrm{d}\xi_1 \ldots\ldots \int_0^\infty \mathrm{d}\xi_n \int_0^\infty \mathrm{d}\xi_{n+1} \frac{p(\xi_1)}{z-\xi_1} \ldots\ldots \frac{p(\xi_n)}{z-\xi_1-\xi_2-\ldots-\xi_n} \cdot$$
$$\cdot\, p(\xi_{n+1})\, f(z-\xi_1-\ldots-\xi_{n+1}).$$

This equality can be changed into an inequality: take the absolute value of both sides and replace the integrand by its absolute value. The right-hand side is increased further if one replaces the denominators $|z - \xi_1 - \dots - \xi_k|$ by $\xi_1 + \dots + \xi_k$, and $|f(z - \xi_1 - \dots - \xi_{n+1})|$ by $N(z)$. One finds, using (A2.2),

$$|f(z)| \leqslant \frac{1}{|z|}\int_0^\infty d\xi_1 \dots\dots \int_0^\infty d\xi_n \frac{|p(\xi_1)|}{\xi_1} \dots\dots \frac{|p(\xi_n)|}{\xi_1 + \xi_2 + \dots + \xi_n} L \, . \, N(z).$$

The integral at the right-hand side is not changed by a permutation of the variables $\xi_1, \xi_2, \dots, \xi_n$ in the integrand. Using the simple algebraic equation

$$\Sigma_P \, \xi_1^{-1}(\xi_1 + \xi_2)^{-1} \dots\dots (\xi_1 + \xi_2 + \dots + \xi_n)^{-1} = \xi_1^{-1} \, \xi_2^{-1} \dots \xi_n^{-1},$$

where the sum is extended over the $n!$ permutations of the n variables, one is led to the inequality

$$|f(z)| \leqslant \frac{1}{|z|}\frac{1}{n!}\int_0^\infty d\xi_1 \dots\dots \int_0^\infty d\xi_n \frac{|p(\xi_1)|}{\xi_1} \dots\dots \frac{|p(\xi_n)|}{\xi_n} L . N(z),$$

or by (A2.2)

$$|f(z)| \leqslant LN(z) \, |z|^{-1} \, . \, M^n/n!.$$

This inequality holds for all n. Hence, noticing that $\lim_{n\to\infty} M^n/n! = 0$, we find $f(z) = 0$ for all non-real z, for which $Re\, z < 0$. This is enough to conclude that $f(z) \equiv 0$ and that the homogeneous integral equation has no non-zero solution which is holomorphic outside the real axis and bounded for $|z| \to \infty$. This proves our statement.

Appendix 3. In section 9 the integral equation (9.14) was solved by means of a Laplace-transformation. We shall prove here that the function $\hat{\varphi}(s)$, given by (9.16), is the Laplace-transform of a function $\varphi(x)$ given by (9.18). The known properties of $p(x)$ imply the absolute convergence of $\int_0^\infty p(x) \exp(-sx)\, dx$ and $\int_0^\infty x^{-1} p(x) \exp(-sx)\, dx$ for $s = 0$ as can be seen from (A2.2). From this we conclude that both $\hat{p}(s) = \int_0^\infty p(x) \exp(-sx)\, dx$ and $\int_0^\infty x^{-1} p(x) \exp(-sx)\, dx$ are analytical functions of s for $Re\, s > 0$ (see e.g. G. Doetsch, Handbuch der Laplace-Transformation I, Satz 1[3.2]). Consequently the same holds true for the functions $\hat{\varphi}(s)$ and $\hat{\varphi}'(s)$ given by (9.16) and (9.15). From the behaviour of $p(x)$ near the origine (9.17) we can determine the asymptotic behaviour of $\hat{p}(s)$ and $\int_0^\infty x^{-1}p(x) \exp(-sx)\, dx$ for large s. Application of one of the Abelian theorems (see e.g. Doetsch, Satz 5 [14.1]) immediately gives

$$\hat{p}(s) = O(|s|^{-1-\alpha}) \text{ and } \int_0^\infty x^{-1} p(x) \exp(-sx)\, dx = O(|s|^{-\alpha}) \text{ for } |s| \to \infty.$$

Hence, from (9.16),

$$\lim_{|s|\to\infty} \hat{\varphi}(s) = 0$$

and from (9.15)

$$\hat{\varphi}'(s) = O(|s|^{-1-\alpha}) \text{ for } |s| \to \infty.$$

This asymptotic property of $\hat{\varphi}'(s)$ is sufficient (see e.g. Doetsch, Satz 3 [7.2]) to ensure the existence of a function $\chi(x)$ such that

$$\hat{\varphi}'(s) = \int_0^\infty \chi(x) \exp(-sx) \, dx.$$

$\chi(x)$ is given by the complex integral

$$\chi(x) = (2\pi i)^{-1} \int_{-i\infty+\delta}^{+i\infty+\delta} \varphi'(s) \exp(sx) \, ds, \; \delta > 0.$$

Another Abelian theorem (see e.g. Doetsch Satz 1 [15.5]) predicts the behaviour of $\chi(x)$ near the origin from the asymptotic behaviour of $\hat{\varphi}'(s)$ for large $|s|$:

$$\chi(x) = O(x^\alpha).$$

This enables us to define the Laplace-transiorm

$$F(s) = \int_0^\infty x^{-1} \chi(x) \exp(-sx) \, dx.$$

$F(s)$ is an analytical function for $Re\, s > 0$, with the same derivative as $\hat{\varphi}(s)$. Both $F(s)$ and $\hat{\varphi}(s)$ tend to zero for $s \to \infty$ and are consequently equal. This proves that $\hat{\varphi}(s)$ is the Laplace-transform of a function $\varphi(x) = x^{-1} \chi(x)$.

Received 8-4-57.

REFERENCES

1) Van Hove, L., Physica **21** (1955) 901 and Physica **22** (1956) 343. These papers will be referred to as H I and H II.
2) Feshbach, H., Porter, C. E. and Weisskopf, V. F., Phys. Rev. **96** (1954) 448.
3) See e.g., Brueckner, K. A. and Levinson, C. A., Phys. Rev. **97** (1955) 1344; also Bethe, H. A., Phys. Rev. **103** (1956) 1353, where an extensive list of references to other work of Brueckner and coll. can be found.
4) Feynman, R. P., Phys. Rev. **76** (1949) 749.
5) Goldstone, J., Proc. Roy. Soc. A, **239** (1957) 267.
6) Wick, G. C., Rev. mod. Phys. **27** (1955) 339.
7) Gell-Mann, M. and Low, F., Phys. Rev. **84** (1951) 350.
8) Van Hove, L., Physica **21** (1955) 517 and Physica **23** (1957) 441 (this issue).
9) Van Hove. L., Physica **18** (1952) 145.
10) Dyson, F. J., Phys. Rev. **75** (1949) 486 and 1736.
11) Frazer, W. R., Private communication.

PERTURBATION APPROACH TO THE FERMI GAS MODEL OF HEAVY NUCLEI

by N. M. HUGENHOLTZ

Instituut voor theoretische fysica der Rijksuniversiteit, Utrecht, Nederland

Synopsis

The general perturbation method presented in an earlier paper [1]) is applied to a study of some aspects of the Fermi gas model of nuclear matter. The two extreme cases of very low and very high particle density are investigated. It is shown that the theory recently developed by Brueckner [2]) can be considered as an improved low density approximation. The validity of some other approximations made in the Brueckner theory, involving the energy denominators in intermediate states are briefly discussed. The study of the case of high density reveals the interesting fact that, contrary to indications presented by Swiatecki [3]) and Bethe [4]), the convergence of the perturbation expansion gets worse with increasing density, while in that case the Brueckner approximation becomes extremely poor.

It is furthermore shown that a slow nucleon, travelling through nuclear matter, can be considered as being in a metastable state and an exact expression for the inverse life-time of such a state is given; this quantity must be identified with the imaginary part of the potential in the optical model.

1. *Introduction.* The Fermi gas model of heavy nuclei, which forms the subject of the present paper, is meant to give a description of properties which are independent of the size or the detailed structure of the individual nuclei. It is to be expected that some properties of nuclear matter, in the interior of large nuclei, such as the binding energy per nucleon or the shift of the energy of an additional nucleon penetrating into the interior of a nucleus, can be studied by considering a large box filled with interacting nucleons, with a particle density equal to the density of actual nuclei. This model might be called the Fermi gas model of nuclear matter.

In the past there have been several attempts to make calculations of the binding energy of heavy nuclei on the basis of the Fermi gas model, in particular by Euler and by Huby [5]). The interaction between the nucleons was treated as a perturbation and the binding energy per nucleon was calculated to second order in the interaction. The results of such calculations were not very encouraging and seemed to confirm the general believe that, due to the strong correlations between the nucleons, perturbation theory is inadequate for the treatment of nuclei.

Recently Swiatecki [3]) re-examined the calculation of Euler. He studied the ratio $\Delta E_0^{(2)}/\Delta E_0^{(1)}$ of the second and first order terms of the binding energy ΔE_0 as a function of the particle density of the nucleon gas. He showed that this ratio decreases rapidly with the density. Hence, in the limit of large density, the first order term becomes predominant. This behaviour raised the hope that, in the case of large densities, the perturbation expansion would converge well. This expectation however is not confirmed, as will be shown in the present paper.

New interest has been aroused in the Fermi gas model by Brueckner e.a. [2]) who proposed a new approach to the many particle problem. The method of Brueckner can be considered as an improved Hartree method. The interaction between two nucleons is treated exactly, whereas the influence of all other particles is taken into account by means of a self-consistent Hartree potential. The method aims at giving the theoretical foundation of the shell model. Although attempts have been made to adapt the method to the treatment of finite nuclei, the method of Brueckner is in essence an approximation method for the imperfect Fermi gas. There has been much discussion on the limits of validity of the Brueckner approximation, but this difficult question is far from settled.

A detailed study of the Fermi gas using perturbation theory was always hampered by the fact that the conventional perturbation theory is very inadequate for the treatment of many particle systems. In particular the occurrence of terms containing arbitrarily high powers of the number of particles in the perturbation expansion was a well known difficulty. In a recent paper [1]) (to be referred to as I) a perturbation formalism was described which is particularly suited for the investigation of systems with many degrees of freedom. In the present paper several of the results of I, where the theory of the Fermi gas was already considered as an example, will be applied to some aspects of the nuclear structure problem.

We base our discussion on a consideration of the two limiting cases of very small and very large densities. In section 2, the case of small density (the average distance between the particles is then large compared to the range of the forces) will be studied. It is shown how, starting from this extreme case, the Brueckner approximation presents itself in a natural way as an approximation for not too high densities. In section 3 we study the opposite case where the particle density is high. The leading term of the nth order ($n \geqslant 2$) contribution to ΔE_0 is shown to be proportional to k_F^{n+1}, where the Fermi momentum k_F is used as a measure for the particle density. This shows that, in the case of high particle density, the perturbation expansion gets worse with increasing density. In the same section the k_F-dependence of the different terms of the Brueckner approximate expansion are calculated asymptotically for large k_F, yielding for the nth order term the factor k_F^{5-n}. Consequently the Brueckner approximation is very poor and misleading at high densities because it leaves out completely the leading effects in this density region.

In section 4 the motion of an additional nucleon with momentum $|k| > k_F$ through nuclear matter is investigated. This is of interest in connection with the optical model for the scattering of nucleons on heavy nuclei. Under some very reasonable assumptions, a state with an additional particle with momentum $|k| > k_F$ is shown to be metastable. The expression derived in I for the inverse life-time of such a state, a quantity which corresponds to the complex part of the potential in the optical model, leads in lowest order of approximation to a formula derived by Brueckner, Eden and Francis [6]).

2. *The case of low particle density.* In I the energy shift ΔE_0 of the ground state of the Fermi gas, caused by the interparticle interaction V, was found to be (see I 9.25)

$$\Delta E_0 = \langle\varphi_0|[V - V(H_0 - \varepsilon_0)^{-1}V + \ldots]_C|\varphi_0\rangle. \tag{2.1}$$

For the meaning of the symbols one is referred to I. By this formula the binding energy $-\Delta E_0$ is expressed in contributions of connected ground state diagrams only. Consequently, for large volume Ω, ΔE_0 is asymptotically proportional to Ω.

If we take spinless particles with central two-body forces (the extension to the case of particles with spin will be given when necessary) the first term of (2.1) gives

$$\Delta E_0^{(1)} = \tfrac{1}{2}\Omega(2\pi)^{-6}\int_0^{k_F} d^3m_1 \int_0^{k_F} d^3m_2\, (v(0) - v(m_1 - m_2)). \tag{2.2}$$

The integration in (2.2) is extended over all momenta m_1 and m_2 inside the Fermi sphere of radius k_F (As in I we use the convention that the symbols k_i (m_i) denote momenta outside (inside) the Fermi sphere.). If k_F is very small, corresponding to the case of low density, the integrand can be expanded in powers of $|m_1 - m_2|$. We get in lowest order

$$\Delta E_0^{(1)} = -\tfrac{1}{2}\Omega(2\pi)^{-6}\int_0^{k_F} d^3m_1 \int_0^{k_F} d^3m_2\, |m_1 - m_2|\, v'(0).$$

This expression is proportional to k_F^7, six factors k_F arising from the 6-fold integration and one from the integrand. This last factor would be absent if we had taken Serber forces between particles with spin $\frac{1}{2}$. The major change in the latter case would be a plus sign in the interaction V instead of a minus sign, and the integrand in (2.2) would not vanish for small $|m_1 - m_2|$.

It is now very easy to see which higher order diagrams give the largest contribution to ΔE_0 for small k_F. They are the diagrams with the smallest possible number of hole lines. In each order in V there is always exactly one diagram with only two such lines. They are of the type as shown in figure 1*a*. It is easily established that the contributions of these diagrams (except the lowest order one) are proportional to k_F^8, two factors k_F arising from the integrand. In the more realistic case of Serber forces the diagrams considered would give a contribution of order k_F^6. All other diagrams give contributions containing higher powers of k_F and can be neglected in the case of very low density.

The leading diagrams for low density are seen to correspond to iterated collisions between two particles. This result has nothing surprising. Indeed, in the kinetic theory of dilute gases it is well known that all but binary collisions can be neglected.

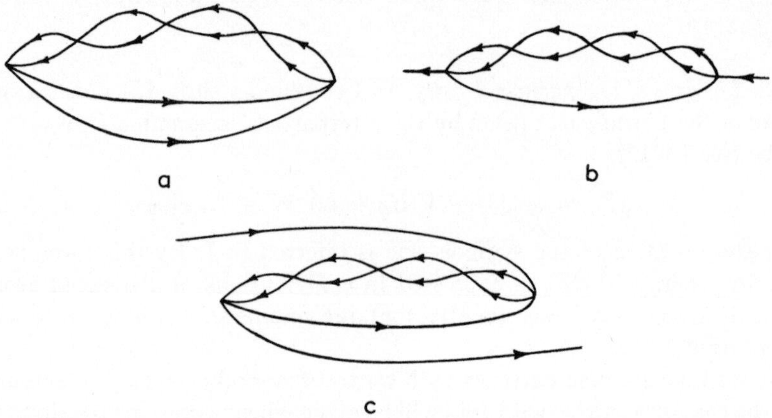

Fig. 1. The diagrams giving the main contribution in the case of extreme low density. The diagrams *a*, *b* and *c* respectively correspond to the ground state, a state with an additional particle and a state with a hole.

For states with the Fermi sea and one additional particle of momentum k, or with one hole of momentum m in the Fermi sea, one has to study the functions $\bar{G}_k(\varepsilon_0 + z)$ or $\bar{G}_m(\varepsilon_0 + z)$, i.e., the function $\bar{G}_\alpha(\varepsilon_0 + z)$ defined in (I 10.2) taken for a state $|\alpha\rangle$ equal to $|k;\rangle$ or $|\ ;\ m\rangle$. The diagrams contributing to these functions have one external line at both ends. Exactly as before it is seen that the diagrams *b* and *c* of fig. 1 give, in the case of low density, the main contributions to $\bar{G}_k(\varepsilon_0 + z)$ and $\bar{G}_m(\varepsilon_0 + z)$ respectively. They all have one internal hole line.

In the approximation where the contributions of all other diagrams are neglected, the energy denominators $(\varepsilon_\gamma - \varepsilon_0)^{-1}$ and $(\varepsilon_\gamma - \varepsilon_0 - z)^{-1}$ for the intermediate states $|\gamma\rangle$ occurring in ΔE_0, $\bar{G}_k(\varepsilon_0 + z)$ and $\bar{G}_m(\varepsilon_0 + z)$ contain the unperturbed energies $\varepsilon_\gamma - \varepsilon_0$. If one wants to improve the approximation and incorporate in the intermediate states the energy shift of the additional particles caused by the presence of all other particles in the gas, the following extension of the low density approximation presents itself in a natural way.

Instead of equation (I 9.25) for the energy shift of the ground state, we take (I 9.26) as our starting point:

$$\Delta E_0 = \langle\varphi_0|[V - V\bar{D}(\varepsilon_0)V + \ldots\ldots]_{\mathcal{LC}}|\varphi_0\rangle. \tag{2.3}$$

Here the matrix element involves the contributions of all irreducible connected ground state diagrams. The factors $\bar{D}_\gamma(\varepsilon_0)$, which replace the factors $(\varepsilon_\gamma - \varepsilon_0)^{-1}$ in the intermediate states of (2.1), are obtained from (I 10.3)

$$\bar{D}_\gamma(\varepsilon_0 + z) = [\varepsilon_\gamma - \varepsilon_0 - z - \bar{G}_\gamma(\varepsilon_0 + z)]^{-1} \tag{2.4}$$

where

$$\delta(\gamma - \gamma')\bar{G}_\gamma(\varepsilon_0 + z) = \langle\gamma'[- V + V\bar{D}(\varepsilon_0 + z)V - \ldots]_{idL}|\gamma\rangle. \tag{2.5}$$

In the latter equation only irreducible diagrams without ground state components are taken into account. The announced extension of the low density approximation is obtained if the irreducible diagrams occurring in (2.3) are restricted to the type *a* of fig. 1, while the irreducible diagrams in (2.5) are restricted to diagonal diagrams the components of which are of the type *b* and *c*. This approximation represents a considerable improvement above the original low density approximation.

As will be shown in section 4 the functions $\bar{D}_\gamma(\varepsilon_0 + z)$ for $|\gamma\rangle \neq |\varphi_0\rangle$ have no pole. However, for small excitation energies, one has in good approximation

$$\bar{D}_\gamma(\varepsilon_0 + z) = \bar{N}_\gamma(\bar{E}_\gamma - z)^{-1} + \bar{\psi}_\gamma(\varepsilon_0 + z).$$

with $\bar{\psi}_\gamma$ small for $z = \bar{E}_\gamma$. $\bar{N}_\gamma$ is defined in (I 10.9). $\bar{E}_\gamma$ is approximately the perturbed excitation energy of the state $|\gamma\rangle$; as shown in I section 10, it is the sum of the perturbed energies of the individual particles and holes of $|\gamma\rangle$. The equations become formally much simpler if in all intermediate states $|\gamma\rangle$ of (2.3) and (2.5) we put approximately

$$\bar{D}_\gamma(\varepsilon_0 + z) = (\bar{E}_\gamma - z)^{-1}. \tag{2.6}$$

If this is done (we come back later on the error involved in this step), the improved low density approximation, described above, becomes equivalent to the Brueckner approximation. To show this equivalence we calculate ΔE_0 and the functions $\bar{G}_k(\varepsilon_0 + z)$, $\bar{G}_m(\varepsilon_0 + z)$ from (2.3), (2.5) and (2.6), thereby limiting ourselves to diagrams of the type of figure 1. We find

$$\Delta E_0 = \tfrac{1}{2}\int_{m_1m_2} v(m_1m_2m_2m_1) + \tfrac{1}{4}\int_{m_1m_2k_1k_2} \frac{v(m_1m_2k_1k_2)\, v(k_1k_2m_2m_1)}{\bar{E}_{k_1} + \bar{E}_{k_2} + \bar{E}_{m_1} + \bar{E}_{m_2}} + \ldots.$$

$$\delta(k'-k)\bar{G}_k(\varepsilon_0+z) = -\int_{m_1} v(k'm_1m_1k) - \tfrac{1}{2}\int_{m_1k_1k_2} \frac{v(k'm_1k_1k_2)\, v(k_1k_2m_1k)}{\bar{E}_{k_1} + \bar{E}_{k_2} + \bar{E}_{m_1} - z} + \ldots.$$

$$\delta(m'-m)\bar{G}_m(\varepsilon_0+z) = \int_{m_1} v(mm_1m_1m') + \tfrac{1}{2}\int_{m_1k_1k_2} \frac{v(mm_1k_1k_2)\, v(k_1k_2m_1m')}{\bar{E}_{k_1}+\bar{E}_{k_2}+\bar{E}_{m_1}+2\bar{E}_m - z} + \ldots$$

Let us define a quantity $G(l_1l_2l_3l_4)$, depending on the 4 momenta $l_1l_2l_3l_4$, by the integral equation

$$G(l_1l_2l_3l_4) = v(l_1l_2l_3l_4) + \tfrac{1}{2}\int d^3k_1 d^3k_2 \frac{v(l_1l_2k_1k_2)\, G(k_1k_2l_3l_4)}{\bar{E}_{k_1}+\bar{E}_{k_2}+\bar{E}_{m_1}+\bar{E}_{m_2}},$$

where it should be remembered that the energy $\bar{E}_m$ of a hole is negative. $G(l_1 l_2 l_3 l_4)$ is the modified scattering matrix of Brueckner. The factor $\frac{1}{2}$ in the second term on the right-hand side takes care of the fact that each intermediate state is counted twice. The above equations now reduce to the simple form

$$\Delta E_0 = \tfrac{1}{2} \textstyle\int_{m_1 m_2} G(m_1 m_2 m_2 m_1), \tag{2.7}$$

$$\delta(k' - k)\bar{G}_k(\bar{E}_k) = - \textstyle\int_{m_1} G(k' m_1 m_1 k), \tag{2.8}$$

$$\delta(m - m')\bar{G}_m(\bar{E}_m) = \textstyle\int_{m_1} G(m m_1 m_1 m'). \tag{2.9}$$

As shown in I, section 10, $- \bar{G}_k(\bar{E}_k)$ and $- \bar{G}_m(\bar{E}_m)$ represent the energy shifts of the particle and hole respectively. If we define the diagonal matrix $\langle l'|W|l\rangle = \delta(l' - l)W(l)$ by

$$W(k) = - \bar{G}_k(\bar{E}_k) \text{ for } |k| > k_F$$
$$W(m) = \bar{G}_m(\bar{E}_m) \text{ for } |m| < k_F,$$

equation (2.8) and (2.9) can be written

$$\delta(l' - l)\, W(l) = \textstyle\int \mathrm{d}^3 m\, G(l' m m l). \tag{2.10}$$

The total perturbed energy of a single particle, with momentum l either outside or inside the Fermi sea (in the latter case this energy is defined as minus the energy of the hole), is thus given by

$$|l|^2/2M + W(l). \tag{2.11}$$

Finally, by (2.7) and (2.9), the energy shift ΔE_0 of the ground state of the system is

$$\Delta E_0 = \tfrac{1}{2}\Sigma_m W(m) = \tfrac{1}{2}\Omega(2\pi)^{-3} \textstyle\int_0^{k_F} \mathrm{d}^3 m\, W(m). \tag{2.12}$$

In these equations we used the definitions for the symbols $\delta(m' - m)$ and $\int_m$ introduced in I section 2. The formulae (2.10), (2.11), and (2.12) correspond with the formulae (9.14), (9.1), and (9.3) of Bethe's presentation of the Brueckner theory [4]).

A remark must still be made on the approximation (2.6), i.e. the replacement of $\bar{D}_\gamma(\varepsilon_0 + z)$ by $(\bar{E}_\gamma - z)^{-1}$. In I section 10 the following formula was derived for $\bar{N}_\gamma$:

$$\bar{N}_\gamma^{-1} = 1 + \bar{G}'_\gamma(\varepsilon_0 + \bar{E}_\gamma).$$

Hence, the deviation of $\bar{N}_\gamma$ from unity is given by $\bar{G}'_\gamma(\varepsilon_0 + \bar{E}_\gamma)$, a quantity which, for small density, has exactly the same k_F-dependence as the energy shift $\bar{G}_\gamma(\varepsilon_0 + \bar{E}_\gamma)$. If the latter is taken into account as a correction to the energy in the intermediate state $|\gamma\rangle$ there is no reason to neglect the former. The same holds true for the function $\bar{\psi}_\gamma(\varepsilon_0 + z)$. Although it might well happen that by accidental cancellations the replacement (2.6) would be justified, there is no indication to this effect and one should consequently not be surprised to find considerable errors brought in by this approximation.

3. *The case of high density*. We investigate in this section how the various terms in the simple perturbation expansion (2.1) of ΔE_0 behave for high density, i.e., how they depend on the Fermi momentum k_F in the case of large k_F. We assume the interparticle potential not to be too singular. For high densities the Fermi sphere has a large radius and the transitions take place only near its surface. Consequently there is a complete symmetry between holes and particles in all terms of (2.1), except the first. The contribution of a diagram (of order $n \geqslant 2$) is not changed if in that diagram all particle lines are replaced by hole lines, and conversely. The first order term of (2.1) forms an exception because in the interaction V the ξ-operators precede the ξ^*-operators (in the order from right to left).

This term was already calculated in section 2 and is given by (2.2). In the present case of large k_F the leading term of (2.2) is clearly the first. In the second term, in view of the factor $v(m_1 - m_2)$, m_1 and m_2 are bound to be close together (relatively to k_F), which gives a strong restriction on the domain of integration. Neglecting the second term in (2.2) the energy shift per particle is found to be

$$\Delta E_0^{(1)}/N = v(0)k_F^3/12\pi^2, \tag{3.1}$$

where we used formula (I 2.9) for the particle number N.

There is only one second order diagram contributing to ΔE_0 in (2.1), the contribution being given by

$$\Delta E_0^{(2)} = -M\Omega(2\pi)^{-9}\int \mathrm{d}^3k_1\,\mathrm{d}^3k_2\,\mathrm{d}^3m_1\,\mathrm{d}^3m_2\,\cdot$$

$$\cdot\frac{v(k_1-m_1)^2 - v(k_1-m_1)\,v(k_1-m_2)}{k_1^2+k_2^2-m_1^2-m_2^2}\,\delta(k_1+k_2-m_1-m_2), \tag{3.2}$$

as is easily found by the method described in I, section 3. The integration is extended over momenta k_1 and k_2 outside the Fermi sphere and over m_1 and m_2 inside it. Let us compare the first and second term in (3.2). In the first term, through the factor $v(k_1 - m_1)^2$, the momenta k_1 and m_1 must be close together, and, through the factor $\delta(k_1 + k_2 - m_1 - m_2)$, also k_2 and m_2. Hence, remembering that $|k_1|$, $|k_2| \geqslant k_F$ and $|m_1|$, $|m_2| \leqslant k_F$, for the integrand to have an appreciable value, the four momenta must be close to the surface of the Fermi sphere, where two of them (e.g., m_1 and m_2) may be chosen arbitrarily. The second term in (3.2) contains the factor $v(k_1 - m_1)\,v(k_1 - m_2)$. There all four momenta must remain in the neighbourhood of each other at the surface of the Fermi sphere, where only one of them can be chosen arbitrarily. Clearly, this term is small compared to the first.

We shall now calculate the main term. Putting $k_1 = m_1 + q$ and $k_2 = m_2 - q$, and remembering that the values of q that contribute to

(3.2) are small compared to k_F one can write

$$\Delta E_0^{(2)} = - M\Omega(2\pi)^{-9} \int \mathrm{d}^3q\, \mathrm{d}^3m_1\, \mathrm{d}^3m_2 \frac{v(q)^2}{2k_F q(\mu_1 - \mu_2)}. \tag{3.3}$$

In the denominator, powers of q higher than the first are neglected. The variables μ_1 and μ_2 are the cosines of the angles of m_1 and m_2 with the vector q, which is chosen in the z-direction. The integration over m_1 and m_2 is restricted by the requirement that the momenta $k_1 = m_1 + q$ and $k_2 = m_2 - q$ lie outside the Fermi sphere. Always neglecting higher powers of q/k_F one finds after some simple manipulations

$$\Delta E_0^{(2)}/N = -\tfrac{3}{2} M(2\pi)^{-4} \textstyle\int_0^\infty \mathrm{d}q q^3\, v(q)^2 \int_0^1 \mathrm{d}\mu_1 \int_0^1 \mathrm{d}\mu_2\, \mu_1\, \mu_2(\mu_1 + \mu_2)^{-1}. \tag{3.4}$$

This term is independent of k_F (in the limit of large k_F) whereas (3.1) is proportional to k_F^3. In the case of high density the first order term (3.1) is much larger than the term of second order, in accordance with the conclusion of Swiatecki mentioned in the introduction. However, as we shall see now, some of the terms of higher order in the perturbation contain increasing powers of k_F.

We consider an arbitrary connected ground state diagram of order n, and investigate how the contribution of this diagram depends on k_F, in the limit of large k_F. The momentum transfer q in each interaction V is small compared to k_F. In order to find the number of factors k_F, we may put simply $q = 0$. Then each interaction V (corresponding to a vertex in the diagram) gives rise to two relations, each of them relating the momentum of an incoming line to the momentum of an outgoing line in that vertex. These relations restrict the number of independent variables in the integration, thereby reducing the number of factors k_F in the result. Such relations can be of three types: $m_i = m_j$, $k_i = k_j$ and $k_i = m_j$. Each relation of the first two types reduces the number of independent integration variables by three. A relation of the latter type, however, gives one additional constraint because both k_i and m_j must be near the surface of the Fermi sphere. In this case the number of independent integration variables is decreased by four. One should notice that the relations corresponding to different points of the diagram can be identical. This, in fact, sometimes reduces the total number of restrictions on the integration variables considerably. Finally, each energy denominator contains a factor k_F (as in (3.3)), which gives an extra factor k_F^{1-n} in the whole contribution.

Counting in this way the number of factors k_F of the leading term of each diagram, one obtains the following result. For arbitrary order $n \geqslant 2$ the diagrams of the type shown in figure 2 give, for large density, the main contribution to ΔE_0. As will be shown now, this contribution is of order k_F^{n+1}. For the relations between the momenta in each vertex we take the following choice:

$$k_i = m_i, \ (i = 1, 2, \ldots, n).$$

The momenta m_i can be integrated independently over the surface of the Fermi sphere, which leads to a $2n$-fold integration, i.e., a factor k_F^{2n}. Together with the factor k_F^{1-n}, arising from the energy denominators, we obtain the total factor k_F^{n+1}. For the energy shift per particle one can write

$$\Delta E_0^{(n)}/N \sim k_F^{n-2}, \tag{3.5}$$

a result in agreement with our earlier conclusion concerning $\Delta E_0^{(2)}$.

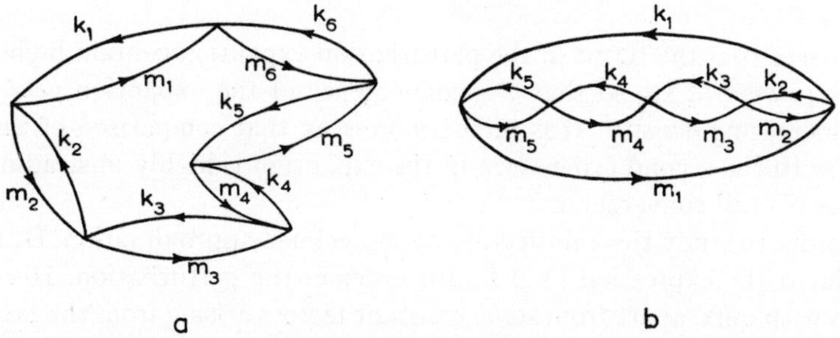

Fig. 2. This figure shows the type of diagrams giving the main contribution to ΔE_0 in the case of large density. Diagram *a* is an arbitrary example of this type. The contribution of the simple diagram *b* is calculated in the text.

The diagram shown in figure 2*b* is a very simple example of the type considered. A straightforward extension of the calculation of (3.4) gives the following result:

$$\Delta E^{(n)}/N = (-1)^{n-1}\, 3(2\pi)^{-2n}\, M^{n-1}\, k_F^{n-2} \int \mathrm{d}q q^3\, v(q)^n$$

$$\int_0^1 \mathrm{d}\mu_1 \ldots \int_0^1 \mathrm{d}\mu_n\, \mu_1 \ldots \mu_n(\mu_1+\mu_2)^{-1} \ldots (\mu_1+\mu_n)^{-1}, \tag{3.6}$$

which is valid for $n \geqslant 3$. For $n = 2$ a factor $\frac{1}{2}$ must be added to account for the two pairs of equivalent lines one has in that case (see I section 3). Apart from this factor (3.6) reduces to (3.4) for $n = 2$. We see further that (3.6) is in agreement with (3.5).

Before commenting on these results we shall calculate the k_F-dependence of the contributions of the Brueckner diagrams of fig. 1*a*. The nth-order diagram of this type contains, in the limit of large density, the factor k_F^{5-n}. For the energy shift per particle, when calculated from these diagrams only, we find for $n \geqslant 2$

$$\Delta E_0^{(n)}/N \sim k_F^{2-n} \text{ (Brueckner approximation)}, \tag{3.7}$$

a contribution which, for large k_F, decreases rapidly with n. It is negligible compared to the main contribution of the same order for high density. It is even very easy to see that the Brueckner diagrams, together with the diagrams obtained from them by interchanging holes and particles, give the smallest contributions in this case.

The conclusion of the above considerations is shown in the following table, where for each order n in the perturbation we give the highest power of k_F occurring in the total energy per particle E_0/N and also the power which would be found from the Brueckner diagram of the same order.

Order n =	0	1	2	3	4	5	6
Main term	2	3	0	1	2	3	4
Brueckner term	2	3	0	—1	—2	—3	—4

One sees that the terms in the perturbation expansion contain higher and higher powers of k_F, so that the convergence of the expansion gets worse with increasing density. It is furthermore seen that comparison of the first order with the second order term in the expansion is highly misleading as a test for overall convergence.

In order to study the validity of the Brueckner approximation Bethe [4]) calculated the expression (3.6) in 3rd order in the perturbation. His result agrees with ours, apart from some constant factors arising from the fact that he uses Serber forces. It depends linearly on k_F for large density. Thus it is indeed small compared to the first order term of the Brueckner approximation, but it is large compared to the Brueckner term of the same order. Our general results show clearly that the Brueckner approximation necessarily is very poor in the case of large densities.

The density of nuclear matter falls in between the two extreme regions considered in the previous and present section. It is certainly not excluded that the Brueckner method, which is in essence an improved approximation method for low densities, is still applicable to actual nuclear matter, at least for qualitative purposes, but one should realize that this important issue cannot be decided on the basis of the numerical calculations, published so far by the various authors working in this field. It nevertheless seems clear that the Brueckner method should not be expected to achieve any degree of quantitative accuracy.

4. *On the metastable character of the excited states*. It was already stated in I that, in the theory of an imperfect Fermi gas, none of the perturbed states, distinct from the ground state, are exactly stationary. In this section we shall show how this conclusion can be reached. We shall base our discussion on the considerations in I, in particular sections 10 and 14.

As shown there, to each unperturbed state $|\alpha\rangle \neq |\varphi_0\rangle$ there corresponds a quantity $\bar{E}_\alpha$, which is defined as the root of equation (I 10.6). This quantity $\bar{E}_\alpha$ is the energy of a stationary state of the perturbed system, provided the function $\bar{G}_\alpha(\varepsilon_0 + z)$ is regular at the point $z = \bar{E}_\alpha$. If, on the other hand,

$\bar{G}_\alpha(\varepsilon_0 + z)$ is discontinuous for z crossing the real axis at $\bar{E}_\alpha$, this energy has in general no simple physical meaning. If, however, the discontinuity of $\bar{G}_\alpha(\varepsilon_0 + z)$ at $z = \bar{E}_\alpha$ is small, $\bar{E}_\alpha$ is the (approximate) energy of a metastable state. The discontinuous change of $\bar{G}_\alpha(\varepsilon_0 + z)$ at $\bar{E}_\alpha$ can then be written as $2i\bar{J}_\alpha(\varepsilon_0 + \bar{E}_\alpha)$, where the positive energy $\bar{J}_\alpha(\varepsilon_0 + \bar{E}_\alpha)$ gives a measure for the inverse life-time. In fact, as shown by (I. 14.10), the inverse life-time is

$$\Gamma_\alpha = \bar{N}_\alpha \bar{J}_\alpha(\varepsilon_0 + \bar{E}_\alpha). \tag{4.1}$$

Without any loss of generality we can limit our considerations to excited states $|\alpha\rangle$ which are either one-particle states $|k\ ;\ \rangle$ (one particle in addition to the Fermi sea) or one-hole states $|\ ;\ m\rangle$. We have to make an assumption concerning the perturbed excitation energies $\bar{E}_k$ and $\bar{E}_m$ of such states (we recall that $\bar{E}_m$ is defined as negative). We shall namely suppose that the energies $\bar{E}_k$ and $\bar{E}_m$ have their minimum values for particles and holes at the surface of the Fermi sphere, an assumption which is quite reasonable in our case. Introducing the perturbed Fermi energy $\bar{E}_F$, which is equal to $\bar{E}_k$ and $-\bar{E}_m$ for $|k| = |m| = k_F$, our assumption is expressed by

$$\bar{E}_k > \bar{E}_F \text{ for } |k| > k_F, \tag{4.2}$$

and $$\bar{E}_m > -\bar{E}_F \text{ for } |m| < k_F.$$

To decide whether the states considered are stationary or only metastable, we study the functions $\bar{G}_k(\varepsilon_0 + z)$ and $\bar{G}_m(\varepsilon + z)$ which were defined in I by the formulae

$$\delta(k' - k)\bar{G}_k(\varepsilon_0 + z) = \langle k'|[-V + V\bar{D}(\varepsilon_0 + z)V - \ldots]_{idC}\,|k\rangle, \tag{4.3}$$

$$\delta(m' - m)\bar{G}_m(\varepsilon_0 + z) = \langle m'|[-V + V\bar{D}(\varepsilon_0 + z)V - \ldots]_{idC}\,|m\rangle. \tag{4.4}$$

From these equations and the inequality (4.2), it can be shown that the line of discontinuity of the function $\bar{G}_k(\varepsilon_0 + z)$ is the same for all k and runs from $\bar{E}_F$ to $+\infty$, while the line of discontinuity of $\bar{G}_m(\varepsilon_0 + z)$ always runs from $-\bar{E}_F$ to $+\infty$. This has, as one can easily see, the consequence that for arbitrary $|k| > k_F$ the function $\bar{G}_k(\varepsilon_0 + z)$ is not continuous at $\bar{E}_k$, whereas $\bar{G}_m(\varepsilon_0 + z)$ is not continuous at $\bar{E}_m$. Thus the states considered are non-stationary.

We limit ourselves to a brief outline of the proof of this important property for the case of $\bar{G}_k(\varepsilon_0 + z)$. The argument for $\bar{G}_m(\varepsilon_0 + z)$ is similar. The essential point is that in (4.3) one has among others intermediate states with energies $\bar{E}_\gamma$ smaller than $\bar{E}_k$ (This situation is in contrast with the case in field theory where, in diagonal diagrams, the energies in the intermediate states are always larger than the energy of the state considered). The proof consists of two steps. In the first step one shows that the line of discontinuity of $\bar{G}_k(\varepsilon_0 + z)$ extends from $\bar{E}_F$ to $+\infty$ when $|k| = k_F$. The second step extends this conclusion to the case $|k| > k_F$.

It must be emphasized that the validity of the proof rests entirely on the use of the equations (4.3) and (4.4), where the energy shift in the intermediate states is explicitly taken into account. The use of more conventional formulae for $\bar{G}_k(\varepsilon_0 + z)$ and $\bar{G}_m(\varepsilon_0 + z)$ involving the unperturbed energy denominators $(\varepsilon_\gamma - z)^{-1}$ would easily lead to erroneous results.

Having thus indicated why no perturbed stationary states correspond to the unperturbed states $|k\,;\,\rangle$ and $|\,;\,m\rangle$ of one particle and one hole respectively, we still have to show that, for momenta k and m close to the surface of the Fermi sphere, these states are metastable. A close examination of different approximate expressions for $\bar{J}_k(\varepsilon_0 + x)$ and $\bar{J}_m(\varepsilon_0 + x)$, which can be obtained from (4.3) and (4.4), reveals that, for $|k|$ and $|m|$ close to k_F and for small $x > 0$, $\bar{J}_k(\varepsilon_0 + \bar{E}_F + x) = O(x^2)$, $\bar{J}_m(\varepsilon_0 - \bar{E}_F + x) = O(x^2)$. This behaviour immediately implies that $\bar{J}_k(\varepsilon_0 + \bar{E}_k)$ and $\bar{J}_m(\varepsilon_0 + \bar{E}_m)$ are proportional to $(\bar{E}_k - \bar{E}_F)^2$ and $(\bar{E}_m + \bar{E}_F)^2$ respectively, for momenta near the Fermi momentum. These quantities are consequently small, thus ensuring the metastable character of the states considered.

The conclusion that a state of one (additional) particle is not stationary but, for not too high energies, metastable is in agreement with experiments on the scattering of nucleons on heavy nuclei. It is found experimentally that slow nucleons travel a considerable, though finite, distance through nuclear matter before their kinetic energy gets absorbed to form a compound nucleus. The results of such experiments can be analysed by means of the optical model [7]), where the interaction between the nucleon and the nucleus is described by a square well potential with a small imaginary component. The imaginary part of this potential corresponds exactly with the decay constant $\Gamma_k = \bar{N}_k \bar{J}_k(\varepsilon_0 + \bar{E}_k)$ given by (4.1).

On the basis of the Brueckner approximation, Brueckner, Eden, and Francis [6]) derived a formula for the imaginary part of the optical potential. This formula can also be obtained from the exact formulae (4.1) and (4.3) if a number of approximations are made. We neglect in (4.3) all terms except the first and replace the function $\bar{D}_\gamma(\varepsilon_0 + z)$ in the intermediate state $|\gamma\rangle$ by $(E_\gamma - z)^{-1}$. The latter approximation was already discussed in section 2; it involves among others the omission of the factor $\bar{N}_\gamma$ belonging to the intermediate state. The decay constant Γ_k is then easily found to be

$$\delta(k' - k)\Gamma_k = \bar{N}_k \pi \int \mathrm{d}\gamma \langle\,;\,k'|V|\gamma\rangle \langle\gamma|V|k\,;\,\rangle\, \delta(\bar{E}_\gamma - \bar{E}_k),$$

a formula which reduces to the formula of Brueckner, Eden and Francis if also the factor $\bar{N}_k$ belonging to the state $|k\,;\,\rangle$ is replaced by one. As stated before, the omission of the two factors $\bar{N}_k$ and $\bar{N}_\gamma$ can easily lead to considerable errors in the result. Our formula (4.1) provides, however, the basis for more accurate calculations of the inverse life-time of metastable states.

Acknowledgements. The author is indebted to Professor L. Van Hove for many helpful discussions and for his continued interest. The author also wishes to thank Professor L. Rosenfeld for his hospitality at the theoretical Institute of Manchester and Dr. E. J. Eden for many fruitful discussions.

This work is part of the research program of the "Stichting voor Fundamenteel Onderzoek der Materie", which is financially supported by the Netherlands Organization for pure scientific Research (Z.W.O.).

Received 13-4-57.

REFERENCES

1) Hugenholtz, N. M., Physica **23** (1957) 481 (this issue).
2) See e.g., Brueckner, K. A. and Levinson, C. A., Phys. Rev. **97** (1955) 1344; also Bethe, H. A., Phys. Rev. **103** (1956) 1353, where an extensive list of references to other work of Brueckner and coll. can be found.
3) Swiatecki, W. J., Phys. Rev. **103** (1956) 265.
4) Bethe, H. A., Phys. Rev. **103** (1956) 1353.
5) Euler, H., Z. Physik **105** (1937) 553.
Huby, R., Proc. Phys. Soc. (London) **A 62** (1949) 62.
6) Brueckner, K. A., Eden, R. J. and Francis, N. C., Phys. Rev. **100** (1955) 891.
7) Feshbach, H., Porter, C. E. and Weisskopf, V. F., Phys. Rev. **96** (1954) 448.

A THEOREM ON THE SINGLE PARTICLE ENERGY IN A FERMI GAS WITH INTERACTION

by N. M. HUGENHOLTZ and L. VAN HOVE

Instituut voor theoretische fysica, der Rijksuniversiteit, Utrecht, Nederland

Synopsis

This paper investigates single particle properties in a Fermi gas with interaction at the absolute zero of temperature. In such a system a single particle energy has only a meaning for particles of momentum $|k|$ close to the Fermi momentum k_F. These single particle states are metastable with a life-time approaching infinity in the limit $|k| \to k_F$. The limiting value of the energy is called the Fermi energy E_F. As a special case of a more general theorem, it is shown that for a system with zero pressure (i.e. a Fermi liquid at absolute zero) the Fermi energy E_F is equal to the average energy per particle E_0/N of the system. This result should apply both to liquid He_3 and to nuclear matter.

The theorem is used as a test on the internal consistency of the theory of Brueckner [1]) for the structure of nuclear matter. It is seen that the large discrepancy between the values of E_F and E_0/N, as calculated by Brueckner and Gammel [2]), arises from the fact that Brueckner neglects important cluster terms contributing to the single particle energy. This neglection strongly affects the calculation of the optical potential.

1. *Introduction.* In Brueckner's theory [1]) on the structure of nuclear matter the interior of a nucleus is considered as a gas of strongly interacting Fermi particles. To each particle a separate energy E_l is assigned, which depends on the momentum l of the particle. This energy is written as the sum of the kinetic energy $l^2/2M$ and a potential energy V_l. The computation of V_l from a set of implicit equations is the main problem in this theory. Once V_l is known, the energy of the whole system in its ground state is given by the simple formula

$$E_0 = \Sigma_{|l|<k_F} (l^2/2M + \tfrac{1}{2}V_l). \quad (1)$$

The summation is extended over all occupied states, *i.e.* over all momenta smaller than the Fermi momentum k_F *).

One might ask the question, what is the physical meaning of this single particle energy E_l or the "potential energy" V_l in a system of strongly interacting particles. To answer this question we consider the theory of Brueckner as a special approximation of a general time-independent

*) We put $\hbar = 1$ throughout this paper.

perturbation formalism which was developed earlier by the authors [3]) (to be quoted as I, II and III). As will be shown in section 2, it then turns out that only to particles with momentum l in the neighbourhood of the Fermi momentum k_F an approximate energy E_l can be assigned. Only in the limit that $|l|$ approaches k_F the energy E_l gets a precise meaning. This limiting value of E_l is called the *Fermi energy* E_F.

Section 3 will be devoted to an important theorem concerning this Fermi energy. It will be shown rigorously that for a system of Fermi particles at its ground state the Fermi energy as defined above is equal to the mean energy per particle, provided the system has zero pressure. Nuclear matter is an example of such a system.

This theorem, which is a special case of a more general formula, derived in the first half of section 3, can be used as a test for the validity of the approximation of Brueckner. In recent calculations of Brueckner and Gammel [2]) the ground state energy per particle is found to be -15 MeV, whereas these authors find for the Fermi energy the value -34 MeV *). The cause of this discrepancy is investigated in the last section. Indications are presented that the largest part of the discrepancy comes from the inaccuracy of E_F.

2. *The single particle energy*. The considerations of this and the following sections are mainly based on I and III. We consider a system of a large number N of Fermi particles enclosed in a box of volume Ω. For simplicity we assume the particles to have no spin or charge. We are interested in particular in the case that both N and Ω are very large with a finite density $\rho = N/\Omega$. The hamiltonian H of the complete system is written as a sum of the kinetic energy H_0 and the interaction V, which in the occupation number representation for plane wave states have the form

$$H_0 = \int_l (|l|^2/2M)\, \xi_l^* \xi_l,$$
$$V = \tfrac{1}{4} \int_{l_1 l_2 l_3 l_4} v(l_1 l_2 l_3 l_4) \xi_{l_1}^* \xi_{l_2}^* \xi_{l_3} \xi_{l_4}.$$

For the notation we refer to III. ξ_l and ξ_l^* are annihilation and creation operators for a particle with momentum l, obeying the anticommutation relations

$$\{\xi_k, \xi_l^*\} = \Omega(2\pi)^{-3}\, \delta_{kl}.$$

In the limit $\Omega \to \infty$ the right-hand side goes over into the Dirac δ-function $\delta(k - l)$.

The ground state $|\varphi_0\rangle$ of the unperturbed system is the state where all states of the Fermi sea, *i.e.* all one particle states with momenta less than the Fermi momentum k_F, are occupied. The Fermi momentum k_F is related to the particle density by $\rho = k_F^3/6\pi^2$.

---

*) As Dr. Brueckner kindly pointed out to us, the numbers quoted here are not quite correct and must be replaced by -14.6 MeV and -27.5 MeV. The discrepancy is therefore 13 MeV. (*Note added in proof*).

All other stationary states of the unperturbed system are characterized by the momenta $k_1, k_2, \ldots.$ of the additional particles present and the momenta $m_1, m_2, \ldots.$ of the holes present (holes are unoccupied states of the Fermi sea). We respectively use the letters k and m to indicate momenta larger and smaller than the Fermi momentum k_F. Because the annihilation of a particle in the Fermi sea is equivalent to the creation of a hole, it is useful to reinterpret ξ_m and $\xi_m{}^*$ for $|m| \leqslant k_F$ as creation and annihilation operators for holes.

We have thus obtained a hamiltonian which exhibits a close formal resemblance to a field theory with pair creation. There is, however, an important difference, which will be considered in this section. Whereas in field, theory, for not too strong coupling, to each unperturbed state corresponds at least one stationary state of the complete system; this is not the case in our system, which is essentially dissipative. In I and II a simple criterion was given for the existence of a perturbed stationary state corresponding to a state $|\alpha\rangle$ of the unperturbed system. It amounts to the existence of a pole for the expectation value of the resolvent $R(z) = (H - z)^{-1}$ for the state $|\alpha\rangle$. As shown in III the expectation value $D_0(z)$ of $R(z)$ for $|\varphi_0\rangle$ has always a pole. Consequently there exists a stationary state $|\psi_0\rangle$, the ground state of the system of interacting particles, which corresponds to the unperturbed ground state $|\varphi_0\rangle$. The energy of $|\psi_0\rangle$ we call E_0. The explicit expression of $|\psi_0\rangle$ and E_0 was determined in III.

Next we consider an unperturbed state with one additional particle with momentum k ($|k| > k_F$); it will be denoted by $|k;\rangle$. According to I we must study the function $D_k(z) = \bar{D}_k(z) * D_0(z)$ *) of the complex variable z. $D_k(z)$ is the expectation value of the resolvent $R(z)$ for $|k;\rangle$ except for a factor $\delta(o)$: $\langle ;k\,|R(z)|\,k';\rangle = \delta(k - k')\, D_k(z)$. The product $*$ is the convolution product defined and extensively used in III. $\bar{D}_k(z)$ was defined in III (section 10) by a series in increasing powers of the interaction V, all terms of which can be represented by means of connected diagrams with one external particle line at both ends (the diagrams used are defined in III, section 3; particle lines have arrows pointing to the left, lines corresponding to holes the opposite direction). The decisive point is now whether or not $D_k(z)$ has a pole. A pole would mean that the complete system has a stationary state corresponding to the unperturbed state $|k;\rangle$. The absence of a pole would reveal the dissipative nature of the unperturbed state $|k;\rangle$. As shown previously (see a fourth paper [4]) to be quoted as IV) $\bar{D}_k(z)$ has no pole and consequently $D_k(z)$ can have none, so that the state $|k;\rangle$ is a dissipative one †). The only singularity of $\bar{D}_k(z)$ is a cut in the complex plane along the real axis, running from some point E_F, independent of k, up to $+\infty$. Whereas the

*) To avoid the unnecessary appearance of the term ε_0 in our formulae the function $\bar{D}_k(\varepsilon_0 + z)$ defined in III is denoted here simply as $\bar{D}_k(z)$.

†) For a further discussion of dissipative states see [5]).

real part of $\bar{D}_k(z)$ varies continuously if we cross this cut, the imaginary part changes its sign. If we now consider the discontinuity of the imaginary part of $\bar{D}_k(z)$ for all points of the cut, we find, in the case that $|k|$ is very close to the Fermi-momentum k_F, a high narrow peak for some point E_k *). This situation is to be compared with the δ-singularity, which one would find if E_k was a pole of $\bar{D}_k(z)$. In the limit $|k| \to k_F$ the point E_k approaches the branching point E_F, the difference $E_k - E_F$ being proportional to $|k| - k_F$. The width Γ_k of the peak decreases as $(E_k - E_F)^2$, so that for $|k| - k_F$ small enough, the width of the peak is small compared to its distance from E_F.

Such a situation was analysed in III (section 14). In the case that $\Gamma_k \ll E_k - E_F$ a state vector $|\psi_k\rangle$ can be constructed, which corresponds to a metastable state with an approximate energy $E_k + E_0$ and a life-time equal to Γ_k^{-1}. The metastable character of $|\psi_k\rangle$ is exhibited by the equation

$$\langle\psi_{k'}\, |e^{-iHt}|\, \psi_k\rangle = \delta^3(k' - k) \exp\left[-i(E_0 + E_k)t - \Gamma_k\, |t|\right],$$

which holds for values of t of the order of Γ_k^{-1} †). The energy E_k can then be interpreted as the energy of a metastable particle with momentum $|k| > k_F$, moving in the Fermi gas with slow dissipation of its momentum and energy into collective types of motion of the gas. The success of the optical model for the scattering of nucleons on heavy nuclei is experimental evidence for the existence of such metastable states in nuclear matter. Conversely we can say that our theory of the Fermi gas with interaction accounts for the low energy behaviour of the optical potential.

In the limit of $|k| \to k_F$ the single particle energy E_k tends to E_F. We call this limit the *Fermi energy*. The life-time Γ_k^{-1} tends then to infinity, and it can even be shown that E_F is the pole (in the somewhat broadened sense defined in III section 9) of the function $\bar{D}_{k_F}(z)$. Hence a state with one additional particle at the surface of the Fermi sea is exactly stationary, with an energy $E_0 + E_F$.

Instead of states with an additional particle one can also consider states with a hole of momentum $|m| < k_F$. This case is very much analogous to the former one. The function $\bar{D}_m(z)$, which is defined in terms of connected diagrams with one external hole line at both ends, has for $|m|$ close to k_F a similar behaviour as $\bar{D}_k(z)$ for $|k|$ close to k_F. This implies for the case that $|m|$ is close to k_F the existence of a metastable state of a hole, with

---

*) In IV this quantity was denoted by $\bar{E}_k$, whereas the notation E_k was there used for $E_0 + \bar{E}_k$. The notation used here agrees with the usual one in the Brueckner theory.

†) In III, eq. (14.8) and the subsequent equation as well as their derivation are incorrect. The definition of the two states $|\psi_\alpha\rangle^\pm$ as given by eq. (14.2) of III, however, is correct. In the case that $|\alpha\rangle = |k;\rangle$ these two states are identical and are denoted by $|\psi_k\rangle$.

an approximate energy $E_0 - E_m$. Here $-E_m$ is the point on the real axis where $\bar{D}_m(z)$ is strongly peaked *). It can be interpreted as the energy of a hole of momentum $-m$ near the surface of the Fermi sea, and E_m therefore can be regarded as the energy of a particle of momentum m in the Fermi sea. In the limit $|m| = k_F$, $\bar{D}_m(z)$ does have a pole which, as was surmised in IV and will be confirmed in the next section, is equal to $-E_F$, where E_F is the Fermi energy as defined above.

We should like to stress here that all our considerations are based on the assumption of convergence of all series involved. It may very well be that in addition to the ground state and metastable excited states here considered for the Fermi gas with interaction there exist another "abnormal" stationary state and metastable excitations of it, depending in a singular way on the two-body interaction and therefore not directly accessible to our methods. The possibility of such abnormal states for a Fermi gas with attractive forces has been established by Bardeen, Cooper and Schrieffer [6]) in their theory of superconductivity. How the abnormal states can be obtained in the perturbation formalism based on diagrams has been shown by Bogolubov [7]). The possible existence and observability of such abnormal states for nuclear matter and liquid helium 3 are questions of great importance which we shall not discuss here.

3. *Theorem on the Fermi energy* E_F. We start this section with the derivation of a formula for $\bar{D}_k(z)$, which brings to light a close similarity between this function and the ground state expectation value $\langle\varphi_0 |R(z)| \varphi_0\rangle \equiv D_0(z)$. We shall make an extensive use of the methods presented in III. Before doing so we want, however, to stress the following point. As is well known, the general perturbation method as developed in I, II and III is only exact if the particle number N and the volume Ω of the system are so large that terms proportional to Ω^{-1} or N^{-1} can be neglected. Nevertheless several definitions and results of III are also exactly valid for systems with arbitrary finite N and Ω. This is the case in particular with the definitions and calculation rules of diagrams, diagonal diagrams, connectedness and also with the theorem on the convolution of the contributions of two diagrams (section 7, eq. 4). We use this important fact in the following derivation.

We take a finite cubic box with volume Ω, and impose, as usual, periodic boundary conditions. Let the state vector $|\varphi\rangle$, which is normalized to one, describe a state of the unperturbed system where N particles occupy N given single particle plane-wave states. This set of N single-particle states we shall call the "sea". The state $|\varphi\rangle$ may be different from the unperturbed ground state $|\varphi_0\rangle$. All other states of the unperturbed system can be obtained from $|\varphi\rangle$ by the application of suitable operators $\xi_k{}^*$ or ξ_m, thereby creating

*) E_m in this paper corresponds to the quantity $-\bar{E}_m$ in IV. The single particle energy for particles in the Fermi sea is now E_m.

additional particles or holes. Clearly the momenta k of the additional particles must be outside the sea, whereas the momenta m of the holes must belong to it.

In calculating the diagonal matrix element $\langle\varphi\,|R(z)|\,\varphi\rangle$ we make use of diagrams. If, just as in III, lines running from right to left (from left to right) represent particles (holes), we obtain diagrams identical with those which were used in III for calculating $D_0(z) \equiv \langle\varphi_0\,|R(z)|\,\varphi_0\rangle$. Their contributions are, however, different, because the momenta k and m of the virtual particles and holes have now to be summed over different, discrete sets of values. The diagrams contributing to $\langle\varphi\,|R(z)|\,\varphi\rangle$ are either connected or consist of two or more connected parts. If we denote the total contribution to $\langle\varphi|R(z+\varepsilon)|\varphi\rangle$ of all connected diagrams by $B(z)$, with ε the energy of $|\varphi\rangle$, the total contribution to $\langle\varphi\,|R(z+\varepsilon)\,|\varphi\rangle$ of all diagrams consisting of two connected parts is equal to

$$\tfrac{1}{2}\,B(z) * B(z).$$

Here we used the convolution in the complex plane introduced in III (section 7). The factor $\frac{1}{2}$ accounts for the fact that this convolution gives each term twice. Proceeding in the same way with diagrams consisting of three and more components, one finds easily

$$\langle\varphi\,|R(\varepsilon+z)\,|\varphi\rangle = -z^{-1} + B(z) + \tfrac{1}{2}B(z) * B(z) + \tfrac{1}{6}\,B(z) * B(z) * B(z) + \ldots. \quad (2)$$

For the special choice where $|\varphi\rangle \equiv |\varphi_0\rangle$ equation (2) leads to

$$D_0(\varepsilon_0 + z) = -\,z^{-1} + B_0(z) + \tfrac{1}{2}B_0(z) * B_0(z) + \\ + \tfrac{1}{6}B_0(z) * B_0(z) * B_0(z) + \ldots.\ {}^{8)}, \quad (3)$$

where $B_0(z)$ is defined as the sum of the contributions of connected ground state diagrams; ε_0 is the energy of the unperturbed ground state $|\varphi_0\rangle$.

We now also apply (2) for another choice of $|\varphi\rangle$. We take for $|\varphi\rangle$ the unperturbed state $|\varphi_k\rangle$, where in addition to the N particles in the Fermi sea of $|\varphi_0\rangle$ there is an extra particle of momentum k ($|k|>k_F$). The total contribution of all connected diagrams (without external lines) to $\langle\varphi_k\,|R(\varepsilon+z)|\,\varphi_k\rangle$, where $\varepsilon = \varepsilon_0 + k^2/2M$, we denote by $B_k(z)$. Equation (2) reads for this case

$$\langle\varphi_k|\,R(\varepsilon_0 + k^2/2M + z)\,|\varphi_k\rangle = -\,z^{-1} + B_k(z) + \tfrac{1}{2}B_k(z) * B_k(z) + \\ + \tfrac{1}{6}\,B_k(z) * B_k(z) * B_k(z) + \ldots..$$

Introducing the notation $B_k(z) - B_0(z) = \bar{B}_k(z)$ we are lead to the equation

$$\langle\varphi_k|\,R(\varepsilon_0 + k^2/2M + z)|\,\varphi_k\rangle = -\,z^{-1} + (B_0(z) + \bar{B}_k(z)) + \\ + \tfrac{1}{2}(B_0(z) + \bar{B}_k(z)) * (B_0(z) + \bar{B}_k(z)) + \ldots..$$

If we compare this series with the exponential series we see immediately that it can be written as the convolution of two functions one of which, by equation (3), is equal to $D_0(\varepsilon_0 + z)$. Thus

$$\langle\varphi_k\,|R(\varepsilon_0 + k^2/2M + z)|\,\varphi_k\rangle =$$
$$= D_0(\varepsilon_0 + z) * [-z^{-1} + \bar{B}_k(z) + \tfrac{1}{2}\bar{B}_k(z) * \bar{B}_k(z) + \ldots]. \quad (4)$$

The state vectors $|\varphi_k\rangle$ and $|k;\rangle \equiv \xi_k|\ \varphi_0\rangle$ describe the same state. Remembering their different normalization we can write

$$|k;\rangle = \Omega^{1/2}(2\pi)^{-3/2}\,|\varphi_k\rangle.$$

Hence

$$D_k(z)\,\delta^3(k - k') \equiv \langle;k'\,|R(z)|\,k;\rangle = \delta_{k',k}\,\langle;k\,|R(z)|\,k;\rangle =$$
$$= \Omega(2\pi)^{-3}\,\delta_{k',k}\,\langle\varphi_k\,|R(z)|\,\varphi_k\rangle = \langle\varphi_k\,|R(z)|\,\varphi_k\rangle\,\delta^3(k - k'),$$

where we used the relation between Kronecker symbol and δ-function for finite Ω (see III, section 2):

$$\delta^3(k - k') = \Omega(2\pi)^{-3}\,\delta_{k,k'}.$$

We see that

$$\langle\varphi_k\,|R(z)|\varphi_k\rangle = D_k(z). \quad (5)$$

As we know $D_k(z)$ can be expressed very simply in terms of $\bar{D}_k(z)$, which is defined by means of connected one particle diagrams, and $D_0(z)$ by the formula (see III (10.1))

$$D_k(\varepsilon_0 + z) = \bar{D}_k(z) * D_0(\varepsilon_0 + z). \quad (6)$$

Comparing (4) and (6) we get

$$\bar{D}_k(k^2/2M + z) = -\,z^{-1} + \bar{B}_k(z) + \tfrac{1}{2}\bar{B}_k(z) * \bar{B}_k(z) +$$
$$+ \tfrac{1}{6}\bar{B}_k(z) * \bar{B}_k(z) * \bar{B}_k(z) + \ldots.. \quad (7)$$

This equation, which is formally quite similar to equation (3) for $D_0(z)$, is strictly valid for a finite system. We are , however, specially interested in the case that both Ω and N are infinite. We therefore study the function $\bar{B}_k(z)$ in this limit. As follows from its definition the function $B_k(z)$ can be obtained from $B_0(z)$, if in the latter each summation $\int_{k_i}$ corresponding to a particle line is replaced by ($\int_{k_i} - (2\pi)^3\,\Omega^{-1} \times$ term with $k_i = k$) and each summation $\int_{m_j}$ for a hole line is replaced by ($\int_{m_j} + (2\pi)^3\,\Omega^{-1} \times$ term with $m_j = k$). Keeping in mind that $B_0(z)$, which was defined in terms of connected ground state diagrams, is proportional to Ω in the limit of $\Omega \to \infty$, we see that $\bar{B}_k(z) = B_k(z) - B_0(z)$ contains a main term independent of Ω, and other terms which vanish if Ω tends to infinity. The function $\bar{B}_k(z)$ is therefore well defined also for an infinitely large system. Replacing summations by integrations and keeping only those terms which are independent of the volume Ω, $\bar{B}_k(z)$ is calculated in the following way. It is a sum of terms, each of which is obtained from the function $(2\pi)^3 \Omega^{-1} B_0(z)$ by putting the momentum of one of the lines equal to k and performing the integration over all other momenta. If the momentum which is put equal to k belongs to a particle line, the corresponding term gets a minus sign. Both sides of equation (7) have well defined finite limits for $\Omega \to \infty$. We can now return to this limiting case.

Although equation (7) for general k is interesting in itself, giving an alternative way of calculating $\bar{D}_k(z)$, we are here particularly interested in the limit of $|k|$ tending to k_F. In this limit the relation between $\bar{B}_k(z)$ and $B_0(z)$ has the following very simple form

$$\bar{B}_{k_F}(z) = 2\pi^2 k_F^{-2} \frac{\mathrm{d}}{\mathrm{d}k_F} (B_0(z)/\Omega). \tag{8}$$

To prove equation (8) we notice that $B_0(z)/\Omega$ depends on k_F only through the limits of integration of the integrals over particle and hole momenta. Differentiation of $B_0(z)/\Omega$ with respect to k_F gives a sum of terms, in each of which the momentum of one line is put equal to k_F. There is in addition a common factor $4\pi k_F^2$ resulting from integration over the surface of the Fermi sphere. Also here one gets a minus sign if the fixed momentum belongs to a particle because then k_F appears in the lower integration limit. The factors $4\pi k_F^2$ and $2\pi^2/k_F^2$ give together exactly $(2\pi)^3$, thus establishing equation (8). Using the well known relation between k_F and the density $\rho \equiv N/\Omega$:

$$\rho = k_F^3/6\pi^2,$$

equation (8) gets the simpler form

$$\bar{B}_{k_F}(z) = \frac{\mathrm{d}}{\mathrm{d}\rho} (B_0(z)/\Omega). \tag{9}$$

We now make essential use of the great formal similarity of equations (3) and (7). Clearly $D_0(\varepsilon_0 + z)$ changes into $\bar{D}_k(k^2/2M + z)$ if in (3) $B_0(z)$ is replaced by $\bar{B}_k(z)$. It was shown in III (section 9) that $D_0(\varepsilon_0 + z)$ can be expressed very simply in terms of the function $\bar{G}_0(\varepsilon_0 + z) \equiv z^2 B_0(z)$. In particular $D_0(\varepsilon_0 + z)$ was found to have a simple pole at $z = -\bar{G}_0(\varepsilon_0)$ with the residue $\exp(-\bar{G}_0'(\varepsilon_0))$, where the prime means the derivative with respect to z. This was a consequence of the fact that $z^2 B_0(z) = \bar{G}_0(\varepsilon_0 + z)$ had no singularities on the negative real axis of the z-plane. The same property holds for $z^2 \bar{B}_k(z)$ when $|k| = k_F$. By analogy we therefore conclude immediately that $\bar{D}_{k_F}(k_F^2/2M + z)$ has a pole at the point

$$z = -\lim_{z_1 \to 0} [z_1^2 \bar{B}_{k_F}(z_1)] = -\frac{\mathrm{d}}{\mathrm{d}\rho} (\bar{G}_0(\varepsilon_0)/\Omega), \tag{10}$$

with a residue

$$\exp\left[-\frac{\mathrm{d}}{\mathrm{d}\rho} (\bar{G}_0'(\varepsilon_0)/\Omega)\right].$$

As follows from the definition of the Fermi energy E_F, the pole of $\bar{D}_{k_F}(k_F^2/2M + z)$ is equal to $\Delta E_F = E_F - k_F^2/2M$. We have thus from (10)

$$\Delta E_F = \frac{\mathrm{d}}{\mathrm{d}\rho} (\Delta E_0/\Omega).$$

The same relation holds for the kinetic parts of E_F and E_0, hence

$$E_F = \frac{\mathrm{d}}{\mathrm{d}\rho} (E_0/\Omega). \tag{11}$$

This equation, if written in the equivalent form

$$E_F = \left(\frac{\partial E_0}{\partial N}\right)_\Omega,$$

where the derivative is taken at constant Ω, shows that the Fermi energy E_F, as defined in the previous section in terms of one-particle diagrams, is equal to the change in ground state energy of the system produced by addition or removal of one particle at constant volume.

For the function $\bar{D}_m(z)$ ($|m| < k_F$), which is the counterpart of $\bar{D}_k(z)$ for holes, one can proceed in exactly the same way. Instead of (7) one finds

$$\bar{D}_m(-m^2/2M + z) =$$
$$= -z^{-1} + \bar{B}_m(z) + \tfrac{1}{2}\bar{B}_m(z) * \bar{B}_m(z) + \tfrac{1}{6}\bar{B}_m(z) * \bar{B}_m(z) * \bar{B}_m(z) + \ldots, \tag{12}$$

where $\bar{B}_m(z)$ is defined in exactly the same way as $\bar{B}_k(z)$, except for the momentum k being replaced by m and the roles of particle and hole lines being interchanged. It is easily seen that the limit of $\bar{B}_m(z)$ for $|m| \to k_F$ is equal to $-\bar{B}_{k_F}(z)$. Forming now the convolution of $\bar{D}_k(k^2/2M + z)$ and $\bar{D}_m(-m^2/2M + z)$ for $|k| = |m| = k_F$ one finds, after an obvious shift of z in both functions

$$\bar{D}_k(z) * \bar{D}_m(z) = -z^{-1}, \text{ for } |k| = |m| = k_F.$$

This equation implies, that the poles of $\bar{D}_k(z)$ and $\bar{D}_m(z)$ for $|k| = |m| = k_F$ add up to zero, while the corresponding residues have a product equal to one. Since the sum of the poles is zero, the energy of a hole at the surface of the Fermi sea is equal to $-E_F$. Therefore the energy E_l of a particle of momentum $|l|$ close to k_F, as defined in section 2 for $|l|$ smaller or larger than k_F, is continuous at $|l| = k_F$.

Equation (11) can be expressed in terms of the energy per particle instead of the energy per unit volume:

$$E_F = E_0/N + \rho \frac{\mathrm{d}}{\mathrm{d}\rho} (E_0/N).$$

In terms of the pressure

$$p = -\left(\frac{\partial E_0}{\partial \Omega}\right)_N = \rho^2 \frac{\mathrm{d}}{\mathrm{d}\rho} (E_0/N),$$

this equation reads

$$E_F = E_0/N + p/\rho.$$

In the case that the system is in equilibrium, *i.e.*, at a density such that the pressure vanishes, we obtain the equation

$$E_F = E_0/N. \tag{13}$$

This equality of the Fermi energy and the average energy, which we have proved generally, was derived recently by Weisskopf [9]) on the basis of the independent particle model. Bethe [10]) considered it to be only a rough approximation.

4. *Test on the accuracy of the theory of Brueckner.* In this last section the theorem (13) derived in section 3 will be used as a test on the validity of the Brueckner theory. Recently very accurate calculations on the basis of this theory have been made by Brueckner and Gammel [2]). The following discussion will be based mainly on the results of their work.

Our considerations will be of special interest because the calculations of Brueckner and Gammel show that their results vary strongly with slight changes in the forces between the particles *). Good agreement with the experiments does therefore not guarantee the accuracy of the theory. The test to be discussed here, on the contrary, is independent of the choice of the forces, for equation (13) must hold for all forces.

For the average energy E_0/N and the Fermi energy E_F Brueckner and Gammel find -15 MeV and -34 MeV respectively. There is a discrepancy of about 20 MeV, which shows that at least one of these values is very inaccurate. To investigate the origin of the discrepancy we consider the theory of Brueckner as an approximation of our exact perturbation formalism, as was done in IV †). It was shown there how one can obtain the theory of Brueckner from the exact theory by selecting only those terms which correspond to a certain class of diagrams. The relevant terms for E_0, E_k and E_m ($|k| > k_F$ and $|m| < k_F$) are represented by the diagrams of type *a*, *b* and *c* of fig. 1 **).

Let us consider equation (3) and equation (7) where $\bar{B}_k(z)$ is obtained

*) We are indebted to Dr. J. L. Gammel for communication of this and many other as yet unpublished results.

†) The equation for the scattering matrix G in IV at the bottom of page 537 contains an error. The energy denominator must read $\bar{E}_{k_1} + \bar{E}_{k_2} - |\bar{E}_{l_3}| - |\bar{E}_{l_4}|$.

**) The additional complications originating from the use of shifted energies in the denominators are not relevant for our discussion and are omitted for simplicity.

from $B_0(z)$ in the way prescribed in section 3. If we approximate $B_0(z)$ in these equations by taking the diagrams of fig. 1*a* only, we must still expect that the approximate values one then finds for E_F and E_0/N coincide (the latter value is the Brueckner approximation for the binding energy).

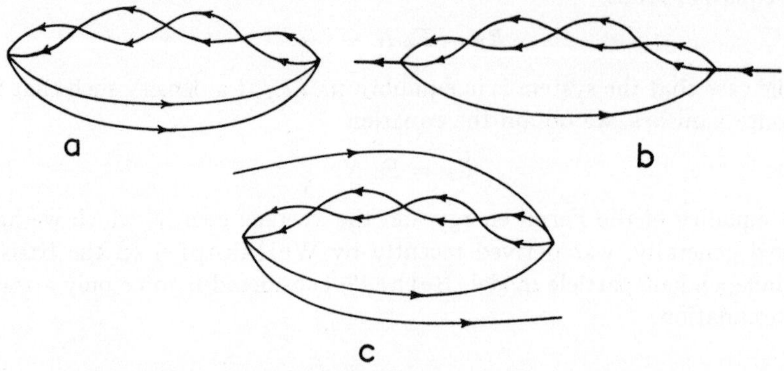

Fig. 1. The Brueckner diagrams. The diagrams *a*, *b* and *c* correspond to the ground state energy E_0 and the energies E_k and E_m of particles and holes respectively.

The function $\bar{B}_k(z)$ in the approximation now considered is equal to the sum of the contributions of all single particle diagrams, obtained from the ground state diagrams of fig. 1*a* by replacing any internal line by two external particle lines. This leads to two types of diagrams. The first type, where one of the hole lines is replaced by two external particle lines, is shown in fig. 1*b*. The other type, shown in fig. 2*a*, is obtained from fig. 1*a* by replacing one of the many internal particle lines by two external particle

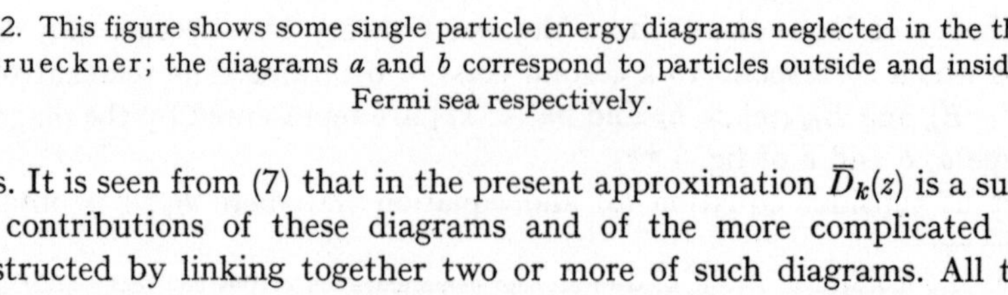

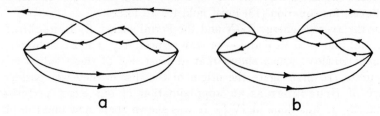

Fig. 2. This figure shows some single particle energy diagrams neglected in the theory of Brueckner; the diagrams *a* and *b* correspond to particles outside and inside the Fermi sea respectively.

lines. It is seen from (7) that in the present approximation $\bar{D}_k(z)$ is a sum of the contributions of these diagrams and of the more complicated ones constructed by linking together two or more of such diagrams. All these single particle diagrams, with the exception of the one in fig. 1*b*, are neglected in the theory of Brueckner. They contain three and more particle clusters. From the numerical discrepancy between E_0/N and E_F found, as mentioned above, by Brueckner and Gammel, we must conclude that for

$|k| = k_F$ the total contribution of the diagrams neglected in the Brueckner theory is considerable. It must account for a difference of about 20 MeV. It seems reasonable to suppose that among the neglected terms the most important ones are those represented by diagrams of the type of fig. 2*a* and the corresponding diagrams for holes in fig. 2*b*. This is also suggested by the following consideration.

The theory of Brueckner can be considered as the first term in the so-called cluster expansion [11]). Using the K-matrix instead of the interaction V all quantities are expressed by means of a very much smaller number of diagrams, namely those diagrams, where no two successive vertices are connected by two particle lines (Goldstone [11]) called them irreducible; we have used this term in III already with another meaning). The diagrams corresponding to the first three terms of the cluster expansion for E_0 are shown in fig. 3. To each dot there corresponds a K-matrix. The first term in the figure gives the Brueckner approximation; it corresponds to diagram *a* of fig. 1. The cluster expansion can be considered as a power series in the

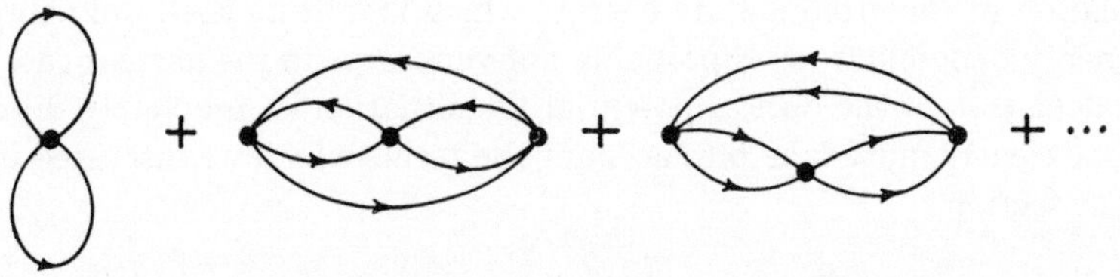

Fig. 3. The first three diagrams of the cluster expansion for E_0.

K-matrix. The Brueckner approximation is based on the assumption that this series converges rapidly. The second term in fig. 3 was calculated by Bethe [10]) for the case of Yukawa forces. It was found to be less than 1 MeV, which is indeed very small compared to the main term. We notice from fig. 3 that the cluster expansion for E_0 contains no term with two K-matrices. This has the consequence that even for a comparatively slow convergence the first term can be a reasonably accurate approximation.

The first two diagrams of the cluster expansion for the single particle energy E_l, are given in fig. 4*a* for $|l| \geqslant k_F$, in fig. 4*b* for $|l| \leqslant k_F$. Also here the first diagrams of *a* and *b* give the Brueckner approximation and correspond to diagrams *b* and *c* of fig. 1. Comparing the first diagrams in fig. 3 and fig. 4*b* we find the well-known relation, characteristic of the Brueckner theory, between the energy shift $\varDelta E_0$ of the ground state and the shift $V_l = E_l - l^2/2M$ of the single particle energy:

$$\varDelta E_0 = \tfrac{1}{2}\Omega(2\pi)^{-3} \int_0^{k_F} d^3m V_m,$$

which is another form of (1). In the case of particles with spin and isobaric spin $\frac{1}{2}$ a factor 4 must be added at the right-hand side. One sees again that (1) is not an exact equation *).

The cluster expansion for E_l involves a term with two K-matrices which might be quite appreciable in case of a slow convergence of the series. This term corresponds exactly to the type of diagrams shown in fig. 2, so that we must expect the neglection of the diagrams in fig. 2 to be largely responsible for the discrepancy between E_0/N and E_F in the theory of Brueckner. We have made a rough estimate of this term, for spin and charge independent Yukawa forces. Making the same approximation as Bethe did in his calculation of the three-particle cluster term in E_0, we find approximately 12 MeV for the second term in fig. 4*a* or *b*, for a momentum $|l| = k_F$. This shows that even for these unrealistic forces the main single-particle energy term left out by Brueckner is quite large. A calculation of this term and other cluster terms neglected in the Brueckner theory, on the basis of more realistic forces with a repulsive core, would be very interesting. We may conclude already, however, that in the theory of Brueckner the single-particle energy is treated very inaccurately. The influence of this inaccuracy on the calculation of the ground state energy, which manifests itself only through the energy denominators, is probably not very large in the nuclear case. For the calculation of the optical potential the situation is completely different and one clearly must take into account the terms which we discussed in the present section.

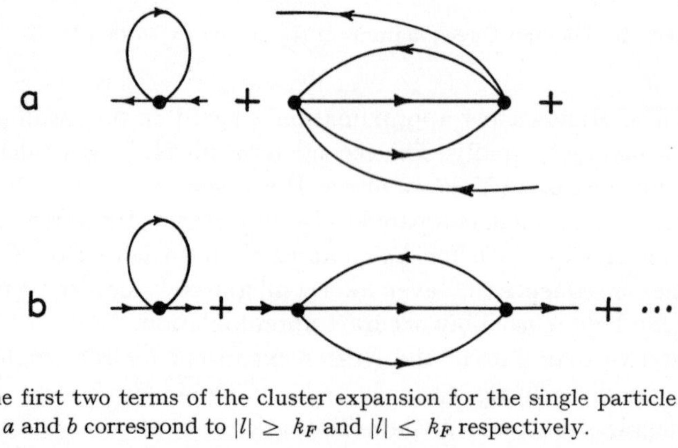

Fig. 4. The first two terms of the cluster expansion for the single particle energy E_l; *a* and *b* correspond to $|l| \geq k_F$ and $|l| \leq k_F$ respectively.

Quite recently, one of the present authors having brought the large internal inconsistency revealed in Brueckner's theory by the theorem here discussed to his attention, Brueckner reconsidered the problem in the framework of his theory and suggested to use the theorem itself for obtaining

*) Differentiation of (1) with respect to the density ρ would lead to (11), provided V_l would not depend on ρ. We know, however, that such is not the case.

a better definition of the single-particle energy *). The new definition amounts to replacing the single-particle energy E_l^B of the original Brueckner approximation (first term in fig. 4*a* of *b*) by a shifted value $E_l^B + \varepsilon$, where the quantity ε, assumed independent of the momentum l, is defined by the condition

$$E_l^B + \varepsilon = E_0/N \text{ for } |l| = k_F.$$

An obvious correction term is then added to the formula expressing E_0 in terms of the single-particle energies. This elementary way of circumventing the inconsistency suffers from two obvious defects. The momentum independence of ε is completely unfounded in a theory where, as in Brueckner's, the potential energy part of E_l^B has an important momentum variation. In the second place, a proper definition of the single-particle energy should be entirely formulated in terms of the propagation of an additional particle (or a hole) of given momentum through the given medium. Such is the case with the definition of E_l in the general theory used here and this is the only reason why our theorem is not trivial. Brueckner's definition of ε, on the contrary, is in fact based on a comparison between two states of the medium with two different densities.

The authors are very grateful to Dr. J. L. Gammel for many stimulating discussions, some of which were at the origin of the present work. They are also indebted to him for much valuable unpublished information on the numerical aspects of Brueckner's theory.

This work is part of the research program of the „Stichting voor Fundamenteel Onderzoek der Materie", which is financially supported by the Netherlands Organization for pure Scientific Research (Z.W.O.).

Received 1-2-58.

REFERENCES

1) Brueckner, K. A. and Levinson, C. A., Phys. Rev. **97** (1955) 1344.
2) Brueckner, K. A. and Gammel, J. L., Phys. Rev. **105** (1957) 1679.
3) Van Hove, L., Physica **21** (1955) 901; Van Hove, L., Physica **22** (1956) 343; Hugenholtz, N. M., Physica **23** (1957) 481. These papers are referred to as I, II and III.
4) Hugenholtz, N. M., Physica **23** (1957) 533.
5) Van Hove, L., Physica **23** (1957) 441.
6) Bardeen, J., Cooper, L. N. and Schrieffer, J. R., Phys. Rev. **108** (1957) 1175.
7) Bogolubov, N., to appear in J. Exp. Theor. Phys. U.S.S.R.
8) This formula was first given in Frazer, W. R. and Van Hove, L., Physica **24** (1958) 137.
9) Weisskopf, V. F., Nuclear Physics **3** (1957) 423.
10) Bethe, H. A., Phys. Rev. **103** (1956) 1353.
11) Brueckner, K. A., Phys. Rev. **100** (1955) 36; Goldstone, J., Proc. Roy. Soc. A, **239** (1957) 267.

*) Private communication and a paper to be published in Physical Review.

THE MANY-BODY PROBLEM
by David Pines
University of Illinois

A Lecture Note and Reprint Volume. The editor sets forth in his critical introduction to this reprint collection both the general physical and mathematical principles that underlie many-body problems, and the relationships that exist between apparently different problems (such as the electron gas and liquid helium). Chapters on General Formulation, Electron Gas, Interacting Fermion Systems, Interacting Boson Systems, and Liquid Helium, Electron-Phonon Interaction, Superconductivity are included along with reprints of articles by the following authors: Goldstone, Hubbard, Galitskii et al., Bohm et al., Pines, Gell-Mann et al., Sawada et al., Brout, Wentzel, Nozières et al., Ehrenreich et al., Landau, Bogoljubov, Lee et al., Beliaev, Hugenholtz et al., Bardeen et al., Migdal, Cooper, Valatin, Anderson, Gorkov, Rickayzen.

464 pp. 6 x 9 Paperbound $3.50

QUANTUM ELECTRODYNAMICS
by R. P. Feynman
California Institute of Technology

A Lecture Note and Reprint Volume. Based on the author's course at Caltech, this text-monograph covers: Interaction of Light with Matter, Résumé of the Principles and Results of Special Relativity, Relativistic Wave Equation, Solution of the Dirac Equation for a Free Particle, Potential Problems in Quantum Electrodynamics, Relativistic Treatment of the Interaction of Particles with Light, Interaction of Several Electrons, Discussion and Interpretation of Various "Correction" Terms, The Pauli Principle and the Dirac Equation, Rules for Feynman Diagrams. Reprints of two articles by the author on quantum electrodynamics are included also.

208 pp. 6 x 9 Paperbound $3.50

NUCLEAR MAGNETIC RELAXATION
by N. Bloembergen
Harvard University

A Reprint Volume. Provides graduate students with an introduction to magnetic relaxation. Includes a new introduction to the author's thesis. Chapters: Introduction, Theory of the Nuclear Magnetic Resonance, The Experimental Method, Theory and Experimental Results, Relaxation by Quadrupole Coupling, Summary, and References. Includes a reprint of one of the author's articles on nuclear spin.

192 pp. 6 x 9 Paperbound $3.50

THE DIAMAGNETIC SUSCEPTIBILITY OF AN ELECTRON GAS
by M. J. Stephen, Oxford University

PROPERTIES OF THE NUCLEAR SURFACE LAYER
by L. Rosenfeld, Nordita, Copenhagen

THE LINEAR RESPONSE FUNCTION OF A MANY-BODY SYSTEM
by A. J. Glick, Weizmann Institute

THE T-MATRIX AND THE CANONICAL TRANSFORMATION
by R. Balian, Centre d'Etudes Nucléaires de Saclay